THE FORGE

THE FORGE

by

ARTURO BAREA

translated from the Spanish by

ILSA BAREA

FABER AND FABER LTD
24 Russell Square
London

First published in Mcmxlvi
Second impression July Mcmxlvi
by Faber and Faber Limited
24 Russell Square, London, W.C.1
Printed in Great Britain by
Western Printing Services Limited, Bristol

To

Two Women

my mother, the Señora Leonor

and

my wife, Ilsa

What the hammer? What the chain?
In what furnace was thy brain?
What the anvil?

WILLIAM BLAKE

CONTENTS

PART I

PART II

PART I

I. RIVER AND ATTIC

The wind blew into the two hundred pairs of breeches and filled them. To me they looked like fat men without a head, swinging from the clothes-lines of the drying-yard. We boys ran along the rows of white trousers and slapped their bulging seats. Señora Encarna was furious. She chased us with the wooden beater she used to pound the dirty grease out of her washing. We took refuge in the maze of streets and squares formed by four hundred damp sheets. Sometimes she caught one of us; then the others would begin to throw mud pellets at the breeches. They left stains as though somebody had dirtied his pants, and we imagined the thrashing some people would get for behaving like pigs.

In the evening, when the breeches had dried, we helped to count them in tens. All the children of the washerwomen went with Señora Encarna up to the top storey of the wash-house. It was a big loft with a roof like a V turned upside down. Señora Encarna could stand upright in the middle, but her top-knot nearly touched the big beam. We would stand at the sides and bang our heads against the sloping roof.

Señora Encarna had in front of her the heaps of breeches, sheets, pants, and shirts. The pillow-cases were apart. Everything had its number. Señora Encarna sang it out and threw the piece to the boy in charge of the set of ten to which it belonged. Each of us looked after two or three groups, the "twenties", or the "thirties", or the "sixties", and had to drop each piece on the right heap. Last of all we stuffed into each pillow-case, as into a sack, one pair of breeches, two sheets, one pair of pants, and one shirt, all marked with the same number. Every Thursday, a big cart drawn by four horses came down to the river to fetch the two hundred bundles of clean linen and leave another two hundred of dirty washing behind.

It was the linen of the men of the Royal Horse Guards, the only soldiers who had sheets to sleep in.

Every morning, soldiers of the Guards rode over the King's Bridge escorting an open carriage in which the Prince of Asturias used to sit, or sometimes the Queen. But first a rider would come out of the tunnel which led to the Royal Palace, to warn the guards on the

9

bridge. They would chase away the people, and the carriage with its escort would pass when the bridge was empty. As we were children and so could not be anarchists, the police let us stay while they went by. We were not afraid of the Horse Guards, because we knew their breeches too well.

The Prince was a fair-haired boy with blue eyes, who looked at us and laughed like a ninny. People said he was dumb and had to go for a walk in the Casa de Campo every day, between a priest and a general with white moustaches. It would have been better for him to come and play with us by the river. And then we would have seen him with nothing on when we were bathing, and would have known what a prince looks like inside. But apparently they did not want him to come. Once we discussed it with Uncle Granizo, the owner of the wash-house, because he was friends with the head keeper of the Casa de Campo, who sometimes spoke to the Prince. Uncle Granizo promised to see to it, but later he told us that the general would not give his permission.

Those military were all alike. A general who had been in the Philippines often came to visit my Uncle José. He had brought back with him an old Chinese who was very fond of me, a pink wooden walking-stick, which he said had been the spine of a fish called the manatee and was the death of anyone who got a whack with it, and a cross which was not a real cross but a green star with many rays, which he wore everywhere, embroidered on his vest and shirt and as an enamel button in his coat-lapel.

Every time this general came to visit my uncle, he grunted, cleared his throat and asked me whether I was already a little man. He would at once begin to scold me: "Keep quiet, boy, a little man mustn't do that. . . . Leave that cat alone, boy, you're a little man now." I used to sit down on the floor between my uncle's legs while they talked about politics and the war of the Russians and Japanese. The war had finished long before, but the general liked to speak of it because he had been in China and Japan himself. When they talked about that, I used to listen, and every time I heard how the Japanese had beaten up the Russians I was glad. I could not stand the Russians. They had a very nasty king who was the Tsar and a police chief called Petroff, Captain Petroff, who was a brute and lashed people with his whip. My uncle bought me a new number of the *Adventures of Captain Petroff* every Sunday. They threw a lot of bombs at him, but he never got killed.

When they stopped speaking of the war they bored me and I went to play on the dining-room carpet.

That other general who was with the Prince must have been just the same. He had to teach the Prince how to make wars when he became king, because all kings must know how to make wars, and the priest taught him how to speak. I didn't understand that. How could he speak if he was dumb? Perhaps he could, because he was a prince; but the dumb people I knew could only talk by signs. And it was not for lack of priests.

It was a nuisance that no ball came floating down, when we needed one to play with that evening.

It was quite easy to fish a ball. There was a small wooden bridge in front of Uncle Granizo's house. It was made of two old rails with planks on top and a railing, all painted green. Underneath flowed a black stream which came out of a tunnel; and that tunnel and that stream were the big sewer of Madrid. All the balls which the children of Madrid dropped into the gutters came floating down there, and we fished for them from our bridge with a net made of a stick and the wire guard of a brazier. Once I caught one made of rubber; it was painted red. Next day at school, Cerdeño took it away from me and I had to keep my mouth shut because he was bigger than I was. But I made him pay for it. In the *Corrala*, the square in front of the school where we used to play, I threw a stone at his head from the top of the railing, so that he went about with a bandage for two days and they had to sew up his brain with stitches. Of course, he did not know who had done it. But I carried a sharp stone in my pocket after that, just in case, and if he had tried to beat me, they would have had to sew him up a second time.

Antonio, the one who limped, once fell from the bridge and nearly drowned. Señor Manuel, the handyman, pulled him out and squeezed his tummy with both hands until Antonio began to spit up dirty water. Afterwards they gave him tea and brandy to drink. Señor Manuel, who was a tippler, took a good swill out of the bottle because his trousers were all wet and he said he was cold.

Nothing doing, no ball came down. I went to dinner, my mother was calling me. That day we had our meal in the sun, sitting on the grass. I liked it better than the cold days with no sun, when we had to eat at Uncle Granizo's. His house was a tavern with a tin-covered bar and some round tables which were all wobbly. The soup would spill over and the brazier stank. It was not really a brazier, but a big portable stove, with an open fire in the middle and all the stewing-pots of the washerwomen placed round it. My mother's was small, because there were only the two of us, but Señora Encarna's pot was as big as a wine-jar. There were nine of them, and they ate out of a washbowl instead of a plate. All nine sat on the grass round their bowl and dipped in their spoons in turn. When it rained and they had to eat indoors, they sat at two tables and divided their stew between the washbowl and a very big earthenware casserole which Uncle Granizo used for stewing snails on Sundays. For on Sundays the washhouse was shut and Uncle Granizo cooked snails. In the evening, men and women came down to the river and they danced, ate snails and drank wine. Once Uncle Granizo invited my mother and me, and I stuffed. The snails were caught in the grass round there, especially after the rain, when they came out to sun themselves. We boys collected them, painted their houses in many colours and let them run races.

The *cocido* tasted better here than at home.

First you cut bread into very thin bits and poured over them the soup of the stew, yellow with saffron. Then you ate the chick-peas, and after them the meat together with fresh tomatoes cut in half and sprinkled with plenty of salt. For dessert we had salad, juicy green lettuce with tender hearts such as you could not have got anywhere in town. Uncle Granizo grew the lettuces on the banks of the sewer, because he said that they grew better on sewage water. And it was true. It sounded nasty. But people spread dung on the corn-fields and chickens eat muck, and in spite of all that, bread and chickens are very good.

The chickens and ducks knew our meal-time. They arrived as soon as my mother turned over her washing-board. A big, fat earthworm had been underneath and now it wriggled. One of the ducks saw it at once. He ate the worm just as I used to eat thick noodles: he dangled it in his bill, sucked—plff—and down it went. Then he plucked at the feathers of his neck, as if some crumbs had fallen there, and waited for me to throw him my piece of bread. I would not give it him in my fingers because he was a brute and pinched. He had a very hard bill and it hurt.

With the washing-board for a table we ate, my mother and I, sitting on the grass.

My mother's hands were very small. As she had been washing since sunrise, her fingers were covered with little wrinkles like an old woman's skin, but her nails were bright and shining. Sometimes the lye would burn right through her skin and make pin-prick holes all over her fingertips. In the winter her hands used to get cut open; as soon as she took them out of the water into the cold air, they were covered with sharp little ice crystals. The blood would spurt as though a cat had scratched her. She used to put on glycerine, and her hands healed at once.

After the meal we boys went to play at Paris-Madrid Motor Races with the wheelbarrows used for the washing. We had stolen four of them from Señor Manuel, without his noticing, and kept them hidden in the meadow. He did not like us playing with them, because they were heavy and he said one of us would have his leg broken one day. But they were great fun. Each barrow had an iron wheel in front which screeched as it rolled. One boy would get into a wheelbarrow and another would push it at top speed until he had enough of it. Then he would suddenly tip up the barrow, and the passenger would topple out. One day we played at train-crashes, and lame Antonio squashed his finger. He was always unlucky. He was lame because of a thrashing his father had given him. He fell into the sewer, too. As he wore out one of his shoes more quickly than the other, his mother made him wear both shoes of a pair on both feet, changing them each day, so that he used up the two equally quickly. When he wore his left shoe on his right foot, which was the sound one, he limped with both legs and it was very funny to see him hopping on his crutches.

I had seen the real Paris-Madrid races in the Calle del Arenal, at the corner of the street where my uncle lived. There were many policemen lined up so that people should not get run over. The cars were not allowed to finish in the Puerta del Sol as they had wanted to, and the goal was at the Puente de los Franceses. Three or four cars crashed there. I had never seen a racing-car before. All the cars in Madrid looked like carriages without their horses, but those racing-cars were different. They were long and low and the driver crouched right down in them so that you saw nothing but his head—a fur cap and goggles with big glasses like a diver's. The cars had thick pipes which let off explosions like cannon-shots and puffs of smoke with a horrid smell. The papers said they could go up to fifty-five miles an hour. The train to Méntrida, which is thirty-five miles from Madrid, took from six in the morning till eleven, so that it was not surprising if some of those racing men smashed themselves up on the road.

But I liked driving very fast. In our quarter we boys had a car of our own. It was a packing-case on four wheels, and you could steer the front wheels with a rope. We used to race it down the long slope of the Calle de Lepanto. At the bottom we went so fast that we kept on rolling along the asphalt of the Plaza de Oriente. The only danger was a lamp-post at the corner there. Manolo, the son of the pub-keeper, ran into it one day and broke his arm. He yelled, but it was not really bad; they put his arm in plaster and he went on driving with us as before. Only then he was afraid. When he got to the bottom of the slope he always braked with his foot against the kerb.

The meadow where we had our races that day was called the 'Park of Our Lady of the Port'. The grass was thick, and many poplars and horse-chestnut trees grew in it. We used to peel the bark off the poplars; it left a clear green patch which seemed to sweat. The chestnut trees grew prickly balls with a chestnut inside which you could not eat, because it gave you a tummy-ache. When we found any of those balls we hid them in our pockets. Then, when one of the boys stooped, the rest of us would throw chestnuts at his behind, and the prickles would prick him, and he would jump. Once we split one of the green balls open, took out the chestnut and stuck the shell under the tail of a donkey grazing in the meadow. The donkey went crazy, rushed all over the place, kicked, and would not even let his master come near him.

I never knew why the meadow was named after Our Lady of the Port.

There was a Holy Virgin in a little chapel; a fat priest lived there who used to take his walks in the meadow and sit down under the poplars. A very pretty girl lived with him. The washerwomen said she was his daughter, but he said she was his niece. One day I asked him why the place was called 'Our Lady of the Port', and he told me that she was the patroness of the fishermen. When they were ship-wrecked they prayed to her and she saved them. If they drowned, they went to Heaven. But I could not understand why they kept this Holy Virgin in Madrid instead of taking her to San Sebastian, where there was the sea and fishermen. I had seen them myself two years before, when my uncle took me along in the summer. But here in the Manzanares were no boats and no fishermen, and nobody could have drowned there, because the water reached just to one's waist in the deepest spot.

It seemed that the Virgin was there because of all the men from Galicia who lived in Madrid. Every August, all Gallegos and Astu-rians went to this meadow; they sang and danced to their bagpipes, ate, and got drunk. Then they carried the Virgin round the meadow in a procession, and all the bagpipes went along. The boys from the Orphanage came down too and played in the procession. They were children without father or mother who lived there in the Home and had to learn music. If one of them played his trumpet badly, the teacher would knock it up with his fist and break the boy's teeth. I had seen a boy who had no teeth left, but he blew the trumpet beautifully. He could even play the couplets of the *jota* all by himself. The others would stop playing, and he would blow the *copla* on his trumpet. The people clapped and he bowed. Then the women and some of the men gave him a few centimos, but secretly, so that the Director should not see it and take them away. For the orphans were paid for playing in the procession, but the teacher took the money and the boys got nothing but the garlic soup in the Home. They all had lice and an eye-sickness called trachoma, which looked as though their eyelids had been smeared with sausage meat. And the heads of some of them were bald from mange.

Many of them had been dumped in the foundlings' home by the mothers when they were still infants-in-arms. That was one of the reasons why I loved my mother very much. When my father died, there were four of us children, and I was four months old. People wanted to make my mother put us into the foundlings' home—so I was told—because she would never be able to keep all of us alive. My mother went down to the river as a washerwoman. I was taken in by my Uncle José and Aunt Baldomera. On the days when my mother was not washing she worked as their servant; she cooked for them, did all the housework, and at night she went back to the attic where she lived with Concha, my sister. José, my eldest brother, at first got his meals in the *Escuela Pía*. When he was eleven, my mother's eldest brother took him into his shop in Cordova. Concha got her meals at the nuns' school. My second brother, Rafael, was a boarder at the College of San Ildefonso, which is an institution for orphan boys born in Madrid.

Twice a week I slept in the attic, because my Uncle José said I was to be the same as my brothers and sister and should not think myself the young gentleman of the family. I did not mind, I enjoyed myself better there than in my uncle's flat. Uncle José was very good, but my aunt was a grumpy old bigot and would not leave me alone. Every evening I had to go with her to Rosary in the Church of Santiago; and that was too much praying. I believed in God and the Holy Virgin. But that did not mean that I wanted to spend the day at prayer or in church. Every day at seven in the morning—Mass at school. Before lessons began—prayers. Then the lesson in religion. In the afternoons, before and after school—prayers. And then, when I was quite happy playing in the street, my aunt would call me to go to Rosary, and on top of it she made me pray before I went to sleep and before I got up. When I was in the attic, I did not go to Rosary, and I did not pray either in the evening or in the morning.

As it was summer then, there was no school. Every Monday and Tuesday I went to the attic; those were the days when my mother went down to the river to wash, and I went with her to play in the fields. When my mother had finished packing up her washing, we went home uphill, up the Cuesta de la Vega. I liked that road because it passed under the Viaduct, a high iron bridge which spanned the Calle Segovia. It was from the top of this viaduct that people threw themselves down if they wanted to take their own lives.

I knew a stone slab in the pavement of the Calle Segovia, which had cracks because a man had smashed his head on it. His head was squashed like a pie, and the stone broke into four pieces. A little cross was engraved on the slab, so that people should know and remember. Each time I passed under the viaduct, I looked up to see if someone was not just about to jump down. It would have been no joke if anyone had squashed my mother or me. If he had fallen on the sack of washing which Señor Manuel carried home for my mother, it would have hurt no-one. The sack was huge, bigger than a man.

I knew exactly what was in it, because I had helped my mother to count the linen: twenty sheets, six tablecloths, fifteen shirts, twelve night-shirts, ten pairs of pants—a great many things. Poor Señor Manuel had to stoop under it when he wanted to get through the door of our attic. He let the sack slide down gently so that it should not burst, and leant against the wall, breathing very fast, with sweat running down his face. My mother always gave him a very full glass of wine and asked him to sit down. If he had drunk water he would have died, for it would have stopped him sweating.

He would drink his wine, and then draw a handful of stubs and big coarse cigarette papers out of his blouse, and roll himself a fat, untidy cigar out of the stubs. One day I stole one of Uncle José's good cigars with a gold band and gave it to Señor Manuel. He told my mother, and she scolded me and told my uncle about it. He scolded me too, but then he gave me a kiss and took me to the pictures, because he said my heart was in the right place. After that I did not know whether it had been right or wrong to give Señor Manuel a cigar. I thought it was right, though, because he had been very happy. He smoked it after his meal and kept the stump which he cut up to roll a special cigarette from it. Afterwards my uncle gave me a cigar for Señor Manuel from time to time, and he had never done that before.

The Viaduct was all of iron, like the Eiffel Tower in Paris, only not so high. The Eiffel Tower was a huge iron tower built by a French engineer in Paris for an exhibition, in the year in which I was born. I knew that story very well, because my uncle had the old numbers of *La Ilustración* with photographs of the tower and the engineer, a gentleman with a long beard like all Frenchmen. Apparently they never managed to take the tower to pieces after the exhibition was over, so they left it standing so that it should fall down by itself. For one day it would fall into the Seine, the river which flows through Paris, and destroy many houses. They said people in Paris were very much afraid of it; a lot of those who lived in the neighbourhood had moved away so as not to get crushed.

It was just the same with our Viaduct: it was sure to fall one fine day. When soldiers had to ride over it, they went very slowly, and even so the whole bridge trembled. If you stood in the middle, you could feel it swaying up and down, like in an earthquake. My uncle said the bridge would crack if it vibrated less; but naturally it would have to break if it vibrated too much, and that was what would happen one day. I thought I would not like to be standing underneath just then, but that it would be interesting to look on. The year before, on *Inocentes* Day, the *A.B.C.*, which always had very good pictures, published a photograph of the Viaduct in ruins. It was an All Fools' joke that time, but many people went to look with their own eyes, because they thought it had to be true when there was a picture of it. Afterwards they were angry with the paper; but I thought it was the same with them as with me: they were angry because it was not true.

At each end of the Viaduct was a policeman on patrol, to keep people from throwing themselves over. If anyone wanted to do it he had to wait until late at night, when the guards were asleep. Then he could jump. The poor men must have got terribly bored, wandering round the streets until they could kill themselves. And then they still had to climb over the railing. The Viaduct was no good for old people because they could not climb. They had to hang themselves or jump into the big lake in the Retiro Park, but someone nearly always pulled them out from there and massaged their stomach, like lame Antonio's, until they spat out the water and did not die.

My mother said they wanted to kill themselves because they had not enough money to buy food, but I would not have killed myself for that. I would have stolen some bread and run away. They could not have put me in prison as I was a child. But if people did not want to do that, why didn't they work? My mother who was a woman worked. Señor Manuel worked too, and he was a very old man. He carried the heavy sacks with the washing, although he had a rupture through which his bowels stuck out. Once he carried a big bundle of linen up to the attic and when he got upstairs he felt very ill. My mother put him on the bed and pulled down his trousers. She had a great fright and called for Señora Pascuala, the concierge, and both together quickly pulled off his trousers and pants. He had a swarthy belly full of hairs which were nearly all white, and a bulgy lump rather like a bullock's was hanging down from his parts. My mother and Señora Pascuala pushed this lump back into his belly with their fists and fastened his truss over it, a kind of belt which had a pad over the hole where his bowels slipped out. Then Señor Manuel dressed and drank a cup of tea and a glass of brandy. Señora Pascuala boxed my ears because I had been watching, and said children should never see such things. But I was glad because now I would know how to push Señor Manuel's bowels back again if ever they slipped out while I was alone with him. The worst would be if it happened in the street and his bowels fell right out, for then he would have to die.

Now, Señor Manuel, who had a ruptured belly and smoked nothing but fag-ends, had no wish to kill himself. He was always cheerful and played with me. He used to let me ride on his shoulders and tell me that he had grandchildren like myself in Galicia. He smoked stubs so that he could visit them every year. My uncle used to get him what they called a charity ticket, and he travelled almost for nothing. When he came back he always brought butter in a round pig's bladder for my uncle. It was sweet, fresh butter which I liked to spread on my bread and sprinkle with sugar. Once I asked him why he did not commit suicide, and he said he wanted to die at home in Galicia. I wondered whether he would kill himself there one summer, but then I thought he probably would not. Besides, he said that people who commit suicide go to hell, and everybody else told me the same.

Our attic was in a large house in the Calle de las Urosas. The ground floor was all stables, with more than a hundred fine carriages and their horses. The boss of the stables was an old man with a queer, flattened-out nose. My mother said he had picked it like I did, and because his nails were dirty, the tip of his nose started rotting one day. They had to cut it off and take a piece off his behind to sew on it instead. Once I wanted to make him angry and asked if he really had a piece of his behind sewn on to his nose, and he threw a scotch at me: one of those heavy wooden wedges which keep the wheels from running backwards on a slope. It missed me and struck the printing-shop opposite. There it hit a rack on which they kept their little boxes with letters and knocked one of them over. The A's and T's got mixed up, and all the boys of our street sat and sorted them out into little heaps.

The gateway of our house was so big that we could play with tops, and at hopscotch and ball there, when Señora Pascuala was not about. Her lodge was very small, squeezed in under the staircase, and the stairs were as big as the gateway; they had a hundred and one steps. When I went down, I jumped them three at a time. Sometimes I used to slide down the banisters, but once I lost my seat and was left dangling outside the railing over the second floor. Nobody saw it, but it gave me a fright so that I thought my heart would burst, and my legs trembled. If I had fallen then, the same would have happened to me as to our water jar. There was no running water in our attic and we had to fetch it from the stables. My mother had bought a very big jar, and even when I went down with it, it was heavy; but when I carried it upstairs filled with water, I had to rest at every landing. And once I dropped it from the second floor and it exploded like a bomb down there. It was from the same spot that I nearly fell myself. When I passed it afterwards, I always kept away from the banisters.

Upstairs there was a large round window with small panes, like some church windows. When the powder-magazine at Carabanchel exploded, the glass broke and was strewn all over the stairs. I was very small then, but I remember how my mother carried me down and into the street in her arms. She ran, because she did not know what had happened. People were very frightened at that time, because so many things occurred one after the other: a few years earlier a huge meteor had come down in Madrid. Then Mount Vesuvius, the big volcano in Italy, had an outburst, and afterwards came the Halley Comet. There was also an earthquake in San Francisco, a city much bigger than Madrid, and another one in Messina. Many people believed that the end of the world would come after the end of the nineteenth century. I saw the Halley Comet myself, but I was not frightened. It was beautiful. My uncle and I watched it from the Plaza de Palacio. It was a ball of fire with a tail of sparks, rushing along the sky. My aunt had not come out with us because she was too much afraid. She kept all the candles burning before a Virgin we had at home and prayed there the whole night. When we went to bed she closed the wooden shutters very tight, and my uncle asked her if she was afraid of the comet entering our balcony. At that time, a ship with dynamite, the *Machichaco*, had exploded in Santander and blown up half the town. An iron girder had pierced two houses before it stuck fast. *Sucesos* printed a picture in colours, which showed chunks of the ship and arms and legs flying in the air.

Opposite the round window began the passage which led to all the attic flats. The first belonged to Señora Pascuala, it was the biggest and had seven rooms; then came Señora Paca with her four rooms, and across the passage Señora Francisca who had only one room, like all the rest.

Paca and Francisca are the same name, but Señora Paca was one thing and Señora Francisca another. Señora Francisca was an old lady who had been a widow for many years. As she had no money she sold things for children on the Plaza del Progreso, a whole lot of things for two coppers, such as monkey-nuts, hazel-nuts, jacks-in-the-box, and bengal lights. But she was a lady. The other was a big fat

19

woman who walked about in a dressing jacket so thin that you could see her breasts with very black nipples through it. One day I saw a few black hairs sticking through the stuff of her jacket and afterwards I always had to think of her when I saw bristles on a bacon-rind. It did not matter, because I did not like bacon. Señora Paca always went round shouting and screaming; once Señora Pascuala, who had quite a good voice herself, told her that she would get herself chucked out.

Señora Paca was a washerwoman too, but she did not wash at Uncle Granizo's place—only at a laundry in the Ronda de Atocha, where there is no river and they had to do their washing in basins filled with water from a tap. I had been there once. I did not like it. It looked like a factory, with rows of basins full of wash, steam hanging in the air over them, and the women jostling each other alongside and screaming like mad. There was no sun and no grass and the linen stank. The drying-yard with the clothes-lines was in a bit of waste ground at the back. Tramps used to climb over the hoardings and steal the washing. Of course they sometimes tried to do the same down by the river, but they were less cheeky there because it was open ground, where the women could run and throw stones after them, and they always got caught. In fact, the decent washerwomen were at the river, opposite the Casa de Campo; but from the Toledo Bridge downstream and in the laundries o fthe *Rondas* there were only slatterns.

Our passage made a bend, and then came a straight bit, thirty-seven metres long; I had measured it myself, metre by metre, with my mother's tape-measure. There was a small window in the corner which let the sun through, and a large window in the middle of the ceiling, where the water came in when it rained. It came through the small window too, whenever a strong wind was blowing from the front. That made two puddles in the passage. When a tile was missing on the roof, the rain trickled through into the attic, and you put a pan underneath where it dripped. The passage and the attics were floored with bricks, or rather with tiles of burnt clay which looked like bricks. They were very cold in winter time, but our attic had a rush-mat with straw underneath and so we could play on the floor.

Our attic was Number 9 in the passage. Next door was the attic of the powder-woman who made up rockets and squibs for children. The neighbours said she could make bombs and was an Anarchist. She had a lot of books and was very kind. One night the police came. They went away without arresting her, but they woke up all the rest of us, because they turned her room upside down and threw things about.

In the attic next to hers lived Señora Rosa and her husband. He was a harness-maker and she was short-sighted; she could not have seen seven-on-a-donkey. They were tiny and very thin and loved each other very much. They always spoke in a low, soft voice and you hardly noticed them. They would have liked to have a child, and their room was a refuge for us when we were afraid of a beating. Then Señora Rosa would stand in front of her door and not let anyone in, nor us out, until they promised her not to touch us. She had a very small, very white face, and very light-blue eyes with lashes so fair that you scarcely saw them. She wore spectacles with thick glasses and my mother said she could see well in the dark. When she looked at you, her eyes were like a bird's.

Then there was still another attic, the smallest of all. An old woman lived there, called Antonia, and nobody knew anything about her because nobody wanted to have anything to do with her. She went begging in the streets and came home at eleven at night, just before the front door was locked. She would come up muttering to herself, drunk with gin. Upstairs she would bolt her door and start talking to her cat. Once she was sick on the stairs and Señora Pascuala made her scrub the staircase from top to bottom.

At the end of the passage lived the cigarette-maker. She and her daughter worked together making cigarettes for the Queen. They were very long cigarettes on to which they stuck cardboard holders with a fine brush dipped into a dusty little pot of gum. And that was what the Queen put in her mouth. The little pot was of thick green glass, and as they used to wipe their brush on its rim, it always had some hardened drops of gum sticking to its outside, like the wax drops on church candles. When they ran short of gum, Señora Maria scraped off the dried blobs, put them into the pot and poured some hot water over them. Once, she had no hot water ready and used stock from her stewing-pot; and her cigarettes got spotted with grease.

In a corner of the passage was the lavatory. At night I was afraid of going there, for a lot of fat cockroaches came crawling out and ran about in the passage to feed on the garbage cans which all the neighbours put in front of their attic doors. In summer, when you had to leave the door open, you heard them running about in the passage outside, making a small noise like crackling paper. They did not get into our room because my mother had nailed a strip of linoleum along the bottom of the door, the kind of linoleum rich people had in their houses. But lots of them got into the room of Señora Antonia, the drunkard, because it was next door to the lavatory and had no linoleum. Her cat ate them, and it made you feel sick, because when she crunched them they sounded like monkey-nuts.

Big rats from the stables used to get into the house and sometimes came up to the attics. In the stables they had many rat-traps and dogs of the ratter kind. In the mornings, the traps were taken out into the street, often with four or five live rats in them. Sometimes the neighbours and all the children of our street would make a circle, and they would open the traps and let loose the dogs to chase and kill the rats. At other times they poured paraffin over the rats and burnt them inside the wire traps, but only rarely because it made the whole street smell of burnt hair and roasted flesh. Once a rat bit a dog in the muzzle and got away. A piece was missing out of the dog's nose after that. He belonged to Señor Paco, the one who had his behind stitched on to his nose. So the two of them looked alike, and the men at the printer's called them the 'pugs'.

We had arrived home, and my mother was very tired. Downstairs the milkman lent her a can to carry her milk, so that we had not to go up and down again for it, and she began at once to cook our supper. We were having fried potatoes with fresh sardines and an egg, and afterwards a little coffee, I with milk, my mother black and boiling hot. I never understood how she could stand it like that. While she was cooking, I sat down to read *The Children of Captain Grant* by Jules Verne. From time to time, I stole one of the potato slices just out of the frying-pan. Then she fried the sardines. They smelt good. But my mother would not let me steal one of them, because they were few.

II. CAFÉ ESPAÑOL

By the time my uncle and aunt had walked down from the third floor and reached our front door, I had already raced down the stairs, banged the glass door, got cursed for it by the concierge, run all the way to the entrance of the Café Español, told Angel I would be with him in a moment, and got back in time for my aunt to take me by the hand, so that I could walk the same way over again with them, very decorously.

The gas jet above our house-door burnt with an open flame like a small slice of melon. A little further on, the pipe from a water main, left without its cap, spilt over on the side-walk. I stepped on it and blocked its round mouth with my sole. The water spluttered out and splashed my aunt's stockings, which made her furious.

It was a clear night with a moon of polished tin plate, which lit up the streets white on black. In the Calle del Arenal, the new street-lamps with their gas mantles seemed to fill the whole street with moonlight. The old jets in our own street looked like the pale yellow flames of matches on the white moonlit side, and on the black moon-less side like blobs of quivering light.

When we came to the corner, Angel stopped crying out the even-ing papers and came up to bid a good evening to my uncle and aunt, cap in hand, his long straight hair falling round his pumpkin-shaped head; he moved like a little old man. He handed my uncle a paper and, as usual, Uncle told him to keep the small change. We winked at each other, Angel and I, because we knew how and when we were going to meet and play.

My aunt was annoyed when I played with Angel, and his mother did not like it during selling hours, because then he left off crying out his papers. Our best time was when I had come to the café before the *Heraldo* was out. By the time the paper arrived all damp and smelly from the press, I had wrung permission out of my aunt to go with Angel, after having driven her into her worst temper. My uncle invariably cut short the dispute by saying: 'Oh, let the boy run along!' I would take myself off while she went on grumbling to my uncle about how she was afraid of my being run over and how she hated people seeing me run round with a newspaper boy who was, after all, nothing but a street urchin, a ragamuffin who might teach me the Lord only knew what.

Angel would take the pile of newspapers, while his mother stayed in the doorway of the café shouting '*Heraldo!*', and we started on our expedition through the almost deserted streets of the quarter. We ran, because you have to be on the spot if you want to sell your paper before your competitors arrive. Here and there, maids would open a front door and shout through the dark: 'Here, an *Heraldo!*' Angel and I would run across the streets, to and fro from door to door, doubling back on our tracks twenty times. Papers for regular custo-mers had to be delivered to their homes. Angel would enter the front door and run up the stairs, while I waited for him outside. More maids kept coming out of house-doors calling for the *Heraldo*, and then I had to go, as I was left with the armful of papers. If I had had to sell papers, I should have felt ashamed, but as I was not the news-paper-seller myself, it amused me. Most of the servant-girls knew that I was Angel's friend, but all new maids were flabbergasted when they saw a newspaper boy in a starched white collar, silk bow tie, sailor blouse with gold braid, and shining patent leather boots. That was how my aunt made me dress up when we were going to the café, because all the people who met there were better class; and it was also one of her reasons against my going with Angel. In daytime, when I played in the street in my drill blouse and rope-soled sandals, she did not mind Angel, who wore a grown man's jacket given him by one of his customers. It had been taken in to fit him, but it was still too big and the weight of the coppers had pulled the pockets out of shape, so that they dragged along the ground when he stooped.

Our rounds through the quarter by night were an adventure, like the adventures in books. While we were running along, cats would jump up and shoot across the street like bullets, scared by our pounding steps and more scared when we clapped our hands to make them run still faster. They would scramble up a wall and dive into a window. There were garbage heaps at the street corners; the gaunt dogs who burrowed there watched us and growled, so that we went out of their way. Sometimes they would run after us and we had to stop and drive them off with stones. On the steps of the Church of Santiago the tramps were getting their bed-chamber ready; children were bringing up theatre-bills torn from hoardings, which they used as mattresses. The men sat on the church steps while the boys made the beds. Sometimes they would go into a huddle and send out boys to keep watch on all the street corners. Then they would play cards and the boys had to warn them when the police or the night-watchman were coming. At other times they spread a newspaper on the ground with all the food people had given them, and everybody ate from it They used their fingers or wooden spoons with a short handle, such as they had in jail or in barracks. In the winter they used to make a bonfire of straw and planks torn from hoardings. They sat round the fire and often the night-watchman or the police patrol would join them for a while to get warm. When it rained very heavily, the big wrought-iron gates of the church would be thrown open and they would sleep under the porch. We never stopped with them, because they often stole children.

Milkmen passed on galloping horses, their milk-cans clattering, and they seemed to us the cowboys of American tales. Sometimes we met the Viaticum. In front walked the priest in his embroidered cope, beside him the sacristan carrying a great square lantern. After them went the neighbours in double file, with burning candles in their hands. There were always a great many old women among them, and all the tramps who had been sleeping at the church gate went along too. They kept the candle-ends they had been given and later sold them to the wax-chandler opposite the church; they bought wine with the money. So the tramps were very pleased when anybody in the neighbourhood was dying.

They did very much the same with timber from the hoardings: they tore it off and took it to a confectioner's in the Calle del Espejo. The master used it to kindle his oven and in exchange gave them great heaps of 'crisps'—broken buns and biscuits. As everybody knew that the planks of the hoardings got stolen by the tramps, we boys of the neighbourhood tore off planks, too, and took them to the same bakery. And the tramps got all the blame.

That night, the *Heraldo* was already out and there were no adventures. It was a pity, because the night was very beautiful.

In the entrance to the café, between the outer and the inner door, there was a square space, some two yards by two. Against one of the walls stood a red-painted cupboard with glass panes, full of matchboxes, cigars, packets of cigarettes, and bundles of tooth-picks. In the lower half there were two shelves with piles of newspapers. The glass panes of the entrance door were plastered with illustrated papers and instalments of boys' serials. Señora Isabel, Angel's mother, sat on a low stool squeezed in between the cupboard and the outer door. In that corner she cooked meals on a spirit lamp, mended Angel's trousers or her own vests, counted newspapers, and made tooth-picks, whittling down small sticks of wood with a very sharp knife which pared off minute shavings like grated cheese. There was hardly room for her in the corner. But when her eldest daughter and her son-in-law visited her, with a baby-in-arms and two toddlers, they all packed themselves in there so as not to block the passage, and they all got in. Angel's mother was a bundle of nerves; when she was alone she never stopped gesticulating, talking to herself and swearing. When she was angry, she was like a mad cat and Angel would not go near her.

As we passed by her, she greeted us and gave me a whole heap of matchboxes with coloured pictures for my collection.

Most of our party was already sitting round our regular table, a table with a round, white marble top, which had room for twelve people: there was Don Rafael, the architect, who was eternally cleaning his glasses with a handkerchief he kept in his breast-pocket. When he got into a discussion, his handkerchief and his spectacles were constantly between his pocket, his nose, and his hands. Don Ricardo—Maestro Villa, the conductor of the Madrid Municipal Orchestra—short, pot-bellied, and always merry, was the only one to drink beer, while the others took white coffee. Then there was Don Sebastian, the father of Esperancita, a little girl who used to play with Angel and me, and Don Emilio, the parish priest of the Church of Santiago, a fat, hairy man; the hairs on his finger-joints were tight little curls which looked like ink-stains, and his stubble pricked my cheeks when he kissed me.

There was Doña Isabel and her sister, Doña Gertrudis. Doña Isabel was the mistress, and Doña Gertrudis her servant, because ever since she had been a widow, she had lived in her sister's house and been supported by her. Doña Isabel wore bright silk dresses and always had a fur or a feather boa round her shoulders. The other dressed in mourning. Doña Gertrudis had a black scarf round her head, and Doña Isabel a huge hat with dyed plumes of the kind known as *pleureuses* which danced like a feather duster when she talked or moved her head. Doña Isabel had a round face and a sagging, lumpy skin. She used a lot of white powder with rouge on top of it, and she painted her eyes and lips. Her dresses were cut so low that it left her whole neck free, and her throat hung in a pouch like a pigeon's crop. The face of Doña Gertrudis was like a church candle, long and yellow. The two sisters had a flat on the same floor as my uncle.

Finally, there were Modesto and Ramiro, the pianist and the violinist of the café, both of them blind. They played very well and had been given prizes in the Musical Academy. In the café, they were paid five pesetas a day, and got their supper and white coffee.

The cleverer of the two was Ramiro, the violinist. He could walk between the tables without using his stick, and when he went up to the piano no-one could have told that he was blind. He recognized everybody by their voice and their step, and could tell false money with his fingers. I was very fond of him, but he made me afraid when he took off his dark glasses, because his eyes were like the white of an egg; he wore the spectacles so as not to frighten people. His hands were small and chubby and they seemed to search you. At times he would call me and pass his hands over my head, face, and body. When his fingers touched my eyelashes, nose, lips, ears, neck, and hair, it seemed to me as if his fingertips had tiny eyes which were looking closely into my skin. Afterwards, he used to tell me with great conviction that I was a handsome boy, and I believed him because he never made mistakes. I had two silk bow ties, exactly alike, both with little white spots, but one was blue and the other red; and Ramiro could tell with his fingers which one I was wearing.

Modesto had empty eye-sockets with glass eyes in them; when they looked at you, they made you uncomfortable, because they did not move. He was very grave, Ramiro very gay. Modesto was tall and thin, and Ramiro short and round, so the two looked like a blind

Don Quixote and a blind Sancho Panza. Modesto often petted me, but he never looked at me with his hands.

My aunt sat down beside Don Emilio, the priest, and began to talk to him about the church. The rest of the men were talking politics and my aunt would not let Don Emilio join in. Whatever she said, he always answered: 'Yes, Doña Baldomera. . . . No, Doña Baldomera,' until in the end she left him alone and started discussing the neighbours in our house with Doña Isabel. In the meantime, she was preparing my special cup of coffee, which was one of my aunt's tricks to save money. The waiter brought a cup for my uncle, another for my aunt, and two glasses of water. I got a thick breakfast-cup of the kind used for chocolate. Manolo, the boy, came with the big coffee-pots and filled my uncle's cup with black coffee and my aunt's with milk. Then he poured a little coffee and a little milk into each of their glasses, and my aunt gave him a copper. She got to work with the two cups and two glasses until she had the same mixture in all of them; then she filled my big cup with white coffee and still had two full cups left for my uncle and herself.

As soon as the mixing was over, I gulped down my coffee and went off with Esperancita who had been pinching me from behind my chair because she wanted to play. We plunged into the labyrinth of screens, chairs, and sofas. The sofas ran along the walls, and we loved to scramble on all fours through the sunk lane between their backs and the tables. When we banged our heads against a table and got bruised, we stood up on a sofa to look at ourselves in the big mirrors. Our shoe-soles left marks on the seat and Señor Pepe, the head-waiter, came and ticked us off. We tried to wipe out the marks by slapping the sofa, but clouds of dust rose up and our hands left red patches outlined in dusty white. Señor Pepe became angry and cleared away the dust with his napkin, without slapping.

At other times we scratched the red velvet the wrong way and drew letters and faces which we rubbed out by stroking down the pile with our palms. When we made our drawings, the little hairs of the velvet tickled our fingertips as if a cat were licking them, and they turned into a cat's back when we smoothed them.

The manager of the café was watching us from behind the counter. We slipped away, up the small staircase to the billiard room, opened the green baize door and crept in.

I see it to-day with eyes I did not then possess:

A huge room with many windows along three of its walls and all the lights out. Yet, coming in through the windows on the one side, the white glare of the arc-lamps in their wire-screened globes, which frightened the moths with the splutters and sparks of their carbon and the sudden crackle of their mechanism, and from the other side the livid flares from the old gas jets in the Calle de Vergara with their hissing, melon-slice flames. In the middle of the room eight massive tables, their square shadows swaying with the shifting, varying lights, their varnish throwing sparks, the blotting-paper of their green cloth sucking in the rays. The long shadows of the window frames, sketching black crosses at broken angles on floor, tables, and walls. All asleep, all silent, and so resonant that a low word wakes murmurs in every corner and the gently pattering noise of a fleeing mouse startles us, as we stand timidly on the threshold. The padded door closes softly behind us.

The sight of the balls, glittering through the netting of their little sacks, encouraged us to carry on our adventure. The sound of the first balls knocking against each other broke the heavy silence, and we snapped out of our tension into mad canters round the tables, snatching all the balls from their pockets, and pouring our booty on to the central table which seemed to us the most dignified, the mother of all the tables. Running round and round its six elephant feet, we jumped through the weaving lights and dipped our hands into the living sea of balls which were running over the green cloth, lighting it up with white and red glints and banging their heads against each other with the dry rap of bones.

The sudden glare from the lamps in the room being switched on all at once, and the black sweep of the manager's ferocious moustache caught us perched on the top of the green lawn and turned us to stone, while the last balls were still running out their course and knocking against their neighbours just when we wanted them to stop and be silent. We leapt from the table like monkeys in flight and rushed down the narrow staircase up which we had gone on tip-toes, jumping the steps three at a time, pursued by the threats of the ogre. We tumbled into the café with faces scarlet from excitement and fright.

My mother had come. When we got near our table, Esperancita ran and hid behind the red curtain over the entrance. I went after her, and through the glass panes saw my mother talking with Angel's mother and Señor Pepe, the waiter. Esperancita was in the secret and we talked things over quickly. She ran out from behind the curtain towards the other door of the café, further down the room, and I followed her. Esperancita disappeared behind the curtain of the other door, and so did I, but instead of hiding there we ran out into the street and went round to the front entrance where the newspapers were. My mother was still there in the little lobby. We kissed and hugged each other, and I told her in a rush all about the trick we had invented so that I could come and kiss her without my aunt seeing it.

We ran back the same way we had come, and went on romping all over the café as though nothing had happened. But I explained to Esperancita once again why we so often had to act a little comedy:

'You see, my aunt gets very angry if she sees me kissing my mother. She wants me only to kiss her, and she doesn't want me to love my mother at all. And when she's angry she says I'm an ungrateful boy, because it's she who's keeping me, and then she has a row with my mother and says my mother's behaving as if she was afraid of my being stolen from her. So if my mother I and want to kiss, we always hide.'

In the meantime my mother had come in and sat down beside my aunt. Pepe had brought her a cup and a little dish with sugar; I went to their table, just gave her a pat on the shoulder, said 'Hullo!' and took one of her lumps of sugar. Then I ran away to go on playing. My aunt was pleased.

We found a set of dominoes on a table near by and began building houses with the stones. I could see my mother quietly drinking her coffee and my aunt talking away to Doña Isabel, probably the same old stories about our neighbours.

My mother was a very small woman, rather plump, with quick movements. Her skin was very fair, her eyes grey like a cat's, and her brown hair had only a few white strands on the temples; she did not look her fifty-odd years. She was wearing a black skirt, a grey calico blouse, a striped kerchief on her head, and a striped apron.

My aunt was sixty years old. She had a black dress with embroidered flowers and a black veil over her white hair. Her face was old, but it looked like fine porcelain and she was proud of the natural pink of her cheeks and the silkiness of her hands. But my mother had hands as soft as my aunt's and even smaller. Sometimes that annoyed my aunt who used to put cream on her hands and rub them with lemon and glycerine; she would tell my mother that she did not understand how anyone could keep such hands, working as my mother did.

My aunt was the mistress and my mother the servant, just like Doña Isabel and Doña Gertrudis. She came and sat down to drink her coffee with the others after she had cleared my uncle and aunt's supper table, scrubbed the pots and pans and swept the dining-room and kitchen. Sometimes she would join in the general conversation, because the others liked her very much and kept asking her questions, but usually she kept silent and waited for an occasion to slip away and have a talk with Angel's mother or Señor Pepe.

'The party broke up at eleven o'clock and we went home, my aunt and I in front, my uncle and my mother behind. It was earlier than usual and we had missed our game with Angel who had just finished selling his papers and looked ruefully after us, for our going meant that he would be alone until closing time. We had to get up very early the next morning, because in the afternoon, my uncle, my aunt, and I were going into the country for the summer holidays. My mother was going to sleep in the flat that night. Although the coach only left in the afternoon, my aunt had to start packing and preparing the food already in the morning. She was sure not to leave us in peace all day with her restlessness. As usual, it would be my mother who would have to put up with her, because my uncle would take me along to see the changing of the guard in the morning and we would not come back until lunchtime. That was his method of getting away from her every Sunday.

When we got home, my cat and I drank my milk together on the dining-room table, as we did every night. My uncle sat down opposite us, while my aunt pottered round in the bedroom next door, preparing the night-light which also had to serve instead of a lamp for her Virgin. Then it suddenly occurred to me to say to my uncle:

'I want to sleep with my mother to-night, because we're going away to-morrow.'

'All right, go to bed with her.'

My aunt appeared in the bedroom door and burst out: 'The child will sleep in his own bed, just as he does every night!'

'But, my dear——' said my uncle.

'None of your "my dears", and none of your "buts"! It's better for the child to sleep alone.'

'But if the boy is going away to-morrow and wants to sleep with his mother for once, why can't you let him? After all, doesn't he sometimes sleep in our bed because you happened to have a fancy for it, and I'm sure he must sleep worse in a bed with two people than with one.'

My aunt bridled and began to scold: 'I said "no", and "no" it is! The boy would never have dreamt of wanting to sleep with his mother if she hadn't put the idea into his head.' And she called shrilly for my mother: 'Leonor, Leonor, the child will sleep in his own bed, because I want him to! There's been quite enough pampering already, and the child gets his own way far too much.'

My mother, who did not know the reason for this to-do, came in looking baffled and said: 'Well, his bed's ready.'

At my mother's quiet voice, my aunt sank into a chair and began to shed tears on to the table.

30

'You're all trying to kill me by breaking my heart! You're all in league to make me suffer! Even you'—she turned to my uncle—'you're in the conspiracy with them. Of course, you say "yes", and then there's nothing to be done about it. I know what it is—you've worked it out between you, and I, poor thing, have to swallow it and say nothing.'

My mother, tense with anger, took me by the arm and said: 'Come along, now, say good night to your uncle and aunt, and go to bed.'

My aunt had another explosion:

'So that's it! Everything's settled! Well, the child will not go to his bed to-night, he will come to bed with me!'

My uncle banged his fist on the table and got up, furious: 'The woman's crazy and she'll drive us all crazy!'

I got violently excited, clutched my mother's skirts and shrieked: 'I want to go to bed with my mother to-night!'

The tears and cries of my aunt redoubled, and in the end she got her way with the help of my mother, who restrained her own emotion and pushed me towards my aunt.

In their bedroom I wept, feeling deserted by my mother and hating my aunt who insisted on undressing me between sobs and cuffs, changing from bursts of tenderness, which smeared my face with tears and slavers, to attacks of rage in which she pinched and shook me. In the end my uncle lost what patience he had left and told her firmly to shut up. We went to bed, and I lay between the two. My aunt began to say her rosary and I had to say it with her, while my uncle read the *Heraldo* by the light of a candle on his night-table. As usual, my aunt went to sleep before she came to the second decade of the rosary; her mouth hung half open and showed the gap left by the two front teeth which were swimming in a glass on her night-table. After a while, I turned cautiously to my uncle and whispered:

'She's asleep now, I want to go to my mother.'

My uncle placed a finger to his lips and very softly asked me to wait. He blew out the candle and we both lay in the semi-darkness of the night-light which threw fearful shadows on the ceiling. After a long while my uncle lifted me carefully out of bed, gave me a kiss and told me to go off without making a noise.

I crept along the passage into my mother's room, next door to the kitchen, touching the bedclothes in the dark, and said that it was me, so that she should not be afraid. She asked me anxiously to go back. But when I told her that my uncle had helped me to get out, she made room for me in her bed. And there I lay with my back to her, rolled into a ball in the crook of her arm. The cat jumped on to the bed and butted his way under the top sheet, as he always did. The three of us stayed very quiet, so as to fall asleep.

A drop of water fell on my neck and the cat licked my face.

III. ROADS OF CASTILE

There was no railway to Brunete. We had to go by coach, in a yellow-and-red coach drawn by six mules, just like one of the old diligences. On the box there was room for two passengers beside the coachman and the groom for the mules. Sometimes, when three passengers had to sit there, the groom would ride on one of the leading mules. The coach itself, tacked on to the box, had room for eight people. Children like myself paid half-fare and had no right to a seat. They had to make the journey on the knees of their relatives until a seat became free at one of the stops, which was usually at Villaviciosa. On the top of the coach were two wooden benches with eight numbered seats; they were called *la vaca*, 'the cow'. The luggage was stowed away there, together with the sack with the National Colours, which carried the letters for the villages along the road.

The coach started in the Cava Baja, from an old coaching-inn called the Inn of San Andrés.

The Cava Baja is a seventeenth-century street which has remained embedded in the city. It begins in the Plaza de Puerta Cerrada, the Square of the Closed Gate, where the only thing left from old times is a huge stone cross whose origin is unknown, but of which popular tradition says that it was erected in memory of the thousands who had died there on one of the many medieval gibbets. And it ends in the Plaza de la Morería between the jails of the Inquisition and the old gallows-yard of the Plaza de la Cebada where hosts of heretics had been burnt at the stake, and men famous in Spanish history, like the liberal General Riego, had been hanged. And yet the street itself is gay. It holds a world of its own.

There are innumerable ancient inns with wide, cross-beamed gateways, enormous courtyards for coaches and sheds for mules; with cobbles, heaped-up dung, flower-pots and impudent chickens everywhere; with narrow staircases, their rails polished by the hands of ten generations; with little taprooms where wine is drunk straight from the paunch-bellied wineskins lying on a shelf, their mouths tied with plaited esparto grass ropes whose other end is fastened to a hook in the wall so that the spout is raised and the wine does not spill. The regular customers, carters and peasants, know exactly how to untie a wineskin and drink the wine not from the spout but from the free jet—wine of sixteen or eighteen degrees of alcohol, which parches your throat with its tannin and stains your lips the colour of mulberry.

The guests in those inns come from the villages of Castile. They are women in layer upon layer of wide, swaying petticoats; girls burnt with the sun of the threshing-floors, in their Sunday dresses of garish silk; stolid men in corduroy trousers that creak at every step, and jackets of thick cloth lined with sheepskin over dazzlingly white shirts and black sashes. In their pockets, a green handkerchief large as a ship's sail, a knife broad as a bull's horn, flint, steel, and a stout rope of tinder which, together with a greasy tobacco pouch and packet of cigarette papers looking like a fat little breviary, compose their smoking outfit. And, knotted into the tucked-in end of the sash, a purse crammed with silver for the trip: a woollen purse knitted in many colours and tied with a cord longer than the man himself, which is wound round and round the purse until it looks like a ball of yarn.

When I was a young boy, it used to fill me with wonder and awe to see how those peasants, seated at an oaken table before a blue-flowered Talavera wine jar, would slowly untie their sashes, letting their trousers sag, unwind the cord which guarded their treasure, and unpick the last knots with their finger nails, merely to throw on the table the small cash for their drinks.

The men have occasion to untie their sashes many times, without leaving the street, for in it are all the trades which cater for the villages:

The ironmongery with its low-slung ceiling, where you can buy iron bars for making horseshoes, and unfinished ploughshares to be hammered out on the anvil of the smithy at home.

The sieve-maker who sells riddles with a mesh for every size of seed and grain, which he himself makes there on the spot with inherited craftsmanship.

The cooper who fits the staves together with his mallet, standing in the open door of his shop in his shirt-sleeves, and who lights an open fire in the middle of the street when he wants to shrink the wood of a cask before adjusting the hoops.

The confectioner who practises the mysterious art of making sticky sweets, red, blue, and poisonous green, stodgy cakes with a crust baked almost black, tiny biscuits of which hundreds go to a pound, and *turrón*, the paste of almonds and honey which seems to tear your teeth out of your jaw.

The picture-shop which sells frames of gilt flowers, coloured lithographs of Saints and Virgins with sweetly pretty faces and red or blue robes, and of wondrous landscapes in which there is everything: the stream, the forest, the snow-capped mountain-peak, the windmill, the bullock-cart, the cottage with smoke rising from its chimney-stack, the footpath leading out of the picture, and preferably a small child with a basket, picking flowers.

The pottery shop, a motley of glazed jugs in outlandish shapes, absurdly and naively decorated with many-coloured flowers, of vases, sugar-basins and glasses all gilt, scarlet and blue scrolls with clumsy Gothic lettering: 'A Present from Madrid'.

The wineskin-maker, who makes leather bottles out of cats' skins and big wineskins out of goats' hides; who sits straddling and paunchy in the doorway of his workshop, between his knees the swarthy belly of an inflated skin from which he scrapes the hair with a curved, two-handled knife, his muscular arms tattooed by the pitch he uses to cure the hides.

The rope-maker, a desiccated man with rotten lungs, whose shop smells of hemp and is full of a fine dust that makes your eyes water and tickles your throat, and who finishes all his deals in the tavern across the street to rid his gullet of the minute fluff which gives him a perpetual thirst.

The saddler, a primitive harness-maker, who lines the collars for mules and donkeys with plaited straw, and makes them gay with tiny bronze bells and tinkling little balls like gilded nuts; who holds the leather strips in a pair of wooden tongs gripped between his knees, while he sews them together with two separate threads, one on each side, which he crosses and re-crosses at every stitch, opening his arms wide in a rhythmical movement each time he pulls the crossed threads into place; who weaves the cinches out of brightly coloured cords and makes the headpieces with the red woollen tassels which the mules toss so proudly.

The grocer in his little shop crammed with dried cod and with pressed sardines in open barrels, silvery disks studded all over the shop which smells like the hold of a fishing-smack.

The draper who sells heavy cloth and the stiff sheets of unbleached linen which turn white with the years and the sun, the cheap silk blouses with their steely sheen, the skirts strewn with gaudy flowers, the jackets with sleeves and collar of curly sheepskin, the hairy, heavy woollen shawls big enough to cover a woman together with her child, and the vests and pants of thick yellow flannel, which protect the men in the hard winters of Castile.

The coaches for the villages round Madrid leave the street in the middle of the afternoon and arrive at their last stop by the light of the moon. At the hour of departure, the street fills with country people carrying bundles and farming tools, and with their relatives in town who come to see them off, daughters in service in Madrid and sons in soldiers' uniform. And the world seems full of the laughter of the young, the wails of the children and old people, a chorus of blasphemies and merry, impudent jokes such as you may find only here or in books as old as the street itself.

Fathers buy their sons their first cigar—because they have become men now they are soldiers—and present them with the mighty tobacco pouch their own fathers had given them on a similar occasion.

A little servant girl, big with child, cowers in a corner of the taproom, shying away from her mother's blast of fury at the 'dishonour' and from her father's heavy hand.

People show each other with awe and in whispers the huge portal of the House of the Inquisition, a lintel of three granite blocks, two upright, the third laid across them as in a druidic monument, on the pediment an AVE MARIA GRATIA PLENA, a primitive monogram and the date 1642, and behind it a stone gateway built of slabs the size of millstones. There, the mummified bodies of two women in the habit of nuns had been found walled in between the stones, standing on their feet. The house bulges, it looks like an old woman with dropsy and you expect it to burst open at any moment, giving birth to its dead in the middle of the street.

An hour before the coach was to start, my uncle, my aunt, and I were already sitting in a corner of the taproom, beside us two suitcases and a basket with food and water bottles, for once on the road one could get nothing but well-water. My uncle took his thick silver watch with its tiny little key from his pocket, opened the case and showed the dial to my aunt:

'Now see how unreasonable you are! We're an hour early.'

'Maybe, but at least I don't have to worry.'

I went into the doorway of the inn where the coach was standing, still without its mules, the wheels cluttered with lumps of mud from the road. Many of the passengers were waiting there, leaning against the wall, baskets and saddle-bags stuffed with parcels at their feet. All were country people: a fat man, made still fatter by his saddle-bags; a little old woman with a blackish face; a big, stout woman with child, accompanied by a big and a little girl; and a few more men and women. I wondered which of them were going with us in the coach and which had come to see their people off. The grooms led the mules out of the gateway in pairs and harnessed them to the coach. The rear pair had to be backed into their place and were tied to the pole with a lot of tackle. It was interesting to see how difficult it is for animals to go backwards.

As soon as the mules were harnessed, all the suitcases and parcels were put on the top of the coach and the people began to take their seats. Of course, my aunt had to be among the first to enter the coach and wanted my uncle and me to get in as well. My uncle left her to grumble all by herself and took me to the confectioner's shop to buy sweets for my cousins in the village. We bought a lot of green peppermint drops which stained your fingers like wet paint and burnt your tongue because they were so strong. But the country people like them best of all. We also bought two pounds of *paciencias*, small round biscuits the size of a copper, of which they gave us a big bag full. We took our parcels to my aunt who at once started to scold because we would not get in; she was afraid the coach would leave without us. My uncle paid no attention to her and went with me to the tavern, to drink beer with lemon fizz.

Among all the people in the tavern, my uncle was the only gentleman from Madrid. Everybody was in country clothes except us: my uncle had his black alpaca suit, his starched shirt, and bowler hat, my aunt wore her embroidered black dress and black mantilla, and I my white sailor suit. That morning my uncle had had a row with my aunt because of our clothes. He wanted to put on an old jacket and an old pair of trousers, and to travel in a cap and carpet slippers, and he wanted me to go in my blouse and rope-soled sandals. But she protested and said that, thank God, we were not beggars. And as usual, she had her way. My uncle, who was stout, already had to push a silk handkerchief under his stiff collar to be less bothered by sweating, and from time to time he took off his hat and wiped the sweat from his bald head. With his starched shirt front, cuffs, and collar, he was cursing the 'stupid ideas' of my aunt, as he said. If I had been in his place, I thought, I would have dressed just as I liked, and if she had been angry, she would have had to swallow it. But he was so good that he put up with all her whims rather than annoy her.

When we entered the coach at long last, it was not easy to squeeze in. All the seats except my uncle's were occupied and we had to push through all the people to get there. I had to stand between my uncle's knees and we waited for the coach to start. The heat was unbearable. The people were wedged together and their heads almost

36

touched the low roof of the coach. On the top, the handyman was tying the bundles fast and loading up the last pieces of luggage; and every step of his shook down dust on our heads and sounded as though the boards were going to crack. The coach was completely full, and the groom for the mules had to get on to the left mule in the lead, because three women went on the box-seat beside the driver, packed as close as sardines. Two men, who only wanted to go to Campamento, were standing on the footboard; they paid fifty centimos fare.

The coach screeched while we were rolling down the steep slope of the Calle de Segovia. The brakes were put on so hard as almost to stop the wheels from turning, and still the coach nearly ran into the mules. It sometimes happened that the coach overturned half-way down the hill and the journey came to an end.

After crossing the Segovia Bridge, we went uphill again along the Extremadura Road. At the Segovia Bridge, Madrid ended and the country began. To call it country was only a manner of speaking, though, because there was nothing but a few shrivelled little trees along the road, without leaves and covered in dust, fields of yellow grass with black patches from bonfires, and a number of shacks built by the rag-pickers out of the sheet-metal from old tins, with big garbage dumps outside the door, which you could smell from the road.

My aunt did what she always did on a journey. As soon as the coach began to move, she crossed herself and started saying the Rosary. Her beads were of olive-wood which had come from Palestine, from the Garden of Olives, and had been blessed by the Pope. At home she had another rosary of silver beads, and a third one of agates which she had brought from France, from Lourdes; its cross had a small crystal set in the middle, and when you looked through it you saw Our Lady in the Grotto.

The road was full of ruts and dust. The coach went bumping along and the dust came in through the open windows so that we were enveloped in a cloud. When you moved your jaws your teeth chewed sand. But the sun was so fierce that we could not have shut the windows without getting stifled. One of the women felt sick. She knelt on the seat and stuck her head out of the window to vomit. In the intervals between vomiting, her head bounced up and down in the window like the head of a stuffed doll. By the time we arrived she would have spat out the lining of her bowels, for she started being sick twenty minutes after we left Madrid, and we still had over four hours to go.

I began to feel hungry. With all that fuss and hurry not to be too late for a seat in the coach, I had not had a bite since lunch. I said so

37

to my aunt, and she got cross with me. She told me to wait until she had said her Rosary, but she was only half-way through. Opposite us sat a fat man. He had taken out a loaf of bread with a *tortilla*—a potato-omelette—inside, sandwich-fashion. It smelt very good. He kept on cutting off pieces with his clasp-knife and eating them, and it made me ravenously hungry to watch him. I would have loved to beg a bite off him. Again I asked my aunt for something to eat, this time in a loud voice; surely the fat man would let me have a piece of his *tortilla* if she did not give me anything. And I wanted to make her so angry that she would refuse to let me eat, for she had taken nothing but bread and chocolate along, and what I wanted was the omelette. She did get angry. She pinched my thigh and gave me nothing. The fat man cut off a large chunk of bread and a slice of *tortilla* the size of half a brick, and offered them to me. My uncle let me take them and scolded my aunt: 'Must you always make a fool of yourself?' Then she produced the bread and chocolate, but I did not want them any more. The *tortilla* was fine, and the man gave me a few slices of dry sausage on top of it. I enjoyed it even more because I had got my way and my uncle had taken my side. He got out the leather bottle with the wine for our supper, accepted the *tortilla* himself, and so the three of us ate and drank. The two men started discussing me; the fat man took my uncle to be my father.

He told us he had a son who was studying law in Madrid, but had failed in his exams, and now was cramming to have another go at them in September. My uncle said that I was a very good scholar, and the fat man answered that his boy was a young rascal who cost him all the money he was earning from his farm. Then the two went on to talk of the crops. The man had a good deal of land in a village near Brunete and knew our whole family there; he had known my uncle's father and grandparents.

After the row about the food, my aunt had started telling the woman with the little girl, who was sitting opposite her, all about the worry and annoyance I caused her. I did not want to hear what she said, because otherwise I would have had to answer back and tell all about how she kept nagging me.

Our coach was going downhill into the valley of the Guadarrama, a river very much like the Manzanares, with hardly any water, nothing but a bed full of sand and a little stream running through rushes. The road made many bends and twists between the town of Móstoles and the river; there we had to cross a very old wooden bridge, so old that the passengers had to get out of the coach to lessen its weight. And then up another long slope, ending in Navalcarnero.

In the market square of Móstoles there stood a half-finished monument hidden under scaffolding and white sheets. It was a statue of the Mayor of Móstoles, and was meant to be inaugurated the following year, 1908, the Centenary of the War of Independence. That Mayor of Móstoles was mayor at the time when Napoleon tried to conquer Spain. He was an old fellow in a coffee-brown cloak with tiers of shoulder-capes, a big, wide-brimmed hat, and a tall staff. When he heard the French were in Madrid, he called the town-crir and gave him a proclamation to read to all the people of the town. And in it he, the Mayor of Móstoles, declared war on Napoleon. Of course it was foolish to think that a little place like that could make war against the armies of Napoleon. But if Napoleon had come to Móstoles and the Mayor had got hold of him all by himself, he would certainly have beaten him to death with his mayor's staff. In my *History of Spain* there was a picture of the Mayor reading out his proclamation, and a portrait of Napoleon in his greatcoat with white lapels, white trousers, and his hand thrust between the buttons of his coat.

Father Joaquín, my history master, a very tall Basque, told us that Napoleon could not conquer Spain, because there were many people like the Mayor of Móstoles, who were not afraid of him. In Madrid, two artillery lieutenants, Daoiz and Velarde, took a cannon and put themselves at the head of the people. In Saragossa, a woman, Agustina of Aragon, egged on the men and started firing off a cannon against the French. In Bailén, all the goadsmen—the herdsmen who kept watch over the wild bulls, riding on a horse and carrying a goad —got together and went out against the cuirassiers. They had nothing but their wooden goads with steel points, while the cuirassiers had strong lances, a plated steel cuirass and a steel helmet with a feather-bush. The cowboys just wore their jackets and their flat-brimmed hats, and there were far less of them than of the cuirassiers. But they gave Napoleon's cuirassiers such a thrashing that an Englishman called Wellington, who came to Spain to help us, was quite taken aback. The people in his country would not believe him when he told them about it.

My grandmother, my mother's mother, was a very small child when Napoleon's soldiers came to those villages. The French killed children with their bayonets, sticking them into their bottoms. So my grandmother's parents put her in a basket, let her down the well of the house, which had a vaulted side-shaft, and hid her there. Her mother went down to give her the breast whenever the soldiers were not looking. My grandmother was ninety-nine years old by now. My brother and sister and I called her our 'Little Grandmother', for she was a tiny, wrinkled old woman, her face and hands covered with

39

coffee-coloured spots. Our other grandmother we called our 'Big Grandmother', because she was much taller than a man and very big. We were going to meet her in Navalcarnero.

The mules were changed at the coaching-inn, and in the meantime, the people had supper, either their own food or a meal from the kitchen of the inn. We had hake fried in batter and pork fillets with fried red peppers, and my uncle invited the fat man to eat with us, because we had eaten up his *tortilla*. We also had black coffee which my aunt had taken along in a bottle wrapped in a thick layer of newspapers, so that it was still hot.

Big Grandmother sat down with us and lifted me on to her lap. It was like sitting in an easy-chair. She and my aunt began to chat, and as usual, they soon quarrelled. When both were little girls, they had played together in their village; they still called each other the first thing that came into their minds. My aunt was a bigot, and my grandmother an atheist. When they were both about twelve years old, their parents sent them to Madrid into service. My grandmother served in many houses before she married. My aunt started as a maid with a very old, very pious lady and stayed with her until she married my uncle. It was being with her old mistress which turned her into a bigot for good.

The two were different even in their manner of eating. My aunt ate tiny morsels, and my grandmother tucked in as much as the fat man, who stuffed as though he had never eaten the *tortilla* and the loaf of bread. And during the meal they discussed me.

'It's high time the boy got a bit of fresh air and stopped being tied to your apron-strings,' said my grandmother. 'You're turning him into a ninny with all your priests and prayers. Just look what a booby-face he has! It's a good job he's going to stay with me for a few days. I'll soon shake him awake!'

'Well, there's nothing the matter with the child,' my aunt bridled. 'The only trouble with him is that he's very naughty, and that's why he doesn't put on weight. As to his education, I can't imagine what you can have against it. Except, of course, that you would like the boy to become an unbeliever like yourself. It would be better for you if you remembered your age, as I do, and that you will go straight to hell if you carry on like this.'

'All the better, it's warmer there. And anyhow, all good-humoured people go to hell, and all tiresome bigots like you go to heaven. And I can tell you frankly, I prefer to be with amusing people. You simply smell of wax.'

'Jesus Christ, you're always saying blasphemous things, and you'll come to a very bad end.'

'I'll be damned! If I say anything blasphemous, it's because somebody's trodden on my corn in the street, or because I pinch my finger in a door. After all, one's a woman, and not a carter! What I am not, and what I don't want the boy to become is a hysterical woman like yourself, who can't get away from the skirts of the priests and sacristans!'

My aunt started to sob, and then my grandmother felt quite miserable. In the end, they made it up and my grandmother said:

'Now, look here, Baldomera, of course I know that you're very kind and that the boy has a very good home with you, but all the same, you're turning him into a nitwit. You go on praying as much as you like, but let the boy play. Because that's what you want, isn't it,' she added, turning to me, 'to play?'

I did not want to make my aunt even more annoyed with me, so I said that I liked going to church very much. And then my grandmother exploded:

'You're a sissy, that's what you are!' And she squeezed me in her big arms and crushed me against her breasts, as though I were being smothered by a feather-bed. I felt hurt and said nothing, but two big tears ran down my face. And then my grandmother lost her head. She took me in her arms, kissed me, hugged me, shook me like a doll, and made me promise to come and stay with her in September and to give her my word that I wasn't angry with her. She took me along to the bar-table of the tavern, filled my pockets with monkey-nuts, and roasted chick-peas, bewildered me with a stream of questions, and only calmed down after I had assured her again and again that I was not angry, but that I wasn't a sissy either, and that, if she called me a sissy again, I would not visit her at Navalcarnero.

We arrived in Brunete at ten o'clock that night. I was completely worn out and only wanted to go to bed.

The village was a heap of houses, deep black shadows or very white walls gleaming with the same light as the moon itself. People were sitting or lying in the doorways to get a breath of air, a few chatting, but most of them asleep. When we walked through the village to the house of Uncle Hilario, my Uncle José's brother, the people got up to welcome us, and some offered us doughnuts and brandy. I didn't want any, the only thing I wanted was to sleep. The night watchman of the village came up to us, slapped my uncle on the shoulder, patted me and said:

'So, you're a man now!'

Then he stood on tip-toe, stretching his neck like a cock about to crow, put one hand to his mouth and shouted:

'Eleven o' the clock, and clear!'

IV. WHEAT LANDS

The sunlight, speckled with flies, streamed through the small square window over the head of my bed. The room smelt of village, of sun-dried grain in the corn-loft opposite, of furze burning in the kitchen, of clinging reek from the chicken-coop and of dung in the stables, and of the mud walls of the house, baked dry by the sun and covered with whitewash.

I dressed and went down the stairs, massive logs hewn with the adze.

The ground floor was a huge room floored with small river pebbles. Beside the doorway were the water-racks which carried eight big-bellied pitchers of white clay, beaded with moisture; their linen cover had a centre-piece with initials a span long, embroidered in red wool. In the middle of the room stood the table of stout pine planks, white from being scrubbed with sand and big enough to seat the whole family and the farm-hands, some twenty in all. Seeds which had to be sorted out were spread out on it, and when Aunt Braulia ironed the household linen, her ironing blanket covered no more than one of its corners. Along the walls stood a great number of chairs of plaited straw, a heavy mahogany commode, and a chest with a rounded lid covered by a tawny-haired hide and studded with gilt nails and a lock like an old door knocker. Above the chest was the cuckoo-clock, its brass weights hanging from gilded chains, its pendulum running from one side to the other without ever bumping against the wall, a little bunch of flowers painted in each of the four corners of the wooden dial, and above it, the little window of the cuckoo, a small wooden bird which chanted the hours and half-hours. When the hand of the clock was about to reach the full hour, it stopped as though it had found a pebble in its path. Then it made a sudden jump on the dial and one of the weights fell down very fast, setting the whole machinery turning so that it rattled like a box full of nails. The din frightened the cuckoo; he opened the door of his little house and began to sing, curtseying and stretching out his neck to see whether this time the weight had not got smashed on the floor. When he had sung the hour he went back and shut the door until the half-hour, when he came out, but only gave a single cry in a surly way, as if he had been disturbed for something silly which was not worth his while.

The cuckoo-clock always reminded me of the village night-watchman, and the night-watchman reminded me of the cuckoo-clock.

The man walked to and fro in the village street the whole night, watching the clock on the church tower and the sky. Every time the clock struck the hour, he had to cry it out and announce the weather: 'Two o' the clock, and clear. . . . Two o' the clock, and cloudy. . . . Two o' the clock, and raining.' In times of drought, when people were afraid of losing their crops, neighbours would wake each other up as soon as the night-watchman sang out the hour and 'raining'. They would go and stand under their doorways to get wet, and some would go out to their fields to make sure that the water was falling on them and not only on the fields of their neighbours.

At the far end of the room there was the hearth, with the larder on one side and the door to the stables on the other. The hearth was a circle of tiles, flanked by two stone benches. Above it was a bell-shaped chimney lined with soot; you could see the sky through the hole at the top. On the wall hung the pots and pans, ancient copper and iron pots, blue-and-white Talavera jars and kitchen irons, spits, grills, and so on. The wide shelf of the mantelpiece was stacked with dishes, bowls, and crocks, in their middle a big, round platter like a sun. It was an earthenware platter half an inch thick, with dirty blue flowers on a greenish-yellow ground and a rim of metallic blue. This was the oldest piece of crockery in the kitchen. On the back it had a curious sign like a tattoo mark and an inscription in blue old-fashioned lettering which said 'Talavera 1742'.

Aunt Braulia used to scour her metal things with lye made from dung ash. Her iron looked like silver and her copper like gold. The ash came from the hearth, for the fire was a big heap of dried dung with a heart of embers smouldering day and night. If you thrust a shovel through the crust you saw a ball of fire red as a pomegranate. You stuck the iron point of a huge pair of bellows into its middle, blew on it, and a flame would leap up. Then you threw furze into the flame to keep it burning, and put the three-legged frying-pan on top of the fire. When you had finished that part of your cooking, you closed the fire-hole with the shovel and nothing was left but the yellow, smoking heap of dry dung and the ring of pots round it, in which the stews were slowly simmering. Red sausages and black-puddings were hung inside the bell of the chimney to be dried and cured by the smoke.

When I came down there was nobody in the room but Aunt Braulia, who was sitting on a low stool beside the fire. The first thing she said was that I must be hungry and she would get me my break-fast at once. They were all crazy about my food whenever I stayed in the village. They had got it into their heads that they had to stuff me and fatten me up. But in reality there were far less things to be had in

43

Brunete than in Madrid. In Brunete, the only fruit was grapes from the grape vines on the house walls, and they were not yet ripe. The only meat they ever saw was lamb and pork from the last slaughtering, laid in pickle or smoke-cured. I knew beforehand the kind of meals I would get: fried eggs for breakfast, a stew of chick-peas with bits of red sausage, bacon and mutton at midday, and potatoes boiled with a piece of meat or dried cod in the evening. Occasionally a man with a donkey brought a few cases of sardines or hake from Madrid, but not in the summer, for the fish would have gone bad on the journey. So the only fish they got in the village were dried-up sardines out of the grocer's barrel, their eyes and bellies yellow with oil, or dried salt cod. There were no green vegetables. Brunete lies in a dry plain without trees or water, where nothing grows but wheat, barley, chick-peas, and vetch. They had to fetch their water with donkeys from two miles away, from a ravine which was just a kind of crack in the ground, petering out in the far distance towards the Sierra.

For food I preferred Méntrida and Navalcarnero to Brunete, above all Méntrida, where my mother's people lived and where I was going to stay after Brunete. Méntrida had orchards and gardens, game, partridges, and rabbits, and there were fine fish and eels in the river near by, the Alberche. They also got fish by train from Madrid. And the village always had plenty of beautiful grapes and tomatoes, cucumbers, and lettuce. In a place called Valdiguera there were hundreds of very old fig-trees which had round, fat figs with bright red flesh and a taste of honey; people called them *melares*, 'honey-sweets'. Every family owned two or three of those fig-trees, and when I came to visit them, they would all invite me to pick myself figs early in the morning when the chill of the night was still on them.

Méntrida had all those things because it lies in the valley of a little river flowing into the Alberche, which has a strip of poplar-grown meadowland with many garden plots.

Brunete had a few wells, but they were very deep and the water was brackish. In Méntrida, every house had a well of its own, and many had to make a ditch from the well to the street, because the water would overflow in winter. It was very cold, sweet water.

Navalcarnero was different again. It lies on the top of a hill and in the town itself there is nothing, but its fields, which all lie on the slope down to the river Guadarrama, produce grapes, fruit, and vegetables as well. Moreover it is so near to Madrid that it gets most of the things to be had in town.

Yet with all that, it was Aunt Braulia who prided herself most on her cooking. Other people in Brunete had nothing but an onion and bread in the morning before going to work in the fields, a *gazpacho* —bread, onions, and cucumber in vinegar and water with very little oil—at midday, and a stew in the evening, made just of chick-peas and a slice of bacon. They tasted meat only two or three times a year. But Uncle Hilario, Aunt Braulia's husband and the eldest brother of my Uncle José, had become one of the richest men in the village.

There had been six brothers, and all escaped when lots were drawn for the call-up, except my Uncle José. At that time, conscript soldiers stayed in barracks eight years. When Uncle José was called up, he was just a yokel like the others and could not read or write. They had been a very poor family, as there were so many children; they only got chick-pea and bacon-rind stews, and at that the poorest chick-peas which they had kept back for seed, because the picked ones fetched more money and they sold them. In barracks, Uncle José learnt to read and write. In the meantime his parents died and his brothers worked their land in common and married. Although my Uncle José had left his share of the land to them, they were starving, what with all the wives and the children who soon arrived. In those years it sometimes happened that they had no money to hire mules or donkeys to till their fields, and then the men and women would draw the plough. Aunt Braulia had drawn it many times. But meanwhile Uncle José, who had no intention of going back to the plough, had become a sergeant and after his discharge he got a post in the War Ministry, because he had beautiful handwriting and was good at figures. Then he began to save up money and to lend it to his brothers, so that they had no more need to beg loans from the village usurer to whom they had to pay a peseta for every five he lent them. And after the wheat harvest they no longer sold the grain to the usurer either, because my uncle sold it in Madrid for them. They all shared in the profits. Then came the Cuban war. My uncle had lent money to other people in the village as well. One day he went there, called all his relations and the older men of the village together and told them that, if they let him have their wheat, he would sell it for them to the army people in Madrid at a much higher price than they got from the usurer. Then they became rich, and my uncle gave them enough money to buy more land and mules. They all worked together under Uncle Hilario, but it was my Uncle José who was in command. The other half of the village lands belonged to the people who were in debt with the usurer.

The usurer was a distant relative of ours, Don Luis Bahía, who had left the village when he was a little boy and later became a millionaire through the Jesuits. He was one of their agents; my Uncle José said he himself really had no money, and the money he lent to people

45

belonged to the Jesuits, who got hold of the land in that way.[1] I knew him from Madrid, for he had dealings with my uncle and I went along to his office a few times; but he scared me. He was old, bald, with a big head and a very fleshy nose curved like the beak of a parrot, and he watched you out of very cold eyes. His skin was like yellow wax. He always wore a black suit, with black office-sleeves up to his elbows, and a round silk cap with a tassel. His office was papered a dark green and the crocheted net curtains on his balcony windows were green too, so that the whole room was in darkness and his face looked like the head of a slimy beast in its lair. Once, in Méntrida, I had seen a big toad sitting among the water weeds, and I thought of him.

I ate the fried eggs and red sausage Aunt Braulia put before me, and then went out to the threshing-floors.

The village was a single street through which the main road passed. The fields, already cut, were yellow with stubble. In a place where the ground rose lay the threshing-floors. They were flat circular spaces paved with round cobbles, which had to be swept very clean before the sheaves were spread out. Then a stout plank studded with spiky flint-stones, a kind of harrow, dragged by a mule, went round and round the carpet of wheat-ears, separating the grain from the straw. The boys rode on the plank, one to guide the mule and all the others as a game. We would jostle and push each other from the rocking plank and tumble on to the mattress of straw. The only risk was of falling in front of the plank and being run over by the harrow. This had happened to one of my small cousins, and it left scarred lines all over his back as though he had been tattooed by Indians.

Further away on the threshing-floors, men winnowed the crushed straw, tossing it into the air against the wind, so that the chaff was blown away and the heavy grains left. We boys ran into the cloud of chaff, rowing with our arms and shutting our eyes, and our skin got full of tiny needles which stuck and would not let us sleep at night. Then we rolled in the hills of clean wheat until the hard grains filled our ears, mouth, and nostrils, and slipped into our socks and pockets. At least, that was what happened to me. But my cousins' skin was so tanned by the sun and dust that the straw needles did not prick them, and they had neither socks nor sandals, for they all went barefoot, and no pockets either, such as I had in my blouse. They wore nothing but a shirt and a pair of knickers tied with string round their middle. What bothered me most was the sun. During the first days in

[1] After the death of Don Luis Bahía, a lawsuit, widely discussed all over Spain, was fought over his will by which he left over thirty million pesetas to the Society of Jesus.—*Author's Note*.

46

the country my skin always went pink, my nose and cheeks peeled, and I kept on changing my skin like a lizard, until I was nearly as brown as my cousins by the time I went back to Madrid. But I never went as brown as Uncle Hilario.

Uncle Hilario was a tall old man with large bones, very much dried-up. He had a completely bald head full of lumps, with a wen on top which looked like a plum; but the skin of his skull was so dark you hardly noticed that he had no hair at all. The skin at the back of his neck was coarse and dry, and seamed by deep wrinkles which looked as if they had been carved with a knife. He used to shave on Thursdays and Sundays, as priests do, and then the shaved part of his face was so much whiter than the rest of his head that it looked as though it had been rubbed with emery paper. Sometimes he took one of my hands, which were rather soft and thin, laid it on one of his own big, broad hands with broken nails, and made a bewildered face. Then he would press my hand between both of his, and I imagined what would happen if he were to rub his hands: he would skin my hand with the hard, calloused lumps on his palms. The wood of the plough-handle shone like the varnished rails of our staircase at home, because Uncle Hilario had rubbed his hard palms over it so often.

At noon the church clock struck twelve, and we all went back to the house to eat. Aunt Braulia had laid the table and put a deep dish in the middle, into which she poured stew from an iron pot over a hundred years old. It had been burnt by the fire until it looked like black porous clay. On each side of the table stood a big, long-spouted flagon of wine, but only my uncle, my aunt, and I had glasses. The others drank from the free jet, holding the flagon at arm's length and tipping the spout. It was the same with the food. The six children all ate from one bowl. The grown-ups ate from the big dish. But as we were there, they had put plates for the three of us, and for Uncle Hilario and Aunt Braulia. The children and farm-hands ate what was left over when we had been served.

After the meal it was too hot to go back to work at once, and all took a short siesta. Some simply lay down on the stones in the doorway which was very cool because the entrances from the street and from the stable were both covered with a thick curtain, so that the sun was shut out but a current of air let through. And, though it was an odd thing to happen, the two stone benches by the fire were very cool, for a strong draught swept up through the chimney, and by the hearth it was like a ventilator fan.

At two the men went back to the fields, but they left me behind because the sun was too strong for me while I was still not used to it So nobody woke me, until I wakened by myself at five o'clock.

47

Both my aunts were standing in the doorway with three other women, telling all the stories of the village since they had been young. I would have liked to play, but my cousins were working now and I was afraid of going out into the street. As there was not a tree in the village and all the houses were white, the street was like an oven and even the stones were too hot to be touched. So I made a voyage of discovery all round the house.

In the corn-loft, which the village people simply called 'the loft', were three big heaps, wheat, barley, and vetch, piled up to the rafters. There were big, dense spiders' webs, and for a time I amused myself catching flies. I tore their wings off and threw the flies into the spiders' webs.

A fly got entangled in the web, and the spider stuck her head out of her hidey-hole. After a short while she came running out, her body like a black chick-pea slung high on legs like bent wires. She wrapped all her legs round the fly and carried it off. When she was running across her web, I thought she was going to jump on to me and bite me. I felt sick and scared, so I took a broom and started to smash up all the cobwebs. From one of them a fat yellow spider with a body like a boiled clam fell on to the floor, ran along the boards and came very near to my feet. I stamped on her and ran down the ladder of the loft. Downstairs I wiped my shoe-sole on the hearth stones. Some bits of hairy legs came off it, still jerking.

There were swallows' nests on the rafters near the doorway. I put a chair on the chest and climbed up to see one of them from close to. I wondered how the Chinese were able to eat swallows' nests; they were nothing but small bowls of hard mud. Inside they were lined with wheat straw. Nobody would have hurt a swallow, for the swallows eat vermin in the fields, and when Christ was crucified, the swallows picked thorns out of His brow.

Once my Uncle José caught a swallow and tied a thin silver wire round one of her legs, and she came back the next year. But after that she never came back again. She had probably died in the meantime, for swallows have a short life. But storks live very long. It was because of the story of the village stork that Uncle José had tried to find out about the swallow.

On the roof of the church there was a stork's nest like a heap of firewood. Once the priest who was in the village at the time, a very old man who used to collect wild insects, caught a stork and put a big copper ring with the inscription 'Spain' round one of his legs. When the stork came back the next year, he had round his other leg a silver ring with letters nobody could read; but a professor who came from Madrid specially to see it said they were in Arabic and read 'Istanbul', which meant a province in Turkey. Then the priest tied a little ribbon with the national colours to the ring, and the stork came back with a red ribbon instead. That stork died in Brunete, and the priest kept the two rings and seven red ribbons in the sacristy of his church.

There were other birds in Brunete too, but none of them could be eaten. There were the black-and-white magpies which liked to walk about in the road, stepping like little women. There were the crows, a smaller kind of raven, which came in flocks and called 'ca-ca-ca-ca'. They turned up when a dead mule had been thrown into the ravine, and ate it. For whenever a mule or donkey died in the village it was taken out to the ravine where the spring was and thrown into a deep hollow there. This hollow was far away from the spring and from the village, but I went there once, and it was full of white skeletons of mules and donkeys. The crows were sitting round the ravine and cackling. They were like malicious old women grousing and grumbling. When you came near they rose into the air and kept flying in circles over your head, cawing and calling until you went away.

There was still another kind of bird, the bats. They came out in the dusk and began to fly through the village street and to bang against the house walls because they were white. We boys hunted them with a tablecloth or other white cloth tied to two sticks which we held over our heads. When the bat bumped against the white cloth, we clapped the sticks together, and the bat was caught in the folds. Then the bats were nailed to a wall by their wings. Their wings were like the thin fabric of an umbrella, but hairy, and tore without bleeding, as easily as an old rag; their body looked like a mouse with a little pig's snout and pointed ears, like the devil's. When they were wrapped in their wings, they seemed old women in big shawls, and when they were hanging asleep from the rafters, they seemed little children such as the storks carry in their bills in fairy-tales.

When the bats were stuck on a wall, the men used to light a cigarette and make them smoke it. The bats got drunk with the smoke and made funny movements with their nose and belly and eyes, which filled with water. We laughed a lot. But when I saw them nailed to the wall, drunken with smoke, I was sorry for them and I thought they were a bit human, a bit like a baby that had slipped out of its swaddling clothes, with its little tummy naked. And once I tried to explain to the people what I had learnt at school: that the bats eat vermin. But they laughed at me and said they were foul beasts which sucked the blood of sleeping people, biting them behind the ears. And they said a girl had died that way; or rather, not quite died—but she had grown whiter and whiter, with no blood left in her, and nobody knew what was the matter with her until they found a bat in her bed, and a small drop of blood behind her ear. They burnt the bat and gave the girl its ashes to eat mixed with wine, on an empty stomach. And she got well. For this reason, they killed all the bats they could, so they said.

But when they grew tired of torturing the bat, one of the lads tore it from the wall, and the poor beast lay on the gutter stones, moving the tatters of its thin wings and wrinkling its little nose, and I could not believe that it had ever been capable of killing anyone.

Brunete was a boring village. Its fields had no trees, and no fruit, and no flowers, and no birds, and men and children were rough and taciturn. Now, when the wheat was harvested and they had made some money, was the only time when they had a little fun, at the fairs. But they were the poorest fairs I knew. A few traders set up stalls in the market square, lit by small oil lamps or candles, where they sold trash for two coppers. But nobody bought anything, so they used to raffle it for a copper, which was the only way to get rid of their stuff. A fireworks-man came to the fair and let off fifteen or twenty rockets in front of the church every night between ten and twelve, that was all; only on the very last day he lit five or six catherine wheels.

The only things which amused those people were the bulls. And even there they showed the kind of brutes they were.

The village square was unpaved, full of ruts, with an iron lamp-post on a stone base in the middle. Round this plaza people would draw up their carts on the eve of a bullfight; the shaft of each cart was riding on the bottom planks of the next and all of them were roped together so that they should not slide apart. This was a sort of barrier and a gangway with an uneven floor, where people could stand. The village lads and the children would squat between the wheels, in reach of the bull's head, and from there they would watch the fight or sally to take part in it. The bulls were kept penned up in a blind alley opening into the square, where the butcher had his corral. It was called Christ Alley.

The fiesta started on the first day of the fair with what they called the 'Bull of the First Drop', because he was let loose almost at dawn, at the time when the men took their early morning glass of spirits. The carts filled with women, old men, and children who shouted when the bull came out—a bull-calf, good enough to be played by the village lads.

At first the little bull attacked and threw the lads. But he was so small and young that they managed to hold him by the horns, drag him to the ground, kick him with their heavy boots and beat him

50

with their sticks. At eleven in the morning he reeled on his legs and gave no more fight, but fled from the gang of lads and boys who by then all dared to come out into the plaza. He backed against the wheels of the carts, but from there they pricked at him with knives and the old men held their burning cigar butts against his haunches to make the beast attack again in blind rage. And so it went on till noon.

We watched from the balcony of the Town Hall, where we stood with the mayor, the doctor, the apothecary, and the priest. The mayor and the priest were both fat men, they roared with laughter and slapped each other on the back as they pointed out each detail to one another.

At four in the afternoon the real bulls began. First the village lads fought two young bulls which had learnt cunning in other village bull-fights and tossed the boys against the carts as though they wanted to avenge the bull-calf of the morning. They stayed in the ring a long time until there was no-one left who cared to brave them. Then they were driven back into the corral, and the 'bull of death' was released.

He had to be killed by a team of four *maletillas*, torero-apprentices who went round the villages fighting bulls, and starving. As they did not come from this village, the mayor had bought a huge old bull with enormous horns, taller than any of the little bull-fighters. The poor lads cowered when he came into the square and they saw his bulk, but the village people began to shout and some of the young men jumped into the ring, brandishing their sticks.

It was a pitiful thing to see those lads in their shabby, patched-up bull-fighter's costume, its gold spangles tarnished or missing, running round the bull's head in little spurts and flicking their cape under his nose, only to flee, and then to clamber up the lamp-post when they were driven away with sticks from the cart barrier. But that was still nothing.

The bugle of the band sounded the banderilla tune, and the public bellowed with joy. For now it was not enough to make little dashes at the bull. Now the banderillas had to be placed, and that meant being at the very horns of the bull. And the little toreros knew only too well that their hope of gain lay in this feat, and in the killing.

It was the custom to dedicate each pair of banderillas to one of the rich men of the place. Then, if they had been placed well, that is to say, in the nape of the bull's thick neck, the rich man would shell out two *duros*—ten pesetas—or even five *duros*, and when the team made the round of the carts to collect, people would fill the cape with big coppers and one or the other silver coin thrown in. If the banderillas were not placed, there was no money, and if all banderilleros failed, they usually got stones instead of cash.

The lean and hungry little torero takes up his stand at the far end of the plaza. He turns his pallid face and looks back distrustfully at the sticks of the village lads threatening his back, some with a spike and some with a knife tied to their points; and he turns again in panic to look at the savage beast in front of him up to whose horns he must get, so as to raise his arms, stretch his belly and chest in a single movement, and drive home the be-ribboned sticks before the horns are driven into his own body.

And there is the 'pass of death'. The matador is as a rule a young lad of seventeen or eighteen, more suicidally inclined than his comrades, with the face of a mystic. He needs an inspired skill to fight bulls in those villages. If he were to kill the bull by a clean sword-thrust, so that it is felled without having to be finished off, the people would feel defrauded. He must play the bull for a long time, he must thrust to kill, not once but many times, with art and courage. He must not jab at the bull's ribs or shoulder-blades from the side, but hurl himself at its horns. And only then, when he has demonstrated his valour and made the women shriek with fear ten times over, may he lunge and thrust in his sword, to the hilt, if he can, wounding the bull in its entrails so that it is left standing in the ring on four straddled legs, vomiting blood in dark gushes until it crumples up, turning over on its back, its legs thrashing the air.

Then the public goes mad with enthusiasm. Silver coins, cigars, and pieces of sausage rain down, and uncorked wine bottles pour wine on the people in gushes as the bull had vomited its blood, and the little torero must drink from those bottles to quench his thirst and to bring some colour back into his cheeks.

For the occasions when the bull gores young flesh, there is a little door in the Town Hall, which says 'First Aid'. Inside is a pine table, scrubbed with sand and lye, and a few pitchers of hot water. On a straw-bottomed chair in a corner lie the doctor's case with a few old instruments and, for safety's sake, the butcher's carving knives and meat saw. The wounded lad is laid on the table, naked, and given a rough and ready treatment. The blood is staunched with wads of cotton wool, soaked in iodine as one might soak sponge-fingers in wine, and pressed on with bare fingers, and the gash is stitched up with thick needles and coarse, twisted silk yarn reeled off a ball, which the old women of the village prepare, just as they prepare the thread to tie the umbilical cord. Then the boy is put on a mattress and taken in a cart to Madrid, along a road full of sun and of dust.

As a quiet little boy, perched on the chair with the doctor's case, I have seen one of those butcher's cures done to a lad with his head dangling from the table, his eyes glazed, his hair dripping sweat, whose torero dress had been slit open with a knife, so that they could get at a gash in his thigh so deep that there was room in it for the doctor's hand.

When the bull-fights are over, the people dance and drink.

V. WINE LANDS

The square iron rod of the axle passed right through the middle of the cart. It had no springs and leapt so violently every time the wheels bumped over a hole or stone in the road that you had to take care not to get a knock. Uncle José and Uncle Hilario sat in the front seats and passed each other the reins of the mule from time to time. My aunt and I sat at the back, facing each other. The small, two-wheeled cart had two lateral wooden seats covered with rush mats, a roof of curved canes with a white canvas tilt, and a pair of canvas curtains in front and at the back. We were going to Méntrida, but Uncle Hilario was going to drive back in his cart that evening so as to sleep at home in Brunete.

When you reach the crest of the hill you see the road-mender's hut and a white-washed well with a cone-shaped roof. It has a window with an iron grille that can be locked and inside a bucket and chain so that all who pass by on the road may drink. From there the hill slopes down, and you can see Méntrida.

The yellow and grey fields of the dry earth, without trees and without water, stay behind, and the green land begins. From the mountains of the Escorial, purple in the distance, to the hills of Toledo at the end of a horseshoe of far-away ridges, the land is utterly green, green with trees and green with gardens. The corn-fields are yellow patches and the vineyards white patches flecked with green; for the soil of the vineyards is whiter and sandier than that of the wheat lands. Scattered between the vines in many of the vineyards are olive-trees, large posies of silver green amongst the bright green of the grape vine.

Méntrida is ringed by a chain of hills, all of them tunnelled: they are its wine-cellars. For if Brunete is the land of bread, Méntrida is the land of wine. When you look at the hills from afar they seem pitted with black holes. Each of these holes has a low oaken door with a padlock and above it a small, square window with crossbars through which the wine draws its breath, the wine in the fat-bellied earthen jars standing in the niches of the cave. If you put your face close to one of the little windows, the hill smells drunk.

The streets of Méntrida climb up the hills around the ravine which passes through the middle of the village and is its sewer. On the highest hill, at the far end of a street too steep for carts, stands the church. The house of my grandmother, my mother's mother, was in the little square before the porch, and our cart had to make a loop round the village to get there.

It was a small house. If you looked at it from the church terrace it had one storey, and if you looked at it from the street on the hillside it had two storeys. If you went in by the front door you had a basement under your feet, and if you walked in by the side door you had a storey over your head, so nobody ever quite knew which floor he was on. The door on the hillside was always locked, and the door on to the church terrace was a swing door with a sign-board on top of it, which showed a high ladies' boot with innumerable buttons and the lettering 'Shoemaker'.

The shoemaker was my Uncle Sebastian, a tiny old man with many wrinkles—but not so many as my grandmother had—who was married to my mother's sister, Aunt Aquilina. Uncle Sebastian made and repaired boots and shoes, but by this time he took in only little work, because he suffered from asthma. Apart from Grandmother, there lived in the house his daughter Elvira with her husband Andrés, and their two children who were much younger than I was. My brother Rafael and my sister Concha were staying there for a time too.

When our cart stopped in the little church square, they all came out of the door, one after the other. Rafael and Concha were first, they came running out to greet Uncle and Aunt to see whether they had brought them anything from Madrid. Then came my two little cousins, shuffling along like two funny little animals. The boy was very thin, with a big tummy and a big head; he was called Fídel and had a yellow face with ears which looked as if they had no blood in them and were of wax. The girl was called Angelita and when she moved, her steel corset and the steel joints of the boots she had to wear creaked. After them came their parents, he a big, strong man and she a woman who was always ailing and limped from an ulcer on her leg. Then Aunt Aquilina and Uncle Sebastian came out arm in arm, a cheery old couple, always happy. And last of all came Grandmother Eustaquia in her black dress, with her nobbly stick,

54

little grey eyes, chin and nose almost touching each other, and a skin like brown parchment, as wrinkled as a dried fig. Next year she would have her hundredth birthday, if she did not die before. But it was more likely that she would bury all the rest. She was up at five every morning, sweeping the house, lighting the fire and making breakfast. She could never keep still for a second and went trotting about from one floor to the other, tapping with her stick so that nobody could go on sleeping. As soon as she saw that our eyes were open, she would chase us out of bed, calling us sluggards and saying that beds were made for sleeping, not for dawdling. And you had to jump out of bed if you did not want to risk a whack from her stick.

Uncle José and Aunt Baldomera were going to spend the night there, but they had to catch the train to Madrid at six in the morning. It was a most boring day, because they were treated like fine folk from Madrid. We stayed in the house all the time, my brother and sister wore their best clothes, and the grown-ups spent the whole afternoon telling each of us in turn to keep quiet and not to quarrel. We would have liked to get out and run about, but as we could not do that, we had a number of rows which all ended with my brother's and sister's ears getting boxed, because of course it had to be their fault. Nobody would have dared to smack me in front of my aunt. But my sister pinched me and whispered:

'You just wait till to-morrow, I'll rub your nose in the dirt for you. You'd better make the best of it while your dear auntie's here!'

And I made the best of it, of course, by repeating her threats out loud, which earned her some more cuffs. In the end they turned the pair of them out into the street so that we should get some peace. I stayed indoors, very cross because I could not go out with them, and at the same time very pleased because everyone had taken my part.

Andrés was a master mason, and he told my uncle stories about how things were going in his trade. Uncle Sebastian was sitting on his cobbler's bench and did nothing but cough and grunt. As he liked me very much and I liked him very much too, I went to him and asked him what was the matter.

'This damned cough's choking me, my boy,' he said between two wheezes, 'and your aunt won't let me smoke, which is the only thing that helps my cough. . . . As though at my age anything mattered anyhow.'

I went to Uncle José and asked him:

'Give me a cigarette for Uncle Sebastian, please.'

They all cried out, but I explained that Uncle's Cuban cigarettes were so mild that they could not do him any harm. So they let him smoke. He stopped coughing and they had to admit I was right. Uncle José gave him a whole packet of cigarettes. Uncle Sebastian smoked them hungrily, one after the other, and at nightfall he had a very bad fit of coughing, I did not know whether because he had run out of cigarettes and wanted some more, or because he had smoked too many.

Next morning we all went down to the station with my uncle and aunt. It was more than three miles from the village and we had to go in the cart of Old Neira, the mail carrier, who took passengers to and from the station. He also owned an inn and wagons which carted wine to Madrid. It was still night when we got up, for the train passed through at half-past six and we had to make our journey to the station in the dawn.

The truth of it was that I was already waiting for my uncle and aunt to be gone. I would have been glad if Uncle had stayed on by himself, for he left me alone, but my aunt was impossible. On the other hand I was afraid that my brother and sister would get even with me for the cuffs of the day before. At the very last moment my aunt started giving good advice to Aunt Aquilina and me: about the right food for 'the child'; about what 'the child' liked best and what disagreed with him; about the clothes I ought to put on; about my going to Mass on Sundays and saying my morning and evening prayers; and that they must take great care so that I should not be run over or be bitten by a dog. When the train started moving, I thought they all were glad to see the last of her; she was still leaning out of the window and shouting instructions.

On our way back to the village, Old Neira stopped at a market garden he had by the roadside, and brought us a heap of cucumbers, tomatoes, and purple-skinned, mild onions. He took bread, dry sausages and a leather bottle of wine from his saddlebags, and we had breakfast there in his garden. The cucumbers and tomatoes still had the night chill on them and they were good to eat, sprinkled with salt. If my aunt had seen me, she would have cried to heaven, for I ate five or six cucumbers, and she would have thought I was going to die on the spot.

We had only just got home, when Aunt Rogelia, another of my mother's sisters, entered in great excitement:

'It's past belief that you shouldn't have come to see us yet! It's one thing that you can't stand my Luis'—she addressed my grandmother—'but it's quite another thing that the boy shouldn't even be allowed to visit his aunt!'

They told her it had not been their fault; that my uncle and aunt had not gone out all afternoon and that we had just seen them off to

Madrid; that in any case I should have gone to see all my relatives that day.

My Aunt Rogelia, who was a plump little woman, strong and energetic, took me by the hand and said firmly:

'Well, all right then, he's coming to eat with me.'

Aunt Aquilina protested, saying she had already prepared a meal, but all her arguments were in vain. I was pleased, because Uncle Luis's place was wonderful. So we trotted through the village and stopped at every house, because my aunt had to show me off to I don't know how many relations and neighbours.

When we got to their house, we found my Uncle Luis surrounded by village lads, sharpening ploughshares. He did not interrupt his work. We had to step gingerly around the crowd, or we should have risked a knock on the head from one of the hammers they were all swinging. In the little house at the back my two girl cousins were just tidying up, and they hugged me and kissed me. Aunt Rogelia brought out some buns and I ate a couple of them, but then I slipped away to the forge.

My Uncle Luis was the village blacksmith, and his two sons, Aquilino who was nineteen, and Feliciano who was sixteen, were his assistants. He was a big, tall, stout man in a leather apron and rolled-up sleeves. The skin of his arms was very white, with black smudges all over. In one hand he would hold the great tongs which gripped the end of a red-hot horseshoe, and in the other hand a little hammer, with which he beat time for the sledge hammers wielded by Aquilino and the other lads and struck the hot iron when he wanted to shape it. That was always a marvellous thing to me.

He would put a piece of iron in the furnace, and Feliciano and I would pull the chain of the bellows—a bellows big enough to hold the two of us—in a regular rhythm, so that it fanned the coal until the iron was glowing white and throwing sparks. He would place the iron on the anvil and the lads struck one after the other with their heavy sledge hammers, flattening and lengthening the iron which spat glowing chunks and grew first red and then purple. Uncle Luis shifted it with his tongs so that each blow struck the right place. Suddenly he would smite a few light blows on the nose of the anvil which rang like a bell, and start hammering the iron all alone until it changed shape, curved, fined down at the points, and became a horseshoe. Last of all he struck a small flap out of the curve itself, which became the calkin for the toe of the hoof. Then he gripped the punch in another pair of tongs, and Aquilino struck it home with his sledge hammer, one blow for each nail-hole. Uncle Luis always had seven holes made, for he said that it brought good luck to find a

57

horseshoe with seven holes, and he wanted to bring good luck to the whole world.

My Uncle Luis belonged to a race of men which has almost disappeared; he was a craftsman and gentleman. He was so deeply in love with his craft that to him the iron was something alive and human. At times he talked to it. Once he was commissioned to make the wrought-iron railings and window-screens for the 'castle' as people called the house of the richest landowner in the place. The masterpiece, a screen for a tall window, as large as a balcony, was to be placed in the middle of the façade over the doorway. He took no money for it, so as to have the right to let his imagination run riot with his hammer and to shape the iron to his taste. Into that screen he poured his vision of a fancy world of leaves and tendrils twining round stout bars, perhaps influenced by his visits to the great silver screen in Toledo Cathedral, which he knew by heart.

Physically he was a Castilian of the old breed, a man with a cast-iron stomach. He rose with the dawn and 'killed the worm', as he said, with a glass of brandy which he himself had distilled in a patched and mended copper still, from the crushed grapes out of which he had pressed the juice for his wine. Then he went to work in the forge. At seven he had his breakfast, a stewed rabbit, or a brace of pigeons, or something on that scale, with a big bowl of salad. After that he forged his iron until noon when, with the stroke of the bell, he stopped and went to eat, even if the iron had just left the furnace.

His midday meal was either the true Castilian *cocido*, chick-peas studded with chunks of bacon, red sausage, and ham, with bits of chicken and large, greasy marrow bones, or else a rich potato stew, with more chunks of meat than potatoes. For dessert he ate half a melon—and the average melon weighed four pounds in Méntrida— or two pounds of grapes, or a platter full of sliced tomatoes. At five he had an afternoon snack, as solid a meal as his breakfast, which only whetted his appetite for a supper as substantial as his midday meal. All day long a gallon jar with red, frothing wine stood by his anvil, to spare its master the taste of water which, as he said, 'bred frogs'.

He owned a field of wheat, a strip of garden land, a vineyard and six fig-trees. In the course of the year he found time and means to till his land, to mill his wheat, to make his wine and to dry his figs in the sun for the coming winter. His house was an ever-full larder. To add to its riches and to please his own palate, he would go out in the dark of night and come home in the small hours, two or three rabbits in his pouch, or his wicker basket filled with fish from the Alberche, still alive.

He had married my Aunt Rogelia against the considered opinion of both their families, for at that time he was half starved and had nothing. The two went to work like donkeys and in time grew more comfortably off than the rest of their relations. The woman, small in stature but strong in body, tackled the job which had fallen to her with inexhaustible energy and gaiety. To cope with his meals alone seemed a miracle, but she also looked after the food and the house, the chickens, and the pigs, she baked the bread and she took care of their four children who arrived one after the other, as though she wanted to waste no time in childbirth. My aunt never took to her bed before giving birth. When she was big with child, she went on washing, scrubbing, and cooking tirelessly, as always. Suddenly she would say to her husband: 'Luis, it's coming.' She would lie down while he called a neighbouring woman who understood about such matters. On the following day a cup of chocolate and a good chicken broth, thick as though stirred with flour, put her on her legs again, and she went back to her cooking and scrubbing as if nothing had happened.

They were a happy couple and had no problems. She was woman enough for all the needs of her powerful male, and in their youth, when the two of them were building up the forge between them, it was no rare thing for the door to be locked and the pair to turn a deaf ear to the knocking of customers. When they opened again, he would stand there, filling the doorway with his mighty body, smiling slyly at his neighbours' jokes. He used to plant his huge hand on her plump shoulder with a smack, wink at the joker, and say: 'Just look at her—small and round, but as hot as red pepper!'

When I came to the forge, the men were still hammering away at the broad blade of the ploughshare, and Feliciano was pulling the bellows-chain without stopping, so that the second ploughshare should be ready when they had finished the first. As I knew that nobody would take any notice of me just then, I took hold of the chain and pulled in time with Feliciano, who slapped my shoulder with his free hand and said: 'Hullo, Madrileño!' That was all; his brain could never hold more than three words at a time. He was the stupidest of the whole family.

When they had finished the ploughshare we had been heating with the bellows, Uncle Luis lifted the gallon jar with one hand, and filled a tall, thick glass with wine. It made the round of the lads and each wiped his lips with the back of his dirty hand. My uncle drank last, filled the glass again and handed it to me: 'Come here, sparrow!'

It was his first word of greeting. He lifted me on to the anvil with only one hand.

'Here, drink it up, you need some blood in you.' He turned to the lads and said: 'I don't know what the bloody hell they give the kids in Madrid to keep them as thin as spooks. Look at the calves he's got!' He squeezed my leg between his forefinger and thumb until I thought my flesh would split. 'You ought to stay here in the forge as my apprentice in your holidays. And no more petticoats for you. What with the old women and the priests, they'll be turning you into a sniffling sissy.'

I drank down the whole glass of wine, like a man. It was a dry, strong wine which made you feel hot. Aquilino, in a gust of affection, picked me up from the anvil and swung me through the air, round and round, like a rag doll. When he set me on the ground I was half choked with fright and wine.

'This afternoon,' he said, 'I'll buy you a spinning top and make you a point with the lathe.'

Making points for spinning tops was something Aquilino was very proud of, and all the village children ran after him for them.

The points he made had a long, square spike at one end which he stuck red-hot into the wood of the top. The other end he either turned on the lathe until it had the shape of an acorn, or else filed it down to a narrow point with a groove spiralling down it. It was not easy to fix a point. You had to get it right into the centre of the top, and then it would hum and 'go to sleep', as we used to say. Otherwise it would wobble and scratch you if you put it on your palm.

I never got bored at Uncle Luis's. Beside the door of the forge stood a work-bench with a vice, and there were rows of tools on the wall, and odd bits of iron all over the floor. You only had to pick up one, fix it in the vice, and start filing it. I liked mechanics; I was going to be an engineer when I was older. This time I wanted to make a wheel. I made a circle on a piece of sheet-iron with the big calipers, and then began to file it down. But my brother and sister turned up. First they went into the house to see our aunt and get their buns, and then they came back for me. Concha took me by the arm and said:

'Come along and let's play. I've told Aunt.'

The forge lay at the end of the village. We only had to climb the slope of a little ravine and were in the open country. Concha went first and I followed. She was very thin and had her hair twisted into a tiny little bun at the back of her neck. Her legs showed under her petticoats; they were sunburnt and her muscles moved like cords while she climbed. Rafael came behind me, silent and sulky. When we reached the top we followed the edge of a harvested field along the wall of brambles which bordered it on the side of the ravine.

I knew my brother and sister better than they thought. I knew that the storm was going to break. Concha would shout at me and shake me until she got tired of it. If I answered back, we would come to blows and then I would get it. I was the smallest and weakest. If I gave her time to let off steam, she would not beat me up in cold blood.

And so it was. When we came to the clearing where the old trees stood round the source of the stream which ran through the village, Concha turned round and clutched my arm:

'Well, now we've got him, the spoilt little baby. But there aren't any aunts or nephews here, nor any petticoats to hide under. So you think because we live in the attic and you at the flat, dressed up like a little gentleman, that we aren't as good as you are? Well, you'd better get it into your head that you're no better than us. You're the son of Señora Leonor the washerwoman, and now I'll bash your mug in so you remember!'

She shook me like an old rag and pinched my arm until it stung. I said nothing and hung my head. Rafael stood watching us with his hands in his pockets. Concha grew more and more excited:

'Look at him, just like a silly old hen. Well, that's just what he is. Now you're not crowing any more, are you? Now you're like a dead fly! Grandmother Inés is right when she says you're a lying Jesuit. Now you dare to hit me, I'm a girl, you just dare!' And she stuck her fists under my eyes.

'Shall I shake him?' asked Rafael.

Concha looked me up and down contemptuously: 'What for? Can't you see he's a sissy?'

The insult struck home, coming on top of my grandmother's insult which I had not forgotten, and I saw red. The three of us rolled on the ground, kicking, hitting, and biting. After a while the big hands of a man cuffed us apart and held my sister and me firmly separated, one on each side of him, while we kicked at one another behind his back. Rafael had become perfectly quiet and glared spitefully at the man. Concha stamped on his foot—he wore only rope-soled canvas shoes—and he swore and boxed her ears. He was my ally then, so I kicked her on the shins. We both wrenched ourselves free and got at each other, I pulling her hair, she clutching my neck. I grabbed handfuls of hair, she dug her nails into me.

The man carried us to the forge, one under each arm, our legs threshing the air. Rafael followed behind us without a word. The man took us in and explained to my uncle:

'Here, take 'em, they're like a pair of wild cats.'

Uncle Luis looked at us calmly. Both our faces and legs were

61

covered with scratches and we glowered at each other under half-shut lids.

'You do look pretty.' He turned to Rafael and said: 'And what have you got to say, Pussyfoot?'

'Me? Nothing.'

'So I see. So it was the two of you against the smallest, was it? You're a nice pair of heroes.'

'He's just a nasty, dirty louse,' screamed my sister.

'They're jealous because I live with Uncle,' screamed I.

'I'll settle this,' said Uncle Luis.:'You make it up now, at once, d'you hear? You've got all worked up, but now you'll be friends again. And the first time I catch you making another shindy, I'll give each of you such a hiding that you'll go lame for a week.'

We washed our faces in the water of the trough where the iron was cooled. Uncle Luis put a thick cobweb over a gash in my knee: 'Now, leave it on, it stops the bleeding and it'll heal your scratch.' And so the plaster stayed there, a web full of dust and blood which grew as hard as clay.

We ate stewed rabbit in a dark, strong sauce of garlic and bay leaf cooked with wine, and the meal meant peace. When we left we were friends, the three of us, but I was the master because I had a silver *duro* in my pocket, and the market square and streets around were full of stalls. A *duro* was five pesetas or a lot of big coppers, and the things on sale did not cost more than ten centimos each. Village people, who recognized me and knew I had just come from Madrid, called me and bought me so many monkey-nuts, hazel-nuts, and roasted chick-peas that all my pockets were full of them. Concha insisted on buying blackberries and got her mouth and fingers stained with purple. Then she stood there, like a silly fool, with her hands sticky and her fingers spread out stiffly, and could not get at her handkerchief to wipe them clean, for fear of making stains on her white dress. In the end she washed in a puddle at the side of the square and dried her fingers on her handkerchief. Rafael stuffed himself with fresh nuts which were sold in their green shells to make them weigh more. But he and I had the same idea, and Concha was in our way: we wanted to smoke aniseed-and-cocoa cigarettes just as the men smoked their tobacco. If we had said so to Concha, she would have told Aunt Aquilina who would have made a fuss. So at first we tried to think out a way of getting rid of her because she was a nuisance, but then I found a solution.

You could buy little squibs which went off with a loud bang, fifty for ten centimos. I suggested our buying a hundred of them and

Concha liked the idea. We would let them off in the streets and throw them under doorways to frighten people. But of course, after we had bought them, we still had to light them before they could go off. Every squib had a fuse, a piece of string soaked in gunpowder. We could have lit them with matches, but that would have meant buying several boxes. I proposed quite innocently that we should buy aniseed cigarettes to light the fuses with. So we bought a packet of ten cigarettes, and Rafael asked a young man for a light. He laughed when he let Rafael have it. We lit ours from Rafael's cigarette, for Concha wanted to throw squibs too. I had to light a cigarette for her, and she carried it hidden in her hand. She only sucked it now and then, with her face to the wall so that people should not see her. The aniseed tickled your throat and eyes and made you cough, but we smoked like men. Then we began to throw the squibs under doorways. At houses where Rafael and Concha knew the people and said some nasty old woman lived there, we all three lit squibs and threw them inside in a bunch. When the first one exploded, all the women ran out to see what had happened, and then the other two went off and frightened them even more. We laughed, hidden round the next corner, ready to bolt if they came after us.

But all girls are fools. When we were going through a street where there was no-one about, Concha had to stick her cigarette into her mouth and puff smoke, and of course a fussy old woman came out of her house and saw us. She smacked Concha's face so that the cigarette jumped out of her mouth, and raised hell, calling her names— pig, beast, hussy, strumpet, and God knows what else. She would not let go of her arm because she wanted to take her home and tell Aunt Aquilina all about it. And the old meddler did drag Concha along, weeping and trying to get away and yelling for us to come with her. The old woman called us names too and said we were shameless good-for-nothings. At every house she passed she told the story to all the women she met, and they all started screaming and slapping Concha's face and shouting at us. Rafael thought of bashing in the old witch's head with a stone. When we came to our house they went inside, and we could hear Concha screaming, but we did not go in. Then Aunt Aquilina came out and hauled us in. We did not like it, but we had to go and then we got it. Aunt Aquilina started dealing out cuffs, mainly to Rafael and Concha, for she said it was their fault. Suddenly she saw that Rafael's pockets were bulging:

'Where are the cigarettes? Empty your pockets at once, all of them, so I can see what's there.'

Rafael, who was sometimes malicious, dug his hands into his pockets and brought out hazel-nuts, walnuts ,and roasted chick-peas.

But when my aunt screamed, 'The cigarettes, where are the cigarettes?' he pulled out a handful of cigarettes mixed with a lot of squibs and threw them into the kitchen fire. My aunt, who did not notice what it was, kept on: 'Throw them all in, all of them!' So Rafael dropped all his squibs into the fire, and I did too. My aunt cried:

'To-night you'll not go and see the fireworks!'

But then the fuses of the squibs caught fire, and things got going.

There were bangs, and ashes and burning straw flew all over the room. Grandmother jumped up from her stool, dragging after her the ball of wool with which she was knitting socks. A frying-pan on the hearth was blown full of cinders, sparks fell on the chairs and on the curtains of the kitchen shelf, and my aunt could not understand what was happening. The two women shrieked and Uncle Sebastian, who had tumbled to it, stayed behind his shoemaker's bench and laughed. We ran out into the street and did not go back until late in the evening.

The table was laid and everybody was most serious. Nobody said a word, only Little Grandmother pattered around muttering, and we watched her out of the corner of our eyes in case she tried to hit us with her stick. We sat down at the table and Aunt Aquilina brought the meal.

'No supper for the wicked children to-night,' she said sternly and handed each of us a chunk of bread. 'That's all you're going to get.'

We said not a word. I was mad with rage. I had never been left without a meal, and my eyes filled with tears of fury. But I did not want to cry. Only my tears trickled down my face, and then Aunt Aquilina saw them and began heaping meat-balls on my plate.

'Well, I'll let you off this once. . . . There's the fiesta to-night and I don't want to get angry, but . . .' and she launched forth into a sermon while she was filling our plates. Uncle Sebastian chuckled and said:

'When all's said and done, it was a funny trick the children played on us!'

Aunt and Grandmother went for him like two wasps:

'That's right, you would go and take their side!'

And a violent row began, so that our poor uncle did not know where to hide from the onslaught. Meanwhile, we finished our meal and got away. We agreed to buy Uncle Sebastian a packet of cigarettes and a roll of cigarette paper. When the fireworks started and everyone had gone to the stone parapet which overlooked the market square, we gave him them in secret. He let me sit on his knee and gave me a kiss, and we watched the rockets burst in the sky. Suddenly he said to Aunt:

'Take the child, I must go to the lavatory.'

When he came back he had a cigarette in his mouth and said a friend had given it him and after all, everybody had to celebrate one day in the year. Aunt grumbled but she left him alone. His eyes sparkled merrily, he winked at us and chuckled behind her back.

The square was full of dancing couples and on the terrace before the church, where we were, was the man with the fireworks, a fat Valencian in a black blouse and round hat, with a cigar in his mouth. In his left hand he held a rocket, which looked like a thick candle, and with his right he put his burning cigar to it. When it spluttered, he suddenly opened his fingers and the rocket went swishing up into the air. We children stood round him in a circle and stared at the sky until we saw it burst into many-coloured stars. The empty shell of the rocket fell down, its last sparks crackling, and bounced over the rooftops. One year a house was set on fire by a rocket.

That day was the Feast of Our Lady, and our aunt began to dress us up in our best clothes very early in the morning. Mine were the finest in the village, of course, for all the others wore country things, while I had Madrid clothes. Rafael had a suit from Madrid, too, but his was cheap, ready-made, and did not fit him; the cloth was so harsh that he could hardly move. Concha also had a cheap dress from Madrid, starched until it was as stiff as a board, and she looked ridiculous with a big blue ribbon in her plait. Both had heavy boots, Rafael's with brass toecaps, and they found it hard to walk in them, and they looked with envy at my sailor suit and patent leather shoes. Concha called me Señorito, because she said I was playing the young gentleman again, and managed to give me a kick so that the varnish of my shoe got all scratched. I pulled her plait and untied her ribbon and we had a fight. But then we all went with Uncle Sebastian to look at the auction for Our Lady's stand.

The Virgin, wrapped in an embroidered velvet cloak and surrounded by burning candles, was carried out of the church on a platform decorated with the heads of little angels painted in natural colours. They stopped with her under the porch and the mayor, dressed in his cape, holding his staff with the gold knob, cried out:

'This year, as every year, we are going to hold an auction for the stand of Our Lady.'

The highest bidders were given the six places at the shafts and the right to carry Our Lady on their shoulders to the hermitage of Berciana, a hill three miles from the village. All the rich men of the place and all those who had made a vow started bidding. The two places in front were the best. One shouted:

'Forty *reales*!'[1]

'Fifty!'

This set them going. When only four bidders for the right shaft in front were left, the mayor cried:

'One hundred and fifty *reales* have been offered. Does nobody offer more?'

After he had repeated it a couple of times, someone offered a hundred and seventy-five, and the bids went up slowly until only two were left who insisted on carrying the Virgin. Then everybody was anxious to see which of the two considered himself the most important man in the place.

'Two hundred and fifty *reales*,' said one pompously.

'Three hundred,' the other snapped.

'Damnation, three hundred and fifty! Don't you go and think you'll carry her off!' the first shouted back.

In the end they quarrelled about who was going to carry Our Lady, cursing and swearing and calling each other cuckolds. The priest took the auction money.

After the auction, the procession to Berciana started, with Our Lady in front, behind her the priest in a golden cope and saying Latin prayers. After him came the mayor, the judge, the doctor, the schoolmaster, and, in a double file, all the neighbours who wanted to carry a lighted candle. Then came the rest of the village in a huddle, the men carrying their hats in their hands, the women with a silk kerchief on their heads. They all wore their best clothes, most of them their wedding-dress, which was too tight for some and too big for others.

The funniest of all were the boys and girls. The boys were dressed like the men, in corduroy suits, a shirt with a collar and silk bow, a straw hat and heavy boots. The girls had stiffly starched dresses in loud colours, showing their very white, starchy petticoats and the edging of their panties. They had bright silk bows in their hair, stockings knitted in very thick wool, and boots with toecaps of metal. None of them knew how to move, because they were used to wearing a smock or knickers, and to going barefoot or in rope-soled sandals. Before we were half-way there, most of the children had to be dragged along by their parents, stumbling over each stone in the road.

When we came to the little Berciana river, the procession crossed through the stream instead of passing over the wooden bridge; I wondered whether they did it because they were afraid the bridge would break or because they wanted to make a sacrifice to Our

[1] At the time of the tale, small sums of money were often given in the obsolete coinage of the *real*. 1 real —25 centimos.—*Translator's Note*.

Lady. They all took off their shoes, and turned up their trousers and skirts. Most of the children and many of the grown-ups did not put on their shoes again afterwards. Some said they had made a vow to Our Lady to walk barefoot to the Hermitage, but it was really because their boots hurt them.

The Hermitage was on the top of a hill which rose up from the stream, at its foot a big meadow of short grass where oak-trees grew. Mass was said in the chapel, but most of the people stayed outside because there was no room for them. In the meantime, loaded carts, mules, and bullocks arrived from the village and were installed on the meadow. The people who came with them unpacked, and out of the carts and hampers came frying-pans and casseroles, rabbits, chickens, lambs, and pigeons. Someone had taken along a calf, cinnamon-coloured, with a white muzzle, which was tied to the back of the cart and strained against the rope round its short horns. Some had brought chairs and set them in a circle in the grass. The best spots were in the shade of the oaks, and people slung ropes between the trees and put blankets on them to get more shade. Away from the trees kitchens were set up, with earthen stewing-pots, plates, glasses, and frying-pans. The big wineskins and leather bottles were left in the shade of the tree-trunks; some people dug holes in the ground near the brook, where they buried their bottles to keep them cool.

After Mass the people came down to the meadow. First everybody had to sample the wine and take a drink from the free jet of a leather bottle, or out of a jar filled from a wineskin. Then everyone, children and grown-ups, collected firewood in the oak copses. The men and women lopped off branches with little axes, and the children carried armfuls of kindling sticks to their own camp fires. Quickly a hundred fires were blazing in the open and the air was full of floating chicken and pigeon feathers. Sheep and rabbits were strung up in trees and skinned by men in shirt sleeves. Tablecloths were spread on the ground and laid with platters of sliced sausages, olives, and gherkins, with tomatoes cut in half and dressed in salt and oil; and everybody had a bite and a drink of wine. We children went from spread to spread and picked out whatever we liked best and drank secretly from the wine jars. Soon all the valley smelt of roast meat and of smoke from burning thyme and broom. People began to feel hungry and to hurry up the cooks.

I remembered the description of the wedding feast of the rich Camacho in *Don Quixote de la Mancha* and it seemed to me that Don Quixote himself might suddenly appear on the crest of one of those hills, astride Rocinante, with Sancho Panza behind him smacking his lips at the good smell.

The children of the fireworks-man went round selling rockets which burst high in the air with bangs like rifle-shots. Wafer-sellers had come from Madrid to the fiesta, young boys from Galicia who made the journey on foot with a tin-box full of thin rolled wafers slung round their shoulders, and the people flocked round them trying their luck at a lottery-wheel and smacking the children who wanted to turn the wheel too.

Even the dogs seemed to have got wind of the fiesta, for everywhere you saw village dogs slinking round the bonfires, with hanging heads and their tails between their legs. A few people threw them a bone, others threw a stone or a log at them, and then they ran off to find another group. Sometimes a few dogs chose the same fire and sat down on their haunches, very tense, their noses in the air, their eyes glued to the hands of the woman who did the cooking. When she threw them a bite, the cleverest caught it and the others growled at him.

Little Grandmother had arrived in Uncle Luis's cart, and both the families joined in one group. We were fifteen in all, and Grandmother began to tell us how one year all her sons with their wives and children, and some with their grandchildren, had come to a fiesta in the village. There had been over a hundred of them. Grandmother had had eighteen children, of whom fourteen were still living. Her eldest son had great-grandchildren at the time of the fiesta, and arrived from Cordova with a family of twenty-odd. Grandmother had married a tailor, and since they did not earn enough money to keep all their children, they had sent them out into the world as they grew up, the girls into service in Madrid, the boys either to Madrid or to Andalusia. One of them went to Barcelona and one to America, but neither of them had ever come back to the village and people knew them only from photographs. The Barcelona one was a man with a broad black beard and a bowler hat, who looked like a secret service agent, and the American was a dried-up man with a clean-shaven face, who looked like a priest. Grandmother had never gone further away from the village than Madrid, and then she had to be taken by cart, because she did not want to get into the train. She said the train was a thing of the devil. And she would die without having been in a train.

Aquilino had fixed up a swing between two trees, and so had many of the others. The girls sat in the swings and the lads pushed them so that they swung high up into the air, shrieking and showing their legs. The lads had their fun out of looking at them, they nudged each other in the ribs, winked and said: 'Did you see? A fine lass, eh?' They laughed a lot and sometimes they pinched the girls' legs or

68

bottoms. Some girls laughed and shrieked and some turned angry. After the meal, when all of them were stuffed and full of wine, the lads pinched more and the girls shrieked less.

That was how engagements started, and quarrels. In the middle of the afternoon they were all a little drunk. The older men stretched themselves on the ground to take their siesta, and the young lads tumbled themselves down beside the girls who were sitting on the grass, but not to go to sleep. The girls played with the lads' hair, and sometimes they slapped at them, if one had touched a girl's leg or thigh or breast. Later, when the sluggishness of digestion had passed, they danced, and danced on into the night. Many of the couples went for a stroll on the other side of the hills.

One couple walked off, their arms wound tightly round each other's waists, and Andrés shouted good advice after them, such as telling them not to drink from the stream because it made big bellies. And everybody laughed.

My Uncle Luis had slept through his siesta and woken with a parched throat, he said. As a little refreshment he ate a bowl of salad and half a dozen oil doughnuts, solid and floury. Then he tucked me under his arm like a parcel and took me for a round.

We went to the top of the hill. The valley with the picnickers disappeared and the land was lonely. Far away you saw the white snow peaks of the Sierra de Guadarrama and the towers of the monastery of El Escorial.

Suddenly Uncle Luis, who was walking behind me, gave a wild howl:

'Uh-huh-huuuh!'

I turned round, frightened. A couple came out of a little gully, she with her blouse unbuttoned, he with his jacket dangling. Uncle Luis held his sides and laughed so that his belly heaved with the laughter. He lifted me on to his shoulders and ran through the gullies, howling his howl. Couples dashed out of thickets and hollows and fled down to the valley, pursued by our shouts and laughter.

When we came back to the crowd, Uncle Luis swung me from his shoulders and lifted a full jar to his mouth, and again his laughter burst out so that the wine spluttered. Everyone turned towards him. He caught the little round figure of Aunt Rogelia in his arms and plastered her face with kisses. Then he lifted her up on his hands, stretching his arms as though he meant to fling her far into the air.

'Huh-huh-huuuh!' he shouted, and his chest and shoulders resounded.

At his cry all the valley fell silent and the echo answered beyond the darkening hills.

69

V. OUTHOUSE OF MADRID

It's good to be here. My head between my mother's knees, on the softness of her thighs under the soft linen of her apron. To look at the flames twisting and dancing in the air. My mother is peeling potatoes at the side of the kitchen fire and talking to Grandmother. She tells her about her life in my uncle's flat, her work and her worries, and about how my aunt is jealous of her because of me. And I watch her face from below, without her seeing me. Her face in the red glow of the flames. Her face tired from work and worry. I bury my head in her apron like a cat. I would like to be a cat. I would jump on her lap and roll myself into a ball there. I'm sick of everybody, sick of my aunt, of school, sick of all the stupid people who think I am only a child, while I know I'm more than they and see everything and swallow down everything and keep it to myself. Jump on her lap, roll myself into a ball, doze, hearing my mother talk without listening to her words, feeling her warmth and the glow of the fire and the smell of burning broom. Stay there quiet, so quiet.

'How tiresome the child is—go and play with your brother and sister.'

'I don't want to.'

I curl up more tightly, trying to get still closer to her. My mother is stroking my head, my tousled hair, my unruly cowlick, and her fingers pass idly over my head, but I feel them inside me. When her hand lies still, I take it and look at it. So very tiny, so thin, worn by the water of the river, with small tapering fingers, the fingertips pricked by the lye, with twisted blue veins, nervous and alive. Alive with warmth and blood, alive in quick motion, always ready to leap and fly, to scrub vigorously, to stroke gently. I love to press them to my cheeks and rub my skin against them, to kiss and nibble her fingertips, here where I have no need to hide behind a door when I want to kiss my mother, with my aunt shouting:

'Where are you, child?'

'Here in the kitchen, Aunt.'

'What are you doing there?'

'I'm going to the lavatory.'

And in the meantime my mother clattering with the pots and pans and I slamming the lavatory door. . . .

What rights has my aunt over me? She keeps me in her house, but then my mother is her servant. Why hasn't she had children? For she is jealous because she has no child of her own, and she would like to take me away from my mother. But not my uncle. My uncle loves me, but he doesn't want to take me away from my mother. Why can't he be my father? My aunt could die, and then my uncle would marry my mother just to be my father. He said so once as a joke, but I think it's true. He too is fed up with my aunt, with her prayers and her crotchets. Once my aunt was cross and said: 'I ought to be dead, then you would be rid of me!' 'Fine,' said my uncle, 'when you're dead I'll marry Leonor and become the boy's papa. What do you think of it, Leonor? Do you accept my snow-white hand?' He said it to my mother with a laugh, and she answered smiling: 'Well, let me think it over in the meantime.' My goodness, what a row! My aunt sobbed and wept, clutching me to her, and I cried too. My uncle furious at my aunt's stupidity, my mother trying to calm her down and bearing with her affronts. 'You ungrateful person, that's the reward I get from all of you for my goodness! That's what you would like—me to go to my grave so that the three of you can do what you like.' And so on. We had no evening meal and did not go to the café. And we were in bed before ten. The day after, everyone went round with sour faces.

Here in the village we are alone. Sometimes I get hold of her and kiss her like mad. 'Now let go, you wheedling rascal!' she says and pushes me away. But I can see that it makes her happy and that she puts up with my aunt for my sake, so that I can get on well and become an engineer soon, because my uncle will pay for my studies and I want to be an engineer. And nothing is too hard for her as long as I kiss her and love her, and she kisses me and loves me more than anyone else. When I'm grown-up she won't have to go down to the river, and I'll be rich so that she's happy and can have all she wants, and she'll be a grandmother like our Little Grandmother, a tiny little granny with lots of wrinkles, in a black dress, an old woman's dress, on which I'll rest my head when I'm tired after work.

Good things do not last. The day before yesterday my mother came, and to-morrow we must both go away, I to Navalcarnero and she to Madrid, back to work.

As the train stopped for a quarter of an hour in the station, I dragged my mother off to look at the engine. It was a small Belgian engine, painted green and almost square, and no good at all. I had been in a big railway engine. Uncle José had a cousin who was an engine-driver at the North Station and always drove the Paris Express. Once he took my uncle and me to Segovia in an engine without a train. The engine was so big that they had to lift me up to the cabin where the driver and stoker were. We went off with nothing but the tender and did not stop at any station until Segovia. The stoker kept on shovelling coal into the open mouth of the furnace so that the flames licked out, and we passed through the country with the track free before and behind us, bounding over the rails and sometimes gliding on them so that it was like flying through the air. In the innards of the engine was a big handle which was the brake. My uncle told me that an engine-driver once tried to save his train from crashing into another and turned the handle so hard that he thrust it through his stomach. He saved the train but he died, spiked by the brake. Then there were thermometers and pressure-gauges and level-tubes with little nickelled taps, and the iron chain of the whistle. When you pulled it the steam whistled and you went deaf with the noise. All the taps were dripping water or oil. There was one which dripped a lot and I wanted to turn it off, but hot oil spurted out in a fan and made spots on all our clothes. When we passed over an iron bridge, everything bounced, the rails, the bridge, and the engine, and I wanted the engine to go faster so that we should be past the bridge when it smashed. We went back by train, but the journey in a carriage was boring.

The train from Méntrida was just as small as its engine. The carriages were matchboxes with dirty wooden seats, full of country people with their saddlebags, baskets, and chickens tied by the legs, which they shoved under the seat. Some carried rabbits with their bowels slit open so that you could see the purple kidneys, and some carried small wine-casks or baskets full of eggs bedded in straw. Sometimes, when we came to a station, we saw people running on the road from the village and making signs for the train to stop. The station-master always waited for them. Then they tumbled into the carriage, pushing each other and stamping on other people's feet or knocking them over with their bundles, and slumped down in their seats, sweating after their run with the baskets and the saddlebags.

Navalcarnero was the biggest station on the line. It had a goods shed with a zinc roof and three lines for shunting. Just beside the station was the flour mill, and a special siding led to the mill from the station itself, made a curve and passed under the iron factory gate. When the gate was closed it made me think that if they pulled the wrong switch, we would run straight through the railing, train and all, and land inside the mill.

Grandmother Inés was waiting for us in the station. Concha had come along with my mother and me; she and I were going to stay in Navalcarnero until the end of the month. When the train with my mother had gone, Grandmother laid her arms on each of our shoulders, her hands hanging down over our chests, and so she walked to the town, with us glued to her sides.

Grandmother's hand was as large as a man's and her arm was a bulky mass. It was right to call her Big Grandmother. She weighed over two hundred pounds and was taller than most men. Her strength was enormous and she ate and drank like a farm-hand. Every time she came to Madrid, Aunt Baldomera invited her to have her meals with us, and she always said no. She used to go to Botín's, a very old Madrid restaurant, and order roast sucking-pig. When none of us was with her, she would eat the sucking-pig all by herself, together with a huge bowl of lettuce salad, and drink two pints of wine with it. She would have been a good match for Uncle Luis.

Navalcarnero was different from the other villages. It was very close to Madrid and the market town of its district. Many of the gentry lived there. They would not have been called gentry in Madrid, but they were gentry in Navalcarnero. The town was divided into two races of people: those who dressed as they did in Madrid, and those who wore blouses and corduroy trousers. There were the women in hat or mantilla, and the women with wide petticoats and apron, with a kerchief round their heads. There was a Poor Man's Casino, a large tavern full of flies, and a Rich Men's Casino, a kind of café with marble-topped tables. In the church there were two rows of benches in the middle, with chairs placed in front of them. The gentlemen sat on the benches and their ladies on the chairs. The rest of the church was for the farmers and the poor. Farmers with money spread out a round mat of esparto grass and put a straw-covered chair on it for the wife. The poor knelt on the flagstones.

I knew this because I sometimes went to church, although my grandmother never took me there. On Sundays she asked:

'Well now, do you want to go to Mass?'

I usually said yes, for two reasons: first, if I did not go it would be a sin, and secondly, it was an odd experience to go by myself. Mass in Navalcarnero was different from other places. At school all the boys heard Mass together, and we filled the whole church. When I went to church with my aunt, I was tied to her and to her caprices, and she spent the whole time telling me to be quiet, to kneel down, to get up, not to cough, not to sneeze, to keep my hands still, and not to disturb her in her devotions.

Here in Navalcarnero it was quite another thing. I went alone, even when one of Grandmother's neighbours had asked me to go with her, because I knew what old women were like. I stayed under the porch, in the little yard behind the iron gate and watched the people going in. When they were all inside, I entered, alone. They were all clustering round the High Altar and I came in very softly and stayed at the back of the church between the pillars. I was always afraid that one of the old women might call me and make me kneel down beside her.

The floor, the pillars, and the lower part of the walls of the church were of stone, the rest white-washed. In the middle was a chandelier shaped like a pear and covered with glass crystals which sparkled like diamonds when the sun shone on them. I did not know why, but that chandelier, which hung on a very long cord from the centre of the cupola, was nearly always swinging very slowly from one side to the other. I liked to watch it moving and filling with coloured sparks whenever it passed through one of the sunbeams which shone through the windows in the lantern of the dome.

At the entrance there was a Christ on the Cross, naked, very thin, and yellow, almost green, in colour. The bloodstains were quite black, because he had not been repainted for many years. His lower parts were covered by a little velvet apron with a gold fringe. Some people lifted the apron and looked underneath. The paint of the toes had peeled off because the women had kissed them so much, and the bare wood showed. There was a black knot in the wood on the big toe of the left foot, which looked like a corn. His head was dangling as if his neck had been broken and he had a dirty, chocolate-coloured beard with cobwebs between hairs and throat. Tears were running from his eyes, and they looked like the hardened wax drippings on a candle. The only beautiful thing about him were the eyes, blue glass eyes which stared at the peeled toes.

At the side of the Christ was the Holy Water stoup, with a puddle underneath where the yokels stamped with their rope-soles—plff! But the ladies took great care not to step in it and leaned over on tip-toe to dip their fingers into the holy water. Fine people wetted their finger-tips, and country folk put their whole hand in. They had made the puddle.

There was a Virgin of solid silver in the church. She was life-size and was standing on a moon, a mass of clouds and many heads of little angels with pigeon's wings. People said she weighed a ton. One day I watched two old women smearing the Virgin full of metal polish and rubbing her with an old rag until she shone. They got the cheeks and chin bright like glass, but some of the white stuff stuck in the eyes and the mouth, and one of the old women tried hard to polish them, spitting on her handkerchief and wiping the eyes of Our Lady just as people do when children have sand in their eyes. The other old woman was rubbing the angels' heads as angrily as if she wanted to smack them. But they hadn't any bottoms.

Up in the choir they had an organ with a keyboard in a very old wooden case, like a barrel-organ. There were two bellows under the keyboard, on which the organist had to pedal; they looked like two old books which had fallen open. Sometimes the organist stepped on one of the books out of time, and then, when he pressed down the keys, there was no sound from the organ but only a blast of air, as when a mule lets off wind. As soon as the blast stopped short, one of the organ pipes mewed out of tune.

Apart from these things the church was nothing but a cold barn where one could stay comfortably only in summer. But it had some real death skulls. When somebody had died and the Mass for the Dead had to be read, they put in the middle of the church a bier covered by a black, silver-embroidered cloth, surrounded by tall candles. On the black cloth they laid a skull and cross-bones. The skull and bones were real. An old, huge chest in the sacristy was filled with skulls and bones which weighed practically nothing because they were hollowed out by worms. They felt like cardboard. When there was a Mass for the Dead, they took out a skull and two long bones. If the dead man had been rich, the priest selected a skull himself, and the sacristan scraped its pate and rubbed it with oil to make it shine. When a skull was cracked they mended it with a drop of wax. One had four or five wax teeth in its jaw. When there was no Mass for the Dead and the priest and sacristan were away, all of us boys who were friends with the altar-boys played with the bones in the little garden behind the church.

I did not like Navalcarnero as much as Méntrida. It lies high on a hill, on the great trunk road from Madrid to Extremadura. From the town, the road leads downhill towards Madrid on one side, and downhill towards Valmojado on the other. Once you came to the foot of the hill on either side there were trees, but the whole hill of Navalcarnero itself had no trees except the few meagre little trees in the Station Avenue, many of which were crippled. On the hillside were cornfields, now shorn and dry, and vines laden with black grapes. The wheat was harvested, but they were just gathering in the grapes for the wine. Big, heavy wagons went along the Extremadura Road with baskets full of grapes, high as a man. The grapes at the bottom of the baskets were crushed and the wagons dripped fat red blobs which mixed with the dust of the street and became purple-black little balls.

The people made their wine, pouring their grapes into a big shallow trough of stone or cement and crushing them there; the trough had a hole through which the must ran down into a huge jar in the cellar. Two or three houses had a hand-press for their grapes, and one house had a hydraulic press. The whole town went to look at it.

When we came to my grandmother's house, we were met by her sister, Aunt Anastasia. She was as tall as my grandmother, but much heavier, for she was older and her legs were swollen from rheumatism. The two sisters were inseparable, but at the same time they could never stay together, for they were both very bossy. Aunt Anastasia lived upstairs and Grandmother on the ground floor. When they had a quarrel, Aunt Anastasia walked up the straight wooden staircase which creaked under her weight, and slammed her door so that bits of plaster fell from the ceiling and the whole house shook. They would not speak to each other for two or three days. Then either Grandmother went upstairs and banged at her sister's door, shouting that the row was now over, or her sister came down and walked into the sitting-room, asking Grandmother if she wasn't ashamed of herself for not having been up to see her sister in three days; and saying that she might be dying before Grandmother's conscience told her to bring her sister a glass of water. So they had to quarrel for another half-hour before they could make peace.

There were also my grandmother's wards. When my father had died—he was the last of her twenty-five children to die—and my mother had gone to stay with my uncle and aunt, Grandmother went as a housekeeper to Señor Molina, a wealthy man of Navalcarnero who had been left a widower with four children. Grandmother, who herself had been a widow for many years, stayed with him. And in his will he made her the guardian and trustee of his four children.

Each of them was a calamity in himself. The eldest, Fernando, was twenty years old and spent the whole day in the Casino; he had a mistress in the town and something on his lungs. The next one, Rogelio, was fifteen, and he was downright bad. He talked of nothing but girls and did all sorts of things. But he had got it into his head that he wanted to become a monk in the monastery of El Escorial and spent his day with the parish priest. Antonio, the youngest, was rickety, and looked like a hunchback, with his head sunk deep between his shoulders. He had small, red-rimmed eyes, always smeared with a yellow ointment. The girl, Asunción, had had smallpox as a child and her face was pitted with marks. The edges of her nostrils were frayed as though birds had pecked them away.

The first thing Grandmother did was to show us where we were going to sleep. Concha had to share a bed with Asunción and I with Rogelio.

My grandmother's house was the house of big beds. Every room

76

had a tall iron bedstead heaped with two or three mattresses so that you had to climb on a chair to get in. When Grandmother wanted to get into her bed, Asunción and Concha pushed at her behind to help her up, and I laughed when I saw her in her white nightdress: she looked just like a big lumpy mattress herself. When she let herself fall on to her bed, all the springs screeched. They were spiral springs, tapering in the middle, and when they were flattened down they squealed.

From Grandmother's house we went to Señor Molino's farm where they were crushing grapes. A ring of men and women, all barefoot, walked round and round in the stone trough and stamped on the grapes so that their legs were spattered with must. We joined them, but I got out quickly because the grape-stalks pricked my feet. The others stayed, I went off with Grandmother.

We crossed the town and came out on the road to Valmojado. Grandmother walked with long steps and slowed down only when we had passed the houses. The road dipped downhill between two steep earthbanks; we sat down on the ridge and watched the wagons with grapes pass below us. Then Grandmother began to talk to herself:

'I'm getting old and they'—she meant Señor Molina's children— 'don't matter to me. My sister'll die before me, and then you'll be the only ones left. You'll become house-owners. You know I've got two houses in this town. You'll have the same trouble with them as I've got now, you'll have to put new tiles on the roofs every year and you'll never get your rents. And then people say there's a God. Like hell there is.'

She looked at me and burst out laughing:

'Now I'm perverting the little angel—if your aunt heard me we'd have a fight! But look, whatever your aunt and her priests may tell you, there isn't a God, except in the collection boxes in church. Well, anyhow, you'll find that out for yourself, because you can't deny the blood in your veins. Your father was one of the sergeants of the Villacampa rising, and it was a miracle he wasn't executed. And I once threw a priest down the stairs because he insisted on his pious tricks and was killing off the only one of your uncles that was left me. When your mother became a widow, all God did for her was to leave her alone in the hotel with two *duros* in her pocket and your father stiff and cold in his bed. Afterwards God was sorry for her, it's true, so He turned her into a servant and washerwoman, and found her an attic and a few priests and nuns to ladle out soup to your brothers. And then there are still people who thank God for His mercy!'

When my grandmother spoke like that in earnest she made me

very sad. I wanted to believe in God and the Virgin, but the things she said were true. If God can do everything, He could have treated us more kindly, because my mother was very good. Really, He might have treated my grandmother worse instead, for she was always saying blasphemous things, but still she was rich and had what she wanted.

Grandmother was silent for a while and changed the subject:

'Well, you've come here to have a good time and not to hear sermons. But—don't forget, the priests are scoundrels!'

She took me by the hand and we walked back to town, she striding ahead and I trotting behind. When we came to the market square she gave me two pesetas and said: 'Run along, and when you hear it strike twelve, you come home for the meal.' And she walked down the street in the middle of the gutter, straight-backed and muttering blasphemies, or so I thought.

Here in the market square of Navalcarnero was a house that belonged to me. Or rather, it was going to belong to me when Grandmother died. It had three storeys and a portico with heavy wooden posts which were greasy from the backs of the men who leant against them. Each post had a square stone base, and the roof of the portico was made of smoke-blackened beams. There the butcher had his shop, with the carcass of a cow, half covered by a white cloth with bloodstains on it, and cuts of meat, liver, and lungs in white china dishes, set out on little marble slabs. In one dish there was the whole heart of a cow. The butcher's daughter chased the flies away with a duster made of long, coloured paper strips; and at the back of the shop hung a whole pig with a tin pail fastened to its tusks, to catch the blood which dripped from its snout.

The butcher called me:

'Hello, Madrileño, have you come for the grape-harvest?'

When I entered his shop I knocked against the pig which was swinging heavily on its hook and it hit me with its greasy back. I pushed it away with my hand; its fatty bacon-flesh was loathsome.

'Come in, come in, I'll give you something for your granny to fry for you.'

He gave me three thick, black blood-puddings shiny with fat, which made grease stains in the newspaper he wrapped round them so that you could read the printed letters on the other side of the sheet. I had to take the warm, flabby parcel, which I hated having to grip with my fingers, and on top of it I had to submit to a kiss from the butcher and another from his wife, both of whom were as fat and greasy as their pig and their black-puddings. Their daughter stood in the doorway; she was a very pretty girl with a delicate face, and she

78

stroked my hair, but did not kiss me. When I went out of the butcher's shop I felt greasy all over.

Next door in the portico was the tavern, where they invited me to have some sweets and a peppermint soda. The tavern smelt of wine, of the pitch of wineskins, and of the tobacco and sweat of the men who drank at the tin-sheathed bar table. Some who knew me explained to the others that I was the grandson of 'Old Anés'. They did not pronounce it Inés. One of the men said he did not know her, and the tavern-keeper cried:

'But you must know her, she's known in all Spain! Now look, you'll remember who she is at once if I tell you she's the fattest woman in town, the only one who doesn't go to Mass, and the owner of this house.'

Then a little old man who was sipping from a half-pint jar, said:

'Hell, she was a fine lass, she was, when she was come twenty. We were all after her, and she boxed all our ears for us. There wasn't one of us who could have said he'd pinched one of her teats. Before you'd lifted your hand, she whipped round and slapped your face and left you all of a daze. Then she married old Vicente who was a wagon-maker along the road. He was a good soul—a short little man —and he liked a good meal better than working with his plane. When they were married, Anés plunked herself down in his work-shop, and then Vicente worked as if he'd been paid by the hour. It wasn't that she said anything to him, she just sat there on a chair and sewed, but old Vicente wouldn't look up from his pegs. So the work-shop went up and up like foam. But Anés had a child every year, or I should say every ten months, and it was lucky they all died off, because if they hadn't she'd have filled the town with them. A good breeding doe, she was. When the two got older, Vicente just died, like a little bird, I should say because he couldn't cope with so much woman.'

The church bell rang twelve and the men went home to eat. The little old man said I should greet Grandmother from him and told me a few times: 'She was a fine lass, she was!'

After the siesta, Concha went with Asunción to visit her girl friends and I went out with Rogelio. We passed through the town and walked downhill through the harvested fields, following the little footpaths along their edges, towards the river Guadarrama. Rogelio said to me:

'You'll see what fun we'll have. All the boys meet here by the river.'

When we came to the stream, whose water did not reach to one's ankles, there were seven or eight boys rolling naked in the sand or splashing in the pools. They were burnt black as cinders from the sun and spurted sand and water at us. Rogelio and I got out of our clothes and joined them. I felt funny with my white skin among all those nigger-boys. Rogelio was the biggest, his under-belly was already grown with black hair. Some of the other boys had hair growing there too, and they were very proud of looking as hairy as men.

When we were tired of playing and running, Rogelio called us together and took the photograph of a naked woman out of his jacket, and showed it to me before the others.

'Fernando gave it me. He says she's been his girl, but I don't believe it, he's such a liar.'

I did not believe it either, for it was simply the picture of an undressed artiste, such as you could see often in Madrid, a woman with one foot on a stool so that you saw her thighs, and nothing on but an embroidered chemise, black stockings, and her hair in a coil on the top of her head. The picture went from hand to hand among the boys, but we were all watching Rogelio, who was stroking his member with one hand. The bigger boys were in the same way. The photograph did not do anything to me, nor to the little boys; but it seemed ridiculous to us not to be like the older boys, so we began to play too. We laughed, but we felt nervous and watched one another to see what happened. When the big boys came to the end, they jeered at us because we could not do what men did. When we dressed we were all very tired and very sad.

On the way back to the town we bound ourselves by an oath not to tell anybody, and Rogelio swore he would break the head of the first boy who said anything. Then he explained to us about women, and the blood mounted to my head with shame and suffocation. In the street, when the other boys went away to their houses, Rogelio told me in confidence:

'To-night we'll have fun together, you and I alone.'

I felt a mixture of shame at what had happened in the afternoon, and of curiosity about what Rogelio wanted to do that night. I was absent-minded and did not look anyone in the face, least of all Grandmother. At supper she noticed it and asked me whether I was ill. I said no, but I knew I was getting scarlet in the face, because I felt my cheeks burning. She got up, put her hand on my forehead, and said:

'You're very hot. In a little while you'll go to bed, because you must be tired after the journey.'

After supper, Fernando, the eldest, said he was going to the Casino, and Grandmother made a row. To keep her quiet he got hold of Rogelio and me and said he would take us along, he was only going to have some coffee and would come back with us at once. As it was very early, Grandmother let us go. On the way, Fernando told us what he had in mind:

'You come along and have something, coffee or whatever you like. Afterwards I'm going to see my girl, and you go home and tell Anés that old Paco's come to see me and I've stayed with him to settle about the grapes.'

    thought we were going to have coffee in the lounge with the marble-topped tables, but Fernando took us up a small, steep wooden staircase at the back. Before I could ask he explained to me:

'The lounge is only the public bar. There's another room upstairs for us members.'

The room upstairs was as big as the lounge; it had two billiard-tables with patched-up tops, a few round marble tables and some square tables with a green cloth where people played cards. At the back, a number of people were huddled round yet another table, under two green-shaded lamps, where you heard the rattling of money. Fernando went straight there.

The table was covered with the same kind of green cloth, and two men were seated there on high stools, one at each side. One held a pack of cards, and the other had big heaps of cash and banknotes in front of him. Rogelio said:

'They're playing "Monte". The man with the cards is the banker and the other with all the dough is the cashier. You see, the banker puts four cards on the table, and everyone places his bet on one of them, whatever he likes. The card which comes out first when the pack is dealt wins, and all the others lose.'

The banker spread out four cards and said: 'Make your bets!'

All hastened to put their pesetas and duros by the side of the card they favoured, and then the banker said: 'Nothing more goes!'

He began to deal cards from the pack which he had turned face upwards, until one of the four cards on the table came out. Then the other man, the cashier, raked in most of the money and paid the people who had betted on the winning card as much money as they had staked. Fernando lost two duros. When the banker spread another four cards on the table, Fernando again betted two duros. And so he went on losing duros. Suddenly he turned round and said we should drink some coffee. Rogelio called the waiter who gave us two glasses of very bad coffee. Fernando kept losing, and Rogelio asked him to let him play instead; but Fernando did not listen to him. He called me:

'Come here, you, Madrileño!'

He put a heap of money in front of me, sat me on his knees and said to me, while the banker spread out his four cards:

'Take as much of this money as you want and put it beside the card you like best.'

There was a knave of spades. I took a peseta and put it on a corner. Fernando said:

'Don't be afraid, put duros, or put as much as you want.'

So I took a heap of duros, four or five, and put them beside the knave. All the men round the table watched me, but I was sure that the knave would come out first. Many who had already laid their bets took them away from their own cards and put them beside mine. The banker said grumpily:

'Now, have we all finished? Nothing more goes.'

He turned the pack face upwards, and there was a knave. Fernando got paid three times as much as I had laid, and the banker, in a very bad temper, had to pay all the others. He turned to Fernando and said:

'Now look here, children can't play.'

Everybody protested, but the banker insisted that I could not play, or he would take away his cards and leave the others to carry on alone. Rogelio and I had to sit down at a little table in the corner, bored and annoyed.

After a long while Fernando and a fat man whom I did not know came to our table. They started talking about land, vineyards, and promissory notes. The fat man told Fernando that he had already given him a lot of money although he was a minor. Fernando answered:

'What does that matter to you? If I give you a note post-dated for when I come of age, there's no hitch in it.'

The fat man said:

'But supposing you die in the meantime? Because, you know you've got the face of a man with T.B., and one can't be sure of you.'

'You needn't be afraid of my dying. A sick cat never dies,' answered Fernando with a grin.

The fat man took banknotes and a stamped form from his pocket. Fernando signed, and the man gave him the money. It astonished me that there was nothing else written on the paper. Fernando said to the fat man:

'You see I trust your word!'

'Now, when have I ever done you down?'

Fernando went back to the gaming-table and the man started to give us explanations:

'You're the grandson of Inés, aren't you? You're already a man now. Here, buy yourself something.' He gave me a duro. 'Are you jealous?' he asked Rogelio. 'Here's one for you, too. Fernando's a good lad. We had to settle this affair with the grapes, and it's all settled now. Your father was a fine man.' He put a hand on Rogelio's shoulder: 'A nice lot of duros we made together, your father and me, my boy. But when he took that Inés into his house, it was all over. She had a grouch against me, because your grandmother'—he nodded towards me—'never could stand me, and so in the end your father and I quarrelled. She knew which side her bread was buttered all right.'

Rogelio stared into the man's face.

'Give me five duros,' he said suddenly.

'But what do you want five duros for, shaver?'

'You give me five duros, or I'll tell Inés that you're giving Fernando money. I'm not a child like him'—he meant me—'and either you give me the money or I'll tell Inés. Everybody knows that you lend money and then seize people's lands.'

'Boy, those are things one doesn't say out loud. You must show respect for your elders and betters. Here's another duro and shut up. And you too,' he said to me. 'Here's another for you—and don't say anything to your grandmother.'

He got up angrily and pulled Fernando away from the table. They began to dispute, first in a low voice and then loudly:

'Go to bed with children, and you wake up mucky,' said the man. 'If only you hadn't brought those babes along! Especially that grandson of hers. It's not so bad with your brother, after all, you give him a duro and he keeps his mouth shut. But I don't trust that little leech. As soon as he gets home he'll tell his grandmother and we'll have a row.'

Fernando answered:

'Don't you worry—what does he know?'

He turned to us and sent us away.

'And remember—I'm staying here because I've got to buy grapes.'

Outside in the street, Rogelio said:

'I get a duro out of that fellow every time, it's a good trick. But don't say a word to Anés, or she'll take all the money away from us.'

I promised silence and we tied our duros into our handkerchiefs so that they should not clink. When we came home, Grandmother grumbled and groused because Fernando was not back, and then we went to bed.

We slept in a whitewashed room with cross-beams, an enormous bed, under it a chamber-pot almost as big as the bed, two chairs and a chest with a rounded lid. The huge window that gave on to the street had an iron grille with a close leaf pattern. The room was chilly, the sheets damp; the stone tiles of the floor were icy cold and sweated moisture. We undressed in haste and clambered on to the bed, which was as high as ourselves. Inside the sheets we slowly got warm, but then it soon became intolerably hot under the blanket. Rogelio asked me:

'Are you hot?'

'I'm almost in a sweat.'

'We must take off everything.' He pulled off his pants and undervest and stayed quite naked.

I felt ashamed. But if we had bathed without anything on, why shouldn't we lie without any clothes now? So we both stayed naked in the bed. Rogelio pressed himself against me. His skin burned. He passed his hand over my body and said:

'You're so cool.'

He began to stroke my sexual organs. I pushed his hand away, but he insisted: 'Let me, don't be silly, you'll see how much you'll like it.'

I let him go on, dazed with shame, burning hot. Suddenly something happened in me, I did not know what; but I went mad with rage and kicked him furiously in his ribs, while he clutched and pulled at my member in the greatest excitement, without letting go. I jumped out of bed. I had hung my belt over the iron bedrail. Now I seized it and started hitting out at his head, sides, buttocks, and belly. He yelled and rolled in the bed. A little trickle of blood ran down his forehead over one eye. Grandmother came into the room in her nightdress, a candlestick in her hand, and big slippers on her feet. She caught us as he was writhing on the bed and I lashing out at him, blind with fury, anger and loathing. Grandmother boxed my ears and I crumpled up in a corner, weeping.

Then, while she stood there in her nightgown and we in our nakedness, came the explanations. Rogelio sat in a chair and did not say a word. I talked and talked, mixing everything up.

'You see, Grandmother, he's a pansy. He's been touching me and wanting to do dirty things. And his brother's a gambler. And all the boys here play with themselves when they're together. He's got a postcard with a naked woman. . . .'

I cried and fumbled for my trousers, to haul the duros out of my pocket, hiccoughing. Grandmother took the money and carried me to her own bed, wrapped me up, let me lie in the curve of her belly, and there I went to sleep. But before that she had given Rogelio a

84

kick on his naked bottom, and her slipper had come off and sailed through the air. I had laughed through my tears.

I woke when the outer door slammed. Fernando was back. It was dawning, and Grandmother shouted at him from the top of her bed. Fernando was drunk.

'Now there, there, Anés. Leave me alone. I'm too sleepy.'

He sat down in the dining-room, drank a glass of brandy and fell asleep on the dining-room table. Grandmother got up in her night-gown, lifted him in her arms and carried him to his bedroom. It was funny to see my grandmother in the half-light of the morning, big as she was, her white nightgown billowing down to her feet, carrying Fernando on her arms like a stuffed doll. I heard him fall on to his bed like a sack, and snore so that you heard it through the whole house.

A wagon passed by in the street, and all the window-panes rattled. The carter was singing. And my grandmother came back into her bed, gathered me in her arms, laid my head on her breast and began to hum a tune.

VII. MADRID

Madrid smells better. It does not smell of mules, or of sweat, or of smoke, or of dirty farmyards with the warm reek of dung and of chickens. Madrid smells of sun. On the balcony of our flat, which is on the third floor, you can sun yourself in the mornings. The cat stays in a corner of the balcony on his square of rug, peers down into the street over the edge of the board placed against the foot of the railings, and sits down and sleeps. From time to time, he opens his golden eyes and looks at me. Then he shuts them again and goes on sleeping. In his sleep he twitches his nostrils and smells everything.

When they water the street below, the fresh scent of moist earth rises up to the balcony just as when it is raining. When the wind blows from the north you smell the trees in the Casa de Campo. When the air is still and the whole quarter lies quiet, the wood and plaster of the old houses smell, the clean linen spread out on the balconies, and the sweet basil in the flower-pots. The old walnut and mahogany furniture sweats beeswax; you smell it through the open balconies while the women are cleaning. In the basement of our house is a smart carriage yard, and in the mornings, when the lacquered carriages are taken out into the street, sluiced and brushed, you can smell them. The horses, white and cinnamon brown, come out for their walk covered with a blanket and they smell of warm hair.

Near our house is the Plaza de Oriente with its bronze horses in the middle and the stone kings round it, with its two marble basins full of water, and of frogs, toads, tadpoles, and fishes, and with two little public gardens at the sides. The whole square smells of trees, water, stone and bronze. Further on is the Royal Palace with its square courtyard, the Plaza de Armas, carpeted with sand, treeless, flanked with a row of balconies. The sun beats down on it from sunrise to sunset, and it is like a sandy beach without its sea. Two cannons point their muzzles towards the open country, and a soldier with white leather straps and shining black cartridge-cases paces between them day and night. The balconies are on the further side of a vaulted gallery with six stone arches, and after crossing the sun-filled yard, you feel as if you were in a cold cellar. The fresh air from the Campo del Moro and the Casa de Campo sweeps through the balconies and cools the sand of the courtyard.

When you look out from one of the balconies, everything is green; when you turn your back to it, everything is yellow. The lawns and woods are green, the grains of sand and the stone blocks are yellow.

There is a clock, so old that it has only one hand, because at the time it was made people did not yet count the minutes. Above the clock is a small turret with the bells and hammers hanging free in the air, always ready to strike the hours. Just under it are sentry boxes of thick stone with slits for windows and a roof like a colander. And there are three great gates which no-one ever enters except ambassadors and foreign kings. Then the soldiers, who are on guard in their sentry boxes so that nobody should pass, let them through and present arms.

Swallows swoop and chatter over the heads of the sentries. There are thousands of them. Every corner of the hundred windows of the façade holds a nest, or even two or three, glued to each other, each with its little opening as if it were a pocket. There are so many of them that the swallows who came later because they were born after the others had to pile their nests into the arches of the two stone galleries. On summer evenings, when the sun is setting, they make you giddy as they flash in and out. They return a thousand times to their nests where their broods shrill, waiting with wide-open beaks for their mothers who in passing leave an insect as though it were a kiss.

Once a day, at eleven sharp, the soldiers come marching into the courtyard in slow step, in full-dress uniform. At the head of the infantry walk the four sappers, their nickeled shovels and picks on their shoulders, then the drummers, the buglers, and the band with their brass instruments sparkling and shining in the sun, and then the commanding officer, sitting very straight on his horse with his decorations and his sword, and behind him the flag. The cavalry in silver-plated cuirasses or fur dolmans, in metal helmets or shaggy busbies with death-head badges. Last of all come the two guns drawn by eight square-crouped horses, the iron gun-carriages loaded with cannon-balls, their muzzles covered with a leather cap shined with blacking. On the other side of the yard, the soldiers who are coming off guard are lined up. The two flags salute one another across the empty square and the two officers ride slowly forward, meet in the middle and whisper to each other the secret pass-word of those who may enter or leave the palace. They salute each other with their naked swords, raising them to their foreheads and lowering them to their feet, filling the square with flashes of light. Then those who are coming off guard march through the courtyard in the same order as those who had come on, and the sound of their bugles dies away in the streets. The people stream into the yard once more, and the new soldiers play with the nursemaids and the children.

During the night, the square stands empty, the heavy clanking iron gates are closed, the birds go to sleep and everything turns white in the moonlight. From outside the railings you hear the steps of the sentries on the flagstones of the entrance sounding across the huge courtyard. The street lamps on the wide pavements of the Calle de Bailén dazzle with their white light the hundreds of hawk-moths that come up from the parks.

Our quarter—for this was our quarter—stretched further on through a maze of old alley-ways as far as the Calle Mayor. They were narrow, twisting streets, as our forefathers had built them for some reason or other. They had wonderful names: the names of saints, like Saint Clara and Saint James; then heroic names of wars like Luzon, Lepanto, Independence; and lastly fancy names—Street of the Mirror, of the Clock, of the Stoop—which were the oldest and most winding alleys, those which were best for playing at 'Thieves and Robbers'. There were bits of waste ground with broken hoardings and ruins inside, old houses with empty doorways, stone court-yards with solitary trees, little squares narrower even than the streets. They twisted and intertwined so that it was easy to hide and to escape in them.

There we used to play at 'I spy'. The one who was left over waited until he heard the shouts of the gang which scattered into the alleys. 'I see you-oo-oo!'

He would start to run and behind his back the boys who had been crouching in the corners came out from the doorways, calling 'Past and safe!'

He would run on, smelling out the holes like a dog until he caught one of the boys squatting on the ground or behind some worm-eaten door: 'I spy!'

Sometimes they both shouted at the same time, and then a quarrel would start and end in blows.

We had our quarter and our law. At times, the gang of a neighbouring quarter invaded our territory, and then we defended our right with stones which ricocheted from the corners. The war usually lasted for days, and cost bumps and bruises. In the end, the attackers would get tired and leave us in peace. At other times, we ourselves attacked a neighbouring quarter because the boys there were stinkers or because they had beaten up one of our gang who was passing through their territory.

Everything in our quarter was ours: the holes in the street where we played marbles: the railings of the square where we played hop-scotch: the frogs and the toads in the fountain of the Plaza de Oriente: the right to the planks of the hoardings which we could exchange for broken biscuits at the pastrycook's in the Calle del Espejo: the right to catch the hawk-moths round the street lights of the Calle del Arenal, to chuck stones at the gas-lamps, to jump down the high steps leading up to the Church of Santiago, and to light bonfires in the Plaza de Ramales.

That was our law.

Our council meetings took place in the doorway of the plasterer's yard. Pablito was the son of the plasterer, and the doorway belonged to him. We sat down, and the plaster fallen from the sacks made our trousers white all over. Pablito was very fair, very thin and very small, but he was the brainiest of us. Eladio, the son of the tavern-keeper of the Calle de la Independencia, was the strongest brute. Between the two of them they settled all our problems, and organized our games and our pranks. Sometimes one of them undid what the other had started, because they were opposites.

In the Calle de Lemus was a piece of waste ground with a broken fence. In the ground were the cellars of a tumbledown house which nobody looked after. One day Eladio dared us all: 'I'm going in there. I won't be beaten until I say I am. But I tell you, don't cry if I bash somebody's head in—and you can bash in mine for all I care.'

He slipped through one of the holes in the fence and disappeared in the cellars, where the grass was growing and bricks piled up together with the muck of all the people who used them as lavatories. We laid a plan of attack. He was the bandit Vivillo and we were the Civil Guard. When we tried to get in through the holes in the hoarding, Eladio received us with a shower of stones which knocked against the planks; we retreated and fetched a supply of bricks and rubble. People went to the other side of the street so as not to get hit by our stones, and shouted at us. Eladio defended himself in his holes like a hero, and each time we invaded the waste ground we had to get out again, because he hit hard, with all the strength of the son of a tavern-keeper from the hills of Asturias.

Pablito sat down behind the fence and started thinking. He got a clue from the *Adventures of Dick Navarro*. We quickly lit a bonfire in the street and wrapped our stones in smouldering paper. When the paper began to burn we threw the stones at Eladio who called us cowards, so as to dare us to invade his territory. The ground was littered with old paper, rags, straw, and rubbish thrown in by the neighbours, and soon bonfires flared up all over the place. Some of us threw stones wrapped in burning paper, some just threw stones, thick as hail, and Eladio paid us back by throwing whole bricks and bounding between the flames in a great fury. In the end we entered in a pack, our pockets full of stones, and carrying burning planks torn from the fence.

Eladio surrendered, and the neighbours kicked us out of the grounds. The ruins of the house had begun to catch fire, and the butcher, the coal merchant, the milkman, and the tavern-keeper had to hurry up with pails of water. Our blouses were full of holes burnt by sparks. Eladio screamed at the neighbours from behind the next corner: 'Dirty pigs, bastards!'

Then we showered all the stones we were carrying in our pockets on the men, and the whole quarter was in an uproar, with doors and balconies banging while they were chasing us. The French baker from the Calle del Espejo came after us with a knobstick and thrashed Antoneja, who was always unlucky.

The next day, the ruins were full of mud and smoke fumes. The Frenchman's loaves got a broadside of horse droppings. We collected them in the stables of the house where I lived, and then our whole gang chucked them on to the rolls and buns heaped on the counter. The Frenchman caught a boy and gave him a hiding with one of the sticks of broom which he used for heating the oven. The boy's mother made a frightful row, she came down with a knife and wanted to kill the Frenchman. All the women and some of the men in the quarter wanted to storm the baker's shop.

'That dirty Frenchie dared to hit my boy!'

We boys bombarded the shop with stones, and the people cheered. Nobody remembered about the ruined house. An old woman said to a man:

'You know, my father—God grant he's in heaven now, poor man—used to tell us that the French stuck their bayonets into schoolboys' bottoms and carried them round the streets like that.'

The baker did not lose his customers, because he baked the best bread in the quarter. But for weeks he had to put up with people handling his rolls and loaves, and saying: 'Christ, this loaf's not baked through—and that's burnt—I want a decent loaf of bread.'

We made peace with the baker when he got a cartload of broom for his oven. The branches were hung with pointed little seeds which danced just like a teetotum. We swarmed up the stack of scented, sticky broom, took all the sticks we wanted and filled our pockets with the tight, resinous, acorn-like pods. The man let us do it without interfering, and after that we went back to his shop to buy rolls warm from the oven, and told him it had all been our fault.

It was only a few days till my school term, and I spent them with Uncle José. In the mornings he took his stick with the silver knob—he had another one with a gold knob—and brushed his silky bowler hat with a tiny brush of very soft bristles, which he passed gently over the rounded crown and the stiff, curved brim. Then we walked slowly in the sun up the Calle de Campomanes and talked. He told me stories of when he was a boy. I could not imagine him as a child, I thought that he had always been as I was seeing him then.

'When I was your age, I was earning my bread. At eight years I was just like the boys you have seen in Brunete. I clambered on to the croup of a donkey and went to the spring to fetch water. I took their meals to my father and my elder brothers, to where they were working in the fields, and looked after the water jars so that they always had fresh water. Of course, I couldn't handle the plough, but I drove the harrow on the threshing floor and weeded the fields with a small hoe. I mowed with a sickle, and tied the sheaves which the men left in a heap for me to tie. At night I got up by starlight and went out into the corral. The well bucket was so big that there was nearly room enough for me to sit in it, and it stood on the curb of the well. I had to let it down the well and haul it up when it was full. It bumped against the wall and was so heavy that I was sometimes afraid the rope would drag me down into the well shaft. When the bucket was at the height of the curbstone I dragged it on to the edge, and then I tipped it and filled the pails for the cattle which were waiting for me in the stable and turning their heads. When it was very cold I picked up my blanket from the hearth stone and lay down between the mules until dawn.'

As I listened to him, I thought this was a marvellous life for a boy, a great game.

He used to speak slowly of men and things, with the leisurely, inexorable, measured pace of an old Castilian accustomed to see the hours pass by with the flat lands before him, forced to seek knowledge from the swaying grass blade and the leaping insect.

'When I was a small boy, I already worked like a man. Our food was bad. There were many of us, and my father used to pick out the black chick-peas, and the ones yellow with rust, for us to eat. He left the good ones for seed, and they were rosy chick-peas with a skin like the dry skin of a man. Our best meals were the cool *gazpoacho* in the summer and potato stew in the evenings. None of my brothers were called up to the Army, but I was, and then, when I was twenty, I started to do what you are doing now: I started studying. I had big clumsy fingers stiff with horny skin, and I wept with rage because I couldn't write. The penholders slipped through my fingers, until I made one for myself. At that time only rich people used pens as you know them. The others had quills which had to be sharpened with a penknife, and I couldn't write with them. We also used canes trimmed like quills. I took a stout cane and made myself a pen that didn't slip through my fingers. I studied hard, but I never came so far as to know half of what you know already now. I learnt about figures, but I never could learn algebra.' He added, as though speaking to himself: 'How is it possible to add up letters?'

'It's quite easy, Uncle,' I answered. 'Just as you add up figures.' Proudly I began to give him a lesson in elementary algebra.

He listened, but he did not understand. He strained himself to follow my reasoning, and I grew almost angry when he would not understand such simple things. He dropped my hand and put his own hand on my shoulder, stroking my neck.

'It's no good. We can't do anything about it, you and I. What you don't learn as a boy, you won't learn as a man. It's just as if one's brain got hardened.'

The Plaza de Callao was full of bookstalls. Every year before the opening of the school term, there was a book fair and Madrid was littered with stalls. The greatest number of them was here, in the booksellers' quarter, and at the Puerta de Atocha, where they filled the Paseo del Prado. My uncle and I liked to go from stall to stall looking for bargains. Between the fairs we went into the bookshops of the Calle de Mesonero Romanos, the Calle de la Luna, and the Calle de la Abada. Most of the shops were just wooden sheds set up

91

on empty building sites. The biggest bookshop was at the corner of the Calle de la Luna and the Calle de la Abada, a green-painted wooden shed as big as a coach mews. The owner, an old man, was a friend of my uncle's and had worked on the land like him. They always started to talk hard about old times and the land. Meanwhile I burrowed in the books and put those I liked in a heap. They were cheap: most of them cost ten or fifteen centimos. Every time my uncle saw the heap of books he grumbled, but I knew very well that the bookseller would not let me go away without them, and would not let my uncle discard half of them either. If my uncle did not buy them, the bookseller would give them to me. At times, though, he would take away books which I ought not to read yet, as he said. The only bad thing about it was that I could not sell those books to him afterwards. When I had read them, we took them back to the bookseller and let him have them for nothing. I also bought books in the Calle de Atocha, but the booksellers there bought them back for half the price I had paid.

There was a Valencian writer called Blasco Ibáñez who had written all these books. The priests at my school said that he was one of the worst anarchists, but I did not believe it. Once he had said that nobody read books in Spain because the people had not enough money to buy them; and I thought he was right, because our school books were very expensive. Then he said: 'I will give the Spaniards something to read.' And he opened a bookshop in the Calle de Mesonero Romanos and started making books. Not his own books, since he said that would not be fair, but the best books you could find in the world, and every copy was sold at thirty-five centimos. People bought them by the thousand and when they had read a book, they sold it to the second-hand bookstalls where the children and the poor bought them. That was how I had read Dickens, Tolstoi, Dostoevski, Dumas, Victor Hugo, and others.

People started at once to imitate Blasco Ibáñez. The publisher Calleja, who used to print all the school books and fairy tales, began a series called 'The Novel of To-day'—*La Novela de Ahora*—so as to fight against Blasco Ibáñez's series which was called 'The Illustrated Novel'—*La Novela Ilustrada*. In that series Calleja published many adventure stories by Mayne Reid and Salgari, as well as Spanish classics. The two firms were fighting each other, but most people bought the issues of both every week. Then the Catalans became jealous and the publisher Sopena started printing very thick volumes on very bad paper, but with a brightly coloured cover. They found less buyers, because there were not many people who could afford to spend one peseta, which was the price of a volume. The masons who were the workers with the highest wages since the strike organized by Pablo Iglesias—one of the revolutionaries like Blasco Ibáñez—earned no more than four pesetas per day at the most, that is to say, if they were skilled workers, and 1·75 pesetas if they were simple labourers. Of course many of them bought books at the second-hand shops, but only books at fifteen centimos.

As it was a long way from our house to school, I always took with me two or three novels to read and to exchange afterwards with the other boys. But we had to take care because of the Fathers at the school. If they caught us with a book of the 'Illustrated Novel' series, they took it away and tore it to bits. We were only allowed a 'Novel of To-day' or one of the thrillers for a few coppers.

I had a funny experience because of this. Both series published one and the same book by Balzac, the 'Illustrated Novel' under the title of *Eugenie Grandet* and the 'Novel of To-day' under the title *Los Avaros de Provincias*. I showed them both to Father Vesga, the most bigoted of all our teachers, and asked him whether I ought to tear up this 'Illustrated Novel' edition as well, although it was the same book as the other one. He got as angry as a wild cat, punished me, and confiscated both books. After that he mounted the dais, banged his fist on the table and on the two books, and explained:

'Here you see how they poison the minds of young children! Yes, gentlemen! So as to make people confuse this edition of Calleja, as you all know, a Christian firm which would never lower itself to printing such filth as Blasco Ibáñez publishes in his dirty 'Illustrated Novel', that man, who was excommunicated by the Holy Father, dares to copy the same work with another title! No, gentlemen, it is not permitted to buy a single volume of the 'Illustrated Novel', whatever it may be, because that only means furnishing arms to Satan! And if by misfortune you should find books of this kind at home it is your duty to talk to your parents about it and tear them up, even if your parents get angry.'

At this the priest had a fit of mad rage; I believe he would have killed Blasco Ibáñez if he had been there. He spoke of him as of a monster who murdered people. In the end he turned to me and said 'You'—he used 'you' in place of 'thou' only when he was furious— 'you will stay on your knees in the classroom for a fortnight, and by then you will have learnt not to read such books!'

We went to my uncle's office which was in the building of the church of San Martín in the Calle de la Luna. That church owned an ancient cemetery in the grounds of Amaniel, in which the members of the Confraternity of Saint Martin used to be buried. Later on the State decreed the closing of the cemetery and prohibited any more burials there, as it was already full. Then many of the people whose relatives were buried there had them dug up and removed to another cemetery, so that they all could be buried in the same grave. Since my uncle was in charge of the cemetery office, people came to him to get the permit to dig up their father or mother or grandfather and take them to another place. It was a very expensive business, because as soon as you fiddled with a dead body, everyone cashed in. You had to pay dues to the State, to the Madrid Town Council, to both cemeteries, the one from which the body was removed, and the other in which it was going to be buried; to the Church of San Martín, to the parish in which the relatives lived, to all the parishes through which the coffin would have to pass; the cost of the exhumation, the fee of the forensic doctor who had to attend the opening of the grave, and the price of the new grave site. Thus it cost more than a thousand duros, or five thousand pesetas, to transfer a body.

People gave gratuities up to five hundred pesetas to my Uncle José so that he should speed up the dispatch of the necessary papers. He ran round to the Town Council, the cemeteries, and the parish offices for them and settled everything.

Often, when my school was closed, I went with him and listened to the conversations; many of them were very curious. Most removals were to the cemeteries of San Isidro and San Lorenzo. In the cemetery of San Lorenzo there was a very fat and jolly chaplain who exclaimed every time we arrived: 'Hullo, Pepe—how many new lodgers are you bringing me?' Then he would produce a bottle of old sweet wine and some biscuits. 'Well, let's drink to the health of the dead!' He would fill his glass first, drink it, smack his tongue, thump my uncle on the back, and say: 'That's the good one, you know, the one I use at Mass! You see, we've always got a few crazy old women who give me things. They pay the three pesetas for the responsories, and then from time to time they bring a little bottle as well to make the recommendation of the defunct to Divine Mercy more effective!'

When we said good-bye to him the bottle was always empty, although my uncle and I had drunk only a small glass each.

My uncle's office was at the end of a very dark corridor which began at a side door of the church and ran alongside a garden neglected for many years. The garden was full of odd plants which grew between the grass and entangled your feet. Some of them had climbed the trees and the walls, and the trees and the walls were covered with leaves. In the middle was a round basin which must have been a fountain once upon a time. The rain-water had collected there and it had rotted the stone. Plants had grown in the broken fountain and hung over its rim down to the ground; and from the ground, plants had climbed up, twined with the others, and crept into the basin, so that you did not know which were growing from the fountain. In spring every corner of the garden was full of flowers. On the walls, on the trees, and in the basin of the fountain bells opened, white or purple with yellow pistils. There were red and orange poppies and there were roses of a very dark red, difficult to pick, because they had thorns like hooks. After rain, snails covered the garden. They came up in thousands, and I never understood from where they came and where they went. There were green lizards a foot long, and from the office window we could see rats big as small cats crossing the garden. The church was full of rats.

In autumn the trees turned yellow and the leaves heaped up in the garden. When you walked on them they crackled like old paper. After the rains they rotted, and then the ground of the garden was as soft as a thick carpet. The trees were very old and very big, and hundreds of birds lived in them; all the birds from the whole quarter, because the children never went into the garden. I was the only one to go there, I and a very old priest who had belonged to the church for many years and who liked to sit in the garden reading his breviary. In winter he used to sit in the sun and sometimes he fell asleep there. As the black cloth of his robes grew very hot, the small lizards sometimes climbed on to his knees. When he woke and saw them, he stroked them gently and they lifted their heads as though they were looking into his face.

Once there was a new parish priest who wanted to tidy up the garden, and the old priest made a row in the sacristy, shaking his stick and crying aloud:

'Damnation, if he touches the garden I'll whack him!'

He was so old that they left his garden as he wanted it. Whenever he saw me, he called me and told the story. 'Those fools,' he would say, 'they think they can do better than God. Wouldn't this garden be nice with a few little pebbled paths and a few small trees with their hair trimmed as if the barber came every morning? You see, all those gardeners only want to correct the works of God, and so they clip the leaves off the trees until they look like a wedding cake. What's your opinion?' he would ask me.

'You see, Father Cesareo, for me this is the best garden in the world. Here I can walk on the grass and pick the flowers I like, but in the Retiro where the trees are trimmed as you say, you mustn't walk on the grass or take a flower. If you do the park-keeper beats you with his stick, or if you are with a grown-up he fines you five pesetas. And then there is barbed wire, and if you don't take care your legs get all torn and scratched. That's why I like going to the Moncloa, where you can run about on the grass and there are flowers and pines, or coming here to this garden.'

But not all priests were like Padre Cesareo. In the sacristy they used to quarrel over the Masses and the confessional. There was a big priest who had a very bad temper; he liked playing cards so much that whenever he had to stay on duty in the church, he went to my uncle's office to play Tresillo. He always boxed the altar boys' ears and had rows with everybody. He quarrelled even with the women who came to the sacristy to bring candles for the altars. When the candle was thin, he took it between the tips of his fingers and said 'Madam, this is just a match-stick. Either you've very little piety, or very little money. But I suppose it's little piety you have, because you've got money enough for trinkets and paint.' When the candle was thick, he grew just as angry: 'Where do you want us to place this pole? Of course, you buy a fat taper so that it should last on the altar many days and you can point it out to all your neighbours and say: "Do you see that big, tall candle in the middle of all the small ones? That's my candle!" So you have a good reason for a little gossip and for showing off. What you're spending on wax you ought to give to our Church, which is in sore need of it.'

The funny thing was that in this way he squeezed money out of everybody. Then he would show the duro or the two pesetas to the other priests and say: 'See what idiots you are. The only argument that helps with these people is a good kick in the pants. With your "Madam this" and "Madam that" and kissing hands you don't get money out of them. If you want to milk a cow you've got to pull her teats.'

He kept the money for himself and the others never dared to say anything. Only once Don Rafael, a small timid priest, went out of his way to tell him that those donations should go into the common pool. The other looked him up and down as if he were going to hit him, and pulled a duro out of his cassock. He flicked it on the palm of his hand and said: 'It's me who's earned this duro. Everyone who likes duros can earn them for himself. It would be a nice thing for me to fill your pockets! *Nequaquam!*' And he put the duro back into his cassock.

There was a seat attendant in the church who was also the janitor of the sacristy and the offices, a kind of watchman. During services he walked about in the church among the people with a collecting-box and made everybody pay the five centimos for his seat. It was a good job, because many people gave him ten centimos or more for keeping a prie-dieu instead of a straw-bottomed chair reserved for them, and others gave him letters or messages for their sweethearts and tipped him a peseta or two. Then, when the girl came to hear Mass he went to her to cash in the copper for the chair, winked, and gave her the letter; and so he would get another tip. The priests took the money out of the collecting-boxes by opening the padlock, but the seat-attendant kept on filching money. He did it with a corset whalebone. He stuck a little pellet of hot pitch on the point of the bone, pushed it through the slit of the box and left it inside to let the pitch cool. Then the money stuck to it, and he fished out the coins one by one.

In the afternoon, when my uncle left his office, we went to the Callao Cinema. It was a big, ugly shed of wood and canvas. In the entrance stood a barrel organ with many drums, flutes, and trumpets, and some figures dressed up as pages, which turned round and round on one foot, nodded their heads to make a bow, and struck an instrument with their hands. One of them had a drum, another a lyre with little bells, and a third a tambourine. Highest of all stood a figure with a baton which conducted the music. Behind them was the machinery; there was a tall box with a very long strip of paper covered with holes, which passed over a cylinder and then fell into another box alongside. When the roll ran over the cylinder, which was also covered with holes, the air passed through the holes of the paper into the hollow inside and made the instruments of the organ sound.

The shed was filled with wooden benches, and at the far end was the screen and the speaker. The speaker was a very amusing man who explained the whole film and cracked jokes at the things which appeared on the screen. The people applauded him very much, especially when one of Toribio's films was running. They called him Toribio, but in reality he was a French actor by the name of André Deed, who always did things that made you laugh. They also gave Pathé films about animals and flowers, which showed you how animals live and how flowers grow. Once I saw a hen's egg with its white and yolk, so large that it filled the whole screen. It began to move slowly and to change its form. First something like an eye appeared, and then the little chick began to shape, and in the end it was already formed, pecked at the shell of the egg, broke it, and came out with a bit of the shell stuck to its behind. You also saw films of the King and Queen looking at horse-races, and of foreign kings and lots of other people.

The owner of the cinema knew us; he was a very kind man who had lived in France for many years. His name was Gimeno. On Thursday afternoons, when there was no class, he did not charge the boys more than five centimos for a ticket. When he saw a boy hanging round the organ he asked him why he did not come in. The boy would say: 'I haven't got the money.' Then Gimeno would take a look at him, and if he wasn't a ragamuffin he would say: 'Come on, get in.' Other boys who had no money begged for it from the people who were passing by, and many bought a five-centimo ticket for them. So the cinema filled with boys on Thursdays; even the passages were full of those who could not squeeze on to the benches. Grown-ups disliked going there on Thursdays because of the row going on, with all the boys squealing and making noises. But Señor Gimeno enjoyed the Thursdays more than any other day, and so did the speaker; on Thursdays he cracked more jokes and told more crazy stories than ever.

Sometimes my uncle and I went to other places in Madrid, to the Retiro Park, when the band was playing there, or to the gardens of the Buen Retiro outside the Park. There in the gardens another band used to play and usually a circus with animals was set up there in summer. A lion-tamer called Malleu, a Spaniard, who was said to be the best lion-tamer in the world, had a lion into whose cage nobody else ever dared to enter. The Circus Parish had another lion-tamer, and Malleu offered him 1,000 pesetas if he dared to enter the cage of his lion. We went sometimes to the Circus Parish, but only when there was no dangerous show on. Once a young girl called Minna Alice who turned somersaults in a wooden hoop mounted on a car had got killed, and my uncle did not want me to go to anything where I might see someone killing himself.

It is difficult to turn back.

You look into the sky, and you see cloud cavalcades heaped up by the air which never tires of giving them new shape, or you see but the blue dome aquiver with sunlight. It is the same at night, although the sun is hidden and the light comes only from the stars and the moon. Invisibly, the waves ride on in that sky by day and by night.

All over the earth voices and songs are thrown into the air at random, mixed, massed as the clouds are massed by the wind. A copper wire slung across the roof of a house catches them all, and its frail thread of a body shudders at the impact. An anode and a cathode hurl those voices and songs at each other, as they arrive in mingled surging waves, and the patient hand of the listener regulates the mad leap of the electrons so as to single out a voice or a symphony. But there is always one strain of sound which dominates everything else, a wave more tenacious than the others, to which you have to listen.

Old Madrid, the Madrid of my childhood, is a great surge of

clouds or of waves, I do not know which. But beyond all those whites and blues, beyond all the songs and sounds and vibrations, there is one predominant strain:

EL AVAPIES.

At that time it was the frontier of Madrid. It was the end of Madrid, and the end of the world. With that critical instinct for the right word, which two thousand years since earned the tag of *vox populi, vox dei,* the people had baptized the limits of El Avapies; there were the *Americas* and there was *El Mundo Nuevo,* the New World. It was another world indeed. So far civilization and the city reached, and there they ended.

There began a world of abstruse things and beings. There the city cast its ash and spume, and so did the nation. The seething waters of Madrid threw their scum from the centre to the periphery, and the scum of the seething waters of Spain was sucked from the periphery to the centre. The two waves met and formed a belt which spanned the town. Only the initiated, the Civil Guards, and we children penetrated into that live barrier.

Gullies and slopes bearded with rough ears of grass, eternally yellow, dry, and harsh. Fumes from factory chimneys and evil-smelling trickles from stables. Allotments with lumpy soil, black and putrid; foul streams and parched cracks in the earth. Epileptic trees, hostile thistles and thorns, gaunt dogs with angular ribs, dusty telegraph poles with their white china cups broken, goats browsing on waste paper, empty rusted tins, huts sunk to their knees in the ground. Gipsies with bold side-whiskers, gipsy women in motley, grease-stained petticoats, beggars with abundant beards and lice, children all bottom and belly, filth trickling down their legs, the navel button protruding from their dusky paunches. This was called the 'Quarter of the Injuries'.

It was the lowest rung in the social ladder that began at the Plaza de Oriente, in the Royal Palace with its gates open to plumed helmets and diamond-spangled *décolletés,* and ended in El Avapies, which then spewed out the last dregs and deposited them in the other world, in the Americas and the *Mundo Nuevo.*

Thus El Avapies was the pointer of the scales, the crucial point between existence and non-existence. One came to El Avapies from above or from below. Whoever came from above had stepped down the last step left to him before the final and absolute fall. Whoever came from below had scaled the first step upwards, which might lead to anywhere and anything. Millionaires have passed through El Avapies before crossing the outer belt of the Rondas and turning into drunken beggars. Rag-pickers, collectors of cigarette stubs and waste paper, filthy from spittle and trampling feet, have climbed the step of El Avapies and come to be millionaires. In El Avapies, all the prides exist side by side, the pride of having been everything and no longer wanting to be anything, and the pride of having been nothing and wanting to be everything.

If those tremendous and wantonly cruel forces were to clash, life would be impossible. But the two waves never break against each other. Between them lies a firm, calm beach which absorbs the impact of both and converts them into currents which ebb and flow: all Avapies works.

In its houses built with prison galleries running round their court-yards, passages open to the winds, a single lavatory for all the in-mates, a door and a window per cell, live the plasterer, the smith, the carpenter, the newspaper-vendor, the blind beggar from the corner, the bankrupt, the rag-and-bone man, and the poet. In those court-yards with their pavement of rounded pebbles, a dripping water-tap in the middle, all the tongues of one language meet: the refined accent of the gentleman, the shameless talk of the pimp, the slang of thieves and beggars, the high-flown rhetorics of the budding writer. You hear horrifying blasphemies and exquisitely tender phrases.

Every day during many years of my childhood I walked from the gates of the Palace down to the gates of the *New World*, and scaled the slope on my way back. At times I went into the Palace and watched from the marble galleries guarded by halberdiers the pageant of the royalty, the princes and the grandees of Spain. At times I crossed the frontier into the no-man's world beyond the New World and watched naked gipsies squatting in the sun and killing the lice which the swarthy fingers of their mother or sister plucked from their hair, one by one. I watched the rag-pickers separating the mountain of refuse into heaps of food for themselves and their animals, and heaps of rubbish which they would be able to sell for a few coppers.

I fought battles with stones against the brats of the gipsies and the rag-pickers, and I played decorously at quoits or at hopscotch with boys in braided sailor suits, with curled hair and white collars and silk scarves.

If El Avapies still resounds in me through all the echoing strains of my life, there are two reasons:

There I learnt all I know, the good and the bad, to pray to God and to curse Him, to hate and to love, to see life crude and bare as it is, and to feel an infinite longing to scale the next step upwards and to help all others to scale it. That is one of the two reasons.

The other is that my mother lived there. But this reason is my own.

VIII. SCHOOL

Mass began at seven sharp in the morning. At a quarter to seven we had roll-call and between then and seven o'clock we gradually went into the church. When only two minutes—one minute—thirty seconds were left, there was a great rush to get in. The big clock in the tower showed us the very last moment at which we had to stop playing and enter the church. In winter we used to go in earlier because then the flag-stones in the little square were covered with ice and its fountain hung with icicles.

Inside the church we formed up in files starting by the last step of the High Altar with its iron grille and bronze hand-rail. As we came in, each of us went to the back of his file and the priest in charge of it crossed him off his list. From the left to the right of the altar, the files of the poor pupils' forms were lined up: 'ABC' form, Second and Third Reading, First, Second, and Third Writing—six forms with in all six hundred boys. Then another long file of boys entered through a side door of the church, the paying pupils; they, too, split up into separate files according to their forms, six forms for the six years of the matriculation course and two elementary forms. Some of the boys were boarders and others merely took their meals at school but slept at home. Altogether there were fourteen files with fourteen priests in charge of them, and there were twelve to fifteen hundred boys in the files.

At six in the morning, the eighty priests of the school heard Mass in their chapel and then came out in double file. When the School Mass was over, we all went back to the school building in double file, split up and entered our classrooms in file. Half-way through the morning and half-way through the afternoon, we formed up in double file and went out into the yards to play. When break ended, we again lined up in double file to return to our classrooms. After school we formed up in the cloisters according to the streets where we lived and left the building in double file, with a priest accompanying each column and not letting us break formation until we were at some distance from the school. The priests returned through the streets of El Avapies and formed up in double file to enter the refectory. In file they went to supper and afterwards to prayers in the chapel before going to bed.

We were not allowed to change places in the file. If two friends were separated because they did not arrive for Mass at the same time, they had to play at General Post with the help of all the others; if they were seen by one of the priests they got a cuff and were sent to the back of the file. The prie ts themselves were not allowed to change places in their file. In front were the oldest among them, and at the back those who had not yet sung Mass and were only used to take the smallest and most backward of the poor pupils for reading forms, boys who still dirtied and wetted themselves in class.

It was the same thing in the parade at the Royal Palace. The soldiers marched in rank and file, at their head the captain, the sergeants, and the corporals. Then, after the corporals, came the sappers, after the sappers the oldest soldiers, and right at the rear came the recruits who had not yet learnt to keep step, whom the sound of the band did not reach and whom the people never looked at. In the Model Jail of Madrid, the convicts were led to meals and to Mass in double file. There, too, the oldest and strongest went in front, and the youngest and smallest at the back. In processions, the first to walk in the double file were the fat canons with their purple birettas, then the others with blue birettas, and after them the simple priests with black birettas; then came the fattest and oldest gentlemen of the confraternities, with scapularies and candles, after them the young men, then the devout old women, then the young women, then the boys and girls in school uniforms, and at the tail end the children from the poor schools, in clean blouses and pinafores, but with torn ribbons and broken candles.

At the booking office of the Royal Theatre people queued up in single file. Those who had money bought the first places in the queues, and so they came first. If anybody else wanted to move up, the police stopped him, just as the priests who walked up and down the file in a procession stopped the children and the impatient women from moving up, and just as the corporals and the sergeants and the captains of troops on parade would stop any soldier from marching half a step in front of the others.

The first thing you were taught was to keep in file and be silent. 'Order—Silence!' shouted priests, captains, and prison warders at all the files. It was a privilege to have acquired a place in a row. Number One—the corporal leading the eight picked sappers of a regiment, or the canon in his purple cassock with an amethyst cross on his chest, or the veteran thief, or the precocious child—felt proud, marched in step, held his head high and looked at the people in the street and on the balconies. Those at the back—the little priest who had just managed to get a job at some low parish of Madrid, the recruit forming up in a regimental parade for the first time, the last boy in the form, or the thief's apprentice caught trying to steal a handkerchief—walked with a hanging head, staring at the back of the last but one in the file and feeling sure that nobody saw them because they did not see anybody.

Before you learnt the letter 'A' you learnt to form up in file and keep silent. After that you were taught to read.

Just as stupidly as people in passing read the sign over a shop or the letters of a luminous advertisement, mechanically, not understanding what it says and yet somehow taking it in so that they do what the advertisement told them to do, as soon as they want to buy cough mixture or a seat in a cinema, just so stupidly and mechanically do you keep to your place in the file of life and go behind those who walk before you, in front of those who walk behind you, without rebelling. And woe to those who try to move ahead! Order breaks out, the order which had been dinned into all the others at school, in church, in barracks, in prison, and in the grocer's store where they buy their sausages. They all feel themselves to be priests, quartermaster-sergeants, jailers, and policemen, they all push and kick the rebel back into his due place in the name of order.

Since I was first in my form I was first in the file. I could see the priest read the Mass and hear all his Latin mumblings. But unless I wanted to lose that privilege I had to go into church before all the others and play less than anybody else. When I dawdled, the priest received me with a glum face and grumbled: 'Aren't you ashamed to come so late?' He would mark me down in his list as number 14 or 15 of the file, and instead of coming into the class as number one I would have to enter as number 14 and fight for my place with the thirteen before me, because the place in the file at church counted as much as good work in class. However clever I might be, I would always remain last in the form if I came in last for Mass.

But with this new term I started in a special position, or rather three of us, Cerdeño, Sastre, and I, started like that. We had no place in the file at all. We stayed behind the others in a little group by ourselves, where nobody saw us or looked at us and where we could talk while we knelt, sitting back on the heels of our boots, with all the thousand boys and the fourteen black-frocked priests towering over the heads of the boys in front of us.

We three were poor pupils. The three of us had gained an honours certificate at the Institute of San Isidro, and the school was going to let us take the matriculation course free of charge. Only wealthy pupils were in the matriculation forms, and we three had to sit among them in class. But as it was wrong for the poor boys to mix with the rich, because it would have set a bad example, and as we could no longer mix with the poor boys because we were not in their forms and the poor and rich boys were on different floors of the school building, we had no file and no place in any file. We heard Mass by ourselves and went out into the street by ourselves. During break the rich boys did not play with us and the three of us played all alone.

In class, we three were the first because of our certificates, and nobody was able to take that from us, for if all the others were against us, we three held together against them all. As soon as one of us was in a fix, the other two would help him out, bending over their books and whispering the right answer or writing it down on a slip of paper; the only thing one had to do was to look down or listen to the whisper.

Cerdeño, whose mother was a widow too, had to go on taking the school meals for poor pupils. But the other poor boys who ate there kept on ragging him until he stopped going downstairs for his meals. Then Father Joaquín, who was in charge of the meals that week, noticed his absence and asked him why he did not come. It was then that we found out that Cerdeño had not had any meal for three days. Father Joaquín arranged for him to have his meal all by himself in the kitchen. It was better for him that way, because the cook gave him a bowlful of food to take home as well.

We could no longer play in our little square. The poor boys thought that we belonged to another caste and cut us out of their games. Several times they tried to thrash one of us, but we beat them off because we always went about together. Things were worst for Cerdeño and Sastre. They lived in the quarter and I didn't. The children in their streets would not let them play, and their mothers had rows with the neighbours, who said that the boys had become nobs. Some of the gossipy old women even said: 'God knows what's behind that kid being with the rich boys. . . .' Of the three, I felt the change least, and I made contact with the paying pupils before the others.

It started with the strongest and slowest boy of the form having a talk with me. He was the son of an Asturian mine-owner. His father wanted him to become a doctor, but the poor boy was unable to learn anything. During break he walked up to the three of us and took me aside.

'Now look here, I simply must find out how you manage to learn. I'm fed up with getting punished all the time, and I must find out. If you tell me, nobody will be against you any more and you'll play with us, because I'll make the others let you.'

I told him the truth:

'I can't tell you anything, because I don't study.'

He stared at me and grew red in the face with rage, for he thought I was pulling his leg. I hastily explained:

'It's perfectly true. I don't have to study for my lessons. If I read a book or a lesson once I know it by heart and don't forget it ever. When Father Pinilla explains our mathematics lesson for the next day I understand it all, and so I don't have to take the book and study. You see, I think that being able to learn things or not is the same as being born a hunchback—you can't help it.'

'That's it. My father's got it into his head that I must become a doctor, and that's why he put me here as a boarder. We've got two hours' homework in the morning and two in the evening, and I always read the lesson twenty times over and write it down and learn it by heart, with full stops and commas and all, but I don't understand a word of it. Now listen——' He reeled off the whole lesson about simple equations without a single mistake and without slipping a phrase, and when he had finished he added half sadly and half proudly:

'There, you see, I know the whole thing, but I don't know anything all the same, because I don't understand what those letters mean. And of course, then they give us problems to solve and I can't do them. And it's the same with everything. Then at the end of the course they don't let me pass to the next form and my father comes and beats me up in the visitors' room and leaves me shut up here in the school to go through the exams again in September, and he doesn't take me home to the country. Here at school they nearly always make me go without my sweet and without break, as you know. And it's really not my fault.'

Through this boy we three began to have our games together with the others. I taught him geography by drawing maps for him and geometry by cutting out the solids in cardboard. He was very good with his hands and learnt easily that way.

The school was at the bottom of the Calle de Mesón de Paredes in El Avapies. It was an old monastery which had stayed empty fifty years before when there was a revolution and all the monks had their throats cut. Afterwards the Ecolapians came—t he 'Clerks Regular of the Pious Schools'—and set up a school in the building, which was called the Escuela Pía, the Pious School of San Fernando. They were not monks as the others had been. They were priests who lived in a community and devoted themselves to teaching, but each of them had the right to come and go without asking anybody's permission. The only special rule they had was that it was forbidden for women to enter the cloisters where the priests lived.

Each priest had a room with a window, divided into a living-room and a bedroom and furnished according to his taste. Some of them were very pious, like Father Vesga who slept on a wooden truckle-bed with a tiny bench in place of a cushion and wore a sackcloth robe and a hair-shirt for sleeping. Some of them liked to show off, like Father Fidel, who had mahogany furniture and a big clock with a luminous dial.

Father Joaquín's room was almost bare; he had nothing but a table, books on pine-wood shelves and a music stand, because he liked playing the oboe. His window was open day and night and he had taught the birds to come in freely. He gave them crumbs in his room, and sometimes they dirtied the papers on his desk, even while he was writing there. But he was never angry with them. When he started playing the oboe the small birds and the pigeons came and sat on the window ledge to listen. The only thing he liked were animals and books, and when he was not in the school you could always find him at the second-hand bookstalls near the Prado or in the Lion House. He was a very tall Basque and had a small head, like all Basques, and the body of a giant. When he punished a boy he tapped him on the head with his fingers, and they were as hard as other men's knuckles. He was our geography and history teacher. We liked him very much, for he was kind and played with us during break instead of walking with the other priests or reading his breviary. He used to take off his cassock, and play *pelota* or tug-of-war with us in his shirt-sleeves. Often all the boys of our form together could not manage to pull him off his feet. When we went back into the classroom he would be flushed and sweaty; he would sit down at his desk and say: 'All right —and now the games are over.' Then he would tell us the story of the king who died because he drank a glass of cold water just after having played *pelota*. We learned with him without being aware of it, because he explained everything as though it were a story.

Father Pinilla was our mathematics teacher. But he learnt his mathematics in step with me. When a priest who wanted to become one of the Escolapians was going to read his first Mass, or had just done so, they sent him to one of their schools and he started by teaching the ABC in an infants' form. As soon as he had finished studying to become a priest, he began to study so as to be able to teach other things, and according to what he learnt he was promoted from form to form up to the highest. When they made Father Pinilla mathematics teacher, he had to study the same textbooks as we did so that he could give the lessons. Priests had no need to be teachers so as to teach. The Father Rector simply ordered a priest to take over a form in mathematics or something else, and the priest managed as well as he could. So it happened once that I was able to solve a problem which beat Father Pinilla, because I was very good at mathematics. He was very much annoyed and was angry with me for four or five days.

Father Vesga was a little man, very thin and small, with grey hair which he wore cropped close. Everything about him was small: he had a notebook of ruled paper of the smallest size there is, with a tiny pencil ending in a needle-sharp point, and he was always noting down something. His pocket watch was a small silver lady's watch. He wore old-fashioned spectacles with small oval lenses and he walked with short little steps without making any noise. He got up at dawn and went round the cloisters hunting for bits of paper, cigarette ends or dusty corners so that he could find something about which to scold the men servants. Then he went to church and did the same thing with the altar-boys. After that he sat down in the confessional and when we heard Mass at seven, he was usually taking the confession of one of the pious old women who were the only ones to take him for their Father Confessor. He always walked by himself, because none of us boys felt like going up to his room and none of the priests went to see him either, or liked to have a talk with him. People said he was a Jesuit and went on many evenings to the Jesuit church in the Calle de la Flor, where they had their monastery, and told them about everything that went on in our school.

He took a long time over hearing confessions, and we often heard him talk very rapidly in a low voice which sounded like scolding, although we could not make out the words. But one day we heard him say very angrily to one of the old women who was confessing with him: 'To-day I won't let you take Communion, and you shall kiss the stones of the High Altar one hundred times.' The poor old wretch kept stooping and rising and kissing the three steps of the High Altar for over half an hour in front of all the boys, and in the end she went off in tears because she could not take Communion.

It was one of Father Vesga's fads to do everything in hundreds. He was our teacher in religion and he made us learn the lessons by heart without missing out a single word. When he heard our lessons he opened the textbook and followed what we were reciting. If we left out a word he told us to copy it one hundred times. If we left out more than three words, he made us copy the whole lesson one hundred times. He insisted on our learning the Credo in Latin, although none of us had yet started learning Latin. When we recited the Credo we all made mistakes, and he told us to copy it fifty times. We agreed not to do it. The following day when he saw that none of us had written it, he made us line up and kept us in the cloisters writing on the ground on all fours, until late in the evening when the Father Prefect came and found us there crouching on the stones. He sent us home and gave Father Vesga a terrible dressing down.

The tavern-keeper in the Calle de Mesón de Paredes caned his son because he thought the boy had gone to fight battles with stones in the *New World*, when he came home at that late hour. The boy was so angry that he took three large drawing-pins, such as his father used for tacking up bullfight posters in the tavern, and put them on Father Vesga's chair. When he sat down he jumped up and had to pull the three tacks out of his bottom. He grew quite purple with rage and at first could not get out a word. Then he asked us who had done it. We did not say anything, but the boy got up, very serious, and told him he had done it.

'You—you? And why?' Father Vesga shook him like a rag-doll.

The boy answered, also in a great fury:

'Because you're a dirty swine. It was your fault that my father thrashed me with a stick last night. And if you touch me—I swear on the Cross, I'll crack your skull open with a stone as soon as I see you in the street!'

Father Vesga fetched the tavern-keeper who cuffed and slapped the boy in the Visitors' Room and told Father Vesga that if he felt like it he could beat the boy to death, because he was a rascal and a good-for-nothing.

Father Vesga took the boy back into the class and we were all frightened. His cheeks and ears were an angry red and his lip torn and bleeding. He had to stand beside the dais, and Father Vesga made us a speech:

'Here you see that reprobate whom his own father has to repudiate because he is rotten seed. A true son of Satan, unworthy to be among human beings. . . .' And so on for half an hour.

Then he thought over what he should do to the boy, and we were all quite still, silent out of fear. Suddenly he got up, took the two largest satchels he could find among our things and filled them with books. He made the boy raise his arms as though he were on the cross, and put one of the satchels into each of his hands. He took a pin from his cassock and stood behind the boy. As the satchels were heavy, the boy kept on dropping his arms, and every time he lowered them the priest stuck the pin into his armpits. The boy started crying and in the end dropped the satchels and said he wouldn't pick them up again. Then Father Vesga took hold of the pointer and began to beat him like mad.

The door opened and the Father Prefect came in. He saw what

was going on and asked the boys about it. He grew very serious and sat down at the teacher's desk. When he had found out about everything, he told us to go out into the courtyard, and shut himself up with the priest. That day we had no more lessons, and the following day Father Vesga did not say a word about it, but he made a very ill-tempered face. Every time one of us made a mistake in the lesson he said in a cold voice: 'Copy it two hundred times by to-morrow,' and made an entry in his little notebook. Later on the servants told the older boys that the Father Prefect had punished him by making him kneel in front of the altar all alone, with his arms stretched out like on the cross, as a penance, and had told him that he could apply for transfer to another school if he did not like it, because he for his part had had enough of Jesuits.

The Father Prefect was liked by all the boys and by everybody in the quarter. He was a straight-backed little old man with curly white hair. The women of the neighbourhood came to tell him all their troubles. Some asked him if their boys could not get meals at the school, because they hadn't any money, others asked for clothes for their children. Some of them told him during confession about their rows with their husbands, and then he would visit them in the tenement houses in the evenings and tick off their husbands for getting drunk or for beating up their wives. Most of the troubles came because the husband spent his wages in the tavern and thrashed his wife and children, or else because the young girls ran around with their boy-friends. Then he would get hold of the two young people and marry them. So it happened that when the Father Prefect walked through the streets of El Avapies everyone greeted him; even the women at the vegetable stalls, who said blasphemies all the time, came to kiss his hand. And he was always left without cash in his pockets because so many came to ask him for something.

Father Fidel was our teacher in Grammar and Logic. He was very young and affectionate, but very nervy. Sometimes it was as though he had fits of madness. Then he would grab a boy and pet and kiss him. Or he would stare into space without seeing anything and we would do nothing for half a lesson. He would simply say: 'Now study your books,' and stay with his elbows on the desk, thinking of God knows what. There was a time when he did nothing but take endless walks, and another time when he shut himself up in his room and turned the key. Occasionally I went up to see him, and he looked as if he had been crying. When he was in that state his nether lip and hands kept trembling. He had very long, thin hands. Often he was feverish and his hands burned. One day I heard the doorkeeper say to one of the servants:

'Father Fidel's crazy. The latest is that he wants to sleep without a mattress and lies on the naked springs.'

'He's not crazy, the trouble with him is that he needs a good wench. He'll be all right as soon as he does the same as Father Pinilla.'

Father Pinilla sometimes went out in his habit and changed into civilian clothes in another house; people said that he went on the spree at night.

The truth was that most of the priests seemed a little mad. There were two or three of them, very young ones, who looked dazed and could not talk properly, for they stuttered and blushed. The year before, one of them had had to be unfrocked because he used to touch the boys' parts. Then there was Father Joaquín with his passion for animals, and Father Fulgencio with his passion for the organ. He used to fetch two or three of us to pull the bellows for him, and he would go on playing the organ for hours, sometimes long, sad pieces, and sometimes things in which he had to strike the keys hard. Then we would stand in the doors of the bellows closet and watch him hopping up and down on the organ bench, sweating, with his hair standing on end. He would jump up suddenly, slam the door and run through the cloisters talking to himself.

At the beginning of the Calle de Mesón de Paredes was the house where Señora Segunda lived. Nearly every morning when I was on my way down to school she was having her breakfast in One-Arm's little café. When I went in to say good morning to her, all the other customers stared at me in surprise because I greeted and kissed her. For Señora Segunda was poor and had to beg alms, and moreover a cancer had gnawed away her nose and you saw the bones of her skull. No other boy dressed like myself went into that café, because it was where the beggars met. They also made *churros* in the place, and the whole quarter and the crisp-hawkers who re-sold them at the street corners came there to buy. The café had marble tables and wooden benches, and two big urns, one for milk and one for coffee. They called this coffee 'tanner's bark', and it was made from the dregs they bought from the cafés of Madrid; I was never sure what the milk was made of, but certainly not of milk. They sold broken crisps which they called 'nibs' and pieces of buns which they called 'stubs'. At nightfall the beggars began to arrive, as well as the Galician porters from the Plaza de la Cebada, who earned their living carrying baskets of fruit to the greengrocers on their shoulders. To make a living, they had to do it cheaper than the carters who charged fifty centimos per basket. The porters asked twenty-five or thirty centimos, and for that money they had to run through the streets, bumping into people, with two baskets of a hundred pounds each on their back, which they sometimes had to carry as far as the Salamanca district. People were never angry when they bumped into them, because the poor fellows were staggering under their burden and did not see where they were going. Also, they had to keep running and could not stop, because of the way in which they carried heavy loads and which made them walk very quickly, but feel the weight less.

There in the little café they had their evening meal, a cup of 'tanner's bark with nibs', which cost them ten centimos. Then they counted the coppers they had earned during the day on the marble table, and sorted out cigarette ends, taking off the paper, so that the tobacco was left. Those of them who had no place of their own took one or two little glasses of spirits, which they called 'petrol', and the owner of the café let them sleep there over the marble top of the tables.

On winter nights, when it rained or was so cold that the beggars could not sleep in the house-doors, the café was filled by ten o'clock. People were packed like herrings and slept on each other's shoulders or on the tables. Sometimes the police came in and searched everybody, but it hardly ever happened that they arrested anyone and took him away, because neither One-Arm nor the beggars would allow a thief to stay there.

Sometimes Señora Segunda invited me to take a cup of 'tanner's bark' and I drank it so as not to hurt her, although I did not like it. She looked after my sister Concha who went to a Nuns' school just below mine. As my mother was washing down by the river or working for my aunt the whole day long, Concha was left all by herself at midday after school. My mother often gave Señora Segunda money to cook a meal for herself and my sister; so both could eat, and my sister did not run about in the streets. My mother also kept things to eat for Señora Segunda, so that she should have an evening meal and keep herself going. She got few alms when she was begging, not enough for her food, because people disliked coming close to her. She lived in a large house just by the cafe, where they let her have a room tucked away in the hollow of the doorway, under the first turning of the staircase. It had only just enough room for her bed and an earthenware stove for her cooking.

All the same she was very kind and fond of all of us. As her nose was the way it was, she did not dare to kiss us, but when we came to her room and gave her a kiss, she was very happy. I did not mind kissing her on the cheek, but it made me feel sick when she kissed me. When she wanted to I let her, because otherwise she was deeply hurt and began to cry. She was crazy about cleanliness; her clothes were very bad, because they were all old clothes people had given her, but she mended them slowly, with tiny little stitches and invisible patches, and then washed and ironed them nearly every day. Her bed sheets were made of bits and pieces of old rags she had picked up in the street and sewn together, but they were so clean and white that they looked bluish.

She was religious, but she went to the Protestant Church which was in her house, not because she herself was a Protestant—for she went to pray in church—but because she said she liked going up there, God being everywhere. Besides, the Protestant priest some-times helped her, although it was not much, since the Protestants had little money. I wanted to see a Protestant church myself; I could not imagine how a church could come to be on an upper floor. So Señora Segunda took me up with her and introduced me to their priest.

I was afraid to go, because the Fathers at my school spoke very ill of the Protestant school and said that anyone who entered it was damned; only the sons of anarchists went there, and then they them-selves turned anarchist and started throwing bombs, as they had thrown bombs at the King. This was something I failed to under-stand, because according to our geography lesson everybody was a Protestant in Germany, England, and a few other countries.

When I came there, I saw a big room with benches and writing desks, where they gave free classes for children; in the same room they had their prayers on Sundays and played a small organ standing beside the priest's desk. Their priest was an old gentleman with a white beard, in ordinary clothes, but with a stiff collar like that of our priests. He gave me sweets and showed me a natural history book with beautiful coloured pictures. I was very curious, so I asked him:

'Is it true that you don't believe in the Virgin and the Saints?'

He smiled and said I was too young to understand such things. Then he gave me a heap of picture cards with drawings of the life of Christ and words from the Gospels of Saint John, Saint Matthew, and Saint Luke. He gave me a lot of them and said I could distribute them among my little friends.

I told the boys at school that I had been in the Protestant School and we shared the picture cards among all of us. Cerdeño was just reading one, keeping it between the pages of a book, when Father Vesga came from behind on tip-toe so that we did not hear him. Suddenly he stretched out his hand, took the picture and read the text.

Lord, what a row! His lips went white and trembled with rage, and his face went purple, and he stamped his feet on the dais, but first he could only stammer, not speak. It always happened when he was in a fury.

Then he asked: 'Who gave you this filth?'

'Barea gave it me, Father,' Cerdeño answered.

'Come here, Barea.' He said it very slowly, through his teeth. 'Who gave you this?'

'A gentleman in the street,' I said. I did not want to say that I had been to the Protestant Church, because I knew what would happen.

'A gentleman—a gentleman—I didn't imagine you'd got it from a donkey! I ask you: who—when—how—where?'

I thought of a lie which was half truth. I knew that on Sundays some men and women met in the Protestant School and then distributed little pictures like these in the street and sold booklets with the Gospels and the Bible. So I said:

'A man who was distributing those things gave them to me in the Calle de Mesón de Paredes, and I kept them because they're from the Gospels.'

'That's just like those Protestant scoundrels! The Gospels—do you call this thing the Gospels?'

'Yes, sir. It says here Gospel of Saint Luke, and here Saint Matthew.'

'These are not the Gospels,' and he banged on the table. 'These are writings of Satan. It is a disgrace that things like this should be tolerated in Spain. All right, it was not your fault, but from to-day on, when they give you one of these prints—prints of the Devil—you must bring them here to me without reading them. Do you hear? Without reading them. And if I catch one of you with one of these pictures, I'll throw him out of the school. Now come along, give me all the prints you have.'

One after the other the cards appeared, and Father Vesga's fury grew greater and greater. Every boy had two or three of them. But as none of them wanted to say that they had had them from me, all told the same story except the boarders who said that we day pupils had handed them on. The Father collected a whole heap on his desk and clutched his head:

'Lord, Lord! This evil must be torn up by the roots.'

The next day we saw that Father Vesga had taken over the file which left the school by the Calle de Mesón de Paredes. When we came to Cabestreros where the file usually broke up, he went on with us towards the Plaza del Progreso, always in rank and file, and dismissed us only at the corner of the square. So it went on day after day until it happened that the rear of our file was supplied with the little cards, at first without our noticing it.

A hunchback with a head like a gourd had slipped into the file and distributed the prints among the boys. Suddenly Father Vesga noticed little pieces of paper in everybody's hands, realized what was happening and seized the hunchback by the throat. He knocked the whole bundle of leaflets out of his hand, slapped his face, and shouted at him. People clustered round and the police came running up from the Calle de la Encomienda. Some people took the part of the priest and some of the hunchback. They started to insult and beat each other up, and wanted to hit Father Vesga and the hunchback as well. The police dragged Father Vesga out of the crowd and escorted him back to the school.

On the following day, our file turned into the Calle de Cabestreros and we did not pass the Protestant School at all. Father Joaquín was in charge. But when we came out of the school gate after Mass on Sunday, there were five young men distributing the little cards among the files and the passers-by. One of them went up to Father Joaquín and gave him a whole bunch, saying mockingly:

'For the children, Father—these are the words of Jesus.'

Father Joaquín came to blows with him and at that all the files broke up, while other boys were still coming out of the church. More of the priests arrived, and the priests and the Protestants were having a fight. We boys started throwing stones at them and in the end the five Protestants ran away up the slope. The butcher from across the street was running after them with a knife in his hand.

'Bastards, buggers! Well I never, coming here and attacking a few poor priests and small children! Come on, tackle real men! I spit on God!'

His son was a boarder in my form and one of the most stupid boys, but he wore a school uniform of silk cloth with real gold braid.

The butcher came back puffing and blowing, with the knife in his hand, his white apron blood-stained, and shouted:

'Come in here, Reverend Fathers, come in here. Those brutes! Sit down, I'll give you a little glass of spirits to steady your nerves. Those rascals have escaped something, I can tell you. If I catch one of them, I spit on God, I'll slit his bowels! Well I never—attacking a few feeble priests who can't defend themselves!'

Father Joaquín, who liked his joke, slapped the butcher on his fat shoulder which sounded like lard, and said:

'Brother, brother, take a hold on yourself. You're blaspheming, and even if God may forgive you for the sake of your good will, there are children present. Besides, we aren't so very feeble, we can defend ourselves too!'

And with his big hand he smacked the butcher's shoulder so that he swayed on his feet.

'Pardon, Father, pardon me—it was only my indignation—may God forgive me!'

They wanted to turn out the Protestant School. But a politician, one of the Socialists, Azcárate, prevented it. The Protestants no longer distributed cards in the street and set up two guards at their house door on Sundays while they had their Mass. The Queen Mother Maria Cristina and the Nunzio of His Holiness did their best to close the school, but as the reigning Queen was from England and Maria Cristina was no longer Queen, some English people protested, and the school did not close down.

The priests inspected our books page by page to discover Protestant picture cards; we sold them among ourselves at fifty apricot stones or ten marbles each.

I made more friends among the other boys of our form, among the rich boys, than the two other scholarship pupils. Although Sastre and Cerdeño came to school with better suits than before they had gone to class upstairs, I was still better dressed than either of them. Also, they lived in tenement houses in El Avapies, while I lived in a wealthy quarter and knew many things they did not know. Sometimes they accused me to my face of avoiding them so as to be with the others. And it was not true. What really happened was that I could get on with the rich boys and they could not, because they remained what they were, street urchins of the slums. When I was with the rich boys, I felt more as if I was with my own kind. When I was with the other two, it always annoyed me that they did not realize we were no longer downstairs and could neither say nor do the same things as before. They came to school with their pockets full of green wheat-ears and nibbled them during the lessons and told stories of how they had been throwing stones together with the Ronda gang in a battle against the boys of the *New World*, how the Civil Guard had come riding and how all the boys had got together, two hundred of them, to throw stones at the Civil Guard. One day Cerdeño arrived with his hands blackened, and when Father Joaquín asked him why he hadn't washed them, he said that the day before, a Sunday, he had been gleaning at the 'Flea Station'. The Flea Station was what they called the shunting station of Las Delicias— The Delights—on the suburban line, where the trains from the North Station were linked with trains from the South Station. The children and women of the quarter went there to the coal dumps with little baskets and collected bits of good coal from among the cinders of the railway engines. They also used to pinch what real coal they could get, and burn it at home or sell it. Cerdeño went there because it was fun for him.

It sometimes happened that he and Sastre produced *gallinejas* for break at eleven: cow's tripe fried in tallow at street stalls and put between two chunks of bread. Whenever they were eating them, they stank from the smell of hot grease. And apart from all that, it was impossible to teach them not to speak as people spoke in El Avapies; they still used any kind of bad word that came to their mind.

It was difficult for me. When I was with the two of them, I was more at my ease, but they looked at me as though I were different. When I was with the others, I found it more pleasant, but they knew that I was different from them, that I was the son of a washerwoman, that I was with them only because I had won the scholarship and the priests paid for my studies. So it happened that when they wanted to insult me, the rich boys called me 'Washerwoman's Son', and the poor boys 'Little Gentleman'.

The oddest thing was that there were many poor boys who were not poor and many rich boys who were not rich. In the non-paying forms there were sons of tradesmen from the quarter, whose fathers had a very good business, and in the forms upstairs there were sons of civil servants whose fathers had to starve themselves so that their boys could shine at school among the rich pupils. And these two groups showed off most, one as being poor and the other as being rich.

It was a Sunday. After Mass I went with Father Joaquín up to his room to collect some books he wanted to lend me. Then we walked down to the cloisters on the first floor, where the relatives of the boarders stayed with the boys after Mass until mealtime. That day it was Father Joaquín's turn to receive the parents and tell them how their boys had done.

Nieto, the Asturian, was with his father, a broad, strong man with the face of a bulldog. Nieto called me, and Father Joaquín and I went over together.

'Look, Papa,' he said, 'this is Barea.'

His father looked me up and down with little grey eyes glinting under shaggy eyebrows.

'Oh yes, that's the son of the washerwoman you told me about. You should learn from him, considering you have cost me good money, only to turn out more of a brute than a washerwoman's son.'

Nieto went quite pale and I felt that I had grown red. Father Joaquín put one hand on my head and took Nieto by the arm, saying: 'Run away for a while.' Then he turned to Nieto's father, very gravely, and said:

'Here the two of them are equal, or rather, here the son of a washerwoman is more than the son of a mine-owner who pays three hundred pesetas per month.'

He turned on his heel and walked away calmly, without bowing his head. The old man gazed after him and then called his son. The two began a discussion, sitting there on the bench.

I passed by them and said to the boy:

'See you to-morrow.' And I walked on without bowing to his father. Father Joaquín stood by the door. He said nothing to me. I said nothing to him. I kissed his hand and went away.

I went down the steps of the entrance without seeing them, for my eyes filled with water. What Father Joaquín had done was against the rules of the school, where people with money were never treated that way. If he were found out, he would be alone against all the other priests. Because things were like that, he played his oboe for the birds and talked to them.

I was alone as he was. Both of us were different from the others.

IX. ROYAL THEATRE

Don Enrique was painting, but one could not see what he painted. He had a smock which reached down to his feet, rope-soled canvas shoes, and his white hair was all mussed. He looked like a madman. Beside him stood a row of pails, of the kind masons use to carry water; they were filled with paint in all colours, which looked like dyed milk, except for a pail which was plain milk and held white paint. In each pail stuck a brush as big as a broom, and a few long slim brushes stood round the big one as if they were children standing round their mother. On the floor there was a huge canvas stuck to the ground with big nails and stiffened with glue. Don Enrique took the big brush out of one of the pails and slapped a few large blobs on to the stretched canvas or shook it so that the paint spattered. In the end the canvas was nailed to a few wooden boards and became a castle or a forest. We always knew what it was going to be: pails filled with greens and blues meant a forest: pails with chocolate and red pepper a castle, and a lot of white and blue the sea.

While he painted we had our games on the stage and made the boards ring hollow. We ran, jumped, and played ball on the stage. On the other side, beyond the fringe of red velvet with the prompter's box in the middle, was the theatre. The theatre had no windows, it was a black cave ringed with pale stripes which faded away far up at the back, near two little squares of light like two eyes.

Nicasio, the son of the concierge—he was our friend and so we could run about in the theatre just like at home—jumped up on the rim of the prompter's box and shouted into the hall:

'Eeeeh!'

The hall answered in a hollow voice: 'Eeeeh!'

We shouted with laughter and the hall laughed with us, sending back our laughter from the back of the boxes and from under the stalls. Up there on the high, painted ceiling it chuckled. Nobody knew so well as we did how the theatre resounded. Away by the two holes of the main entrance, so far from the stage that people looked minute, you could hear the slightest sound. When the theatre was full it was silent, because the people could hear it, and so it no longer laughed with us. Then it did not mock the conductor of the chorus any longer either, as it did during rehearsals, when it echoed all the little cries of the tiny Italian. For the conductor of the chorus was a little old man with a broken voice who mounted on the square stool of the organ in the wings, buried himself behind a huge score and from there began to shriek and gesticulate, like a monkey in a sideshow.

'One—two—three—now!'

He opened his arms and shut them with a smack, nodding his head so that his spectacles almost fell off his nose. When the chorus sang out of tune he went crazy. He started hopping on his seat until he almost stood on his toes, and the adam's apple in his throat, thin as a plucked bird's, stuck out.

'No, noooo, dammit!'

Someone in the chorus would stay there with his mouth open and swallow the note half-way.

'Repeat—attention—one, two, three—now!' Smack, sounded his palms.

Up at the roof the theatre laughed to itself and showered down a cascade of hand-claps. After the rehearsal he took his small bowler hat which was like a child's, passed his sleeve over the crown to make its grease shine, pulled the tails of his jacket, which were always too long because the tailors did not know how to make small enough coats, and went trotting through the corridors like a wound-up toy. Agustín the carpenter, who ran about during the intervals with his big hammer and his mouth full of nails, was always bumping into him and shouting:

'Get out of the way! One day I'll tread on you without meaning to, and then you'll get squashed.'

Once the old man answered back in a temper:

'I'm as much of a man as you!'

Then Agustín caught him between the legs with one hand and lifted him over his head, just like that, astride his hand. The conductor dangled in the air, and the girls of the chorus and ballet rocked with laughter so that their breasts and bellies danced under their tights. The public thought that they were naked, but in reality they had cotton tights on. The prima ballerina had silk tights. Some of the girls who had thin breasts wore two pads of cotton wool sown into their tights, and when they were hanging in the chorus girls' dressing-room, those tights looked like bodies of women put through a wringer, with the breasts left untouched.

When the girls dressed they had to be quite naked before putting on their tights, and therefore there was a notice on their door saying 'Entry forbidden'. But on nights when there was a performance great gentlemen with top hats came to see it and entered the chorus girls' room even while the girls were naked. Later on, after the show, they took them to supper. Once it happened that one of them married a chorus girl.

The corridors led to a circular room, like the spokes of a wheel. There was a velvet-covered sofa in the middle, and a large vase filled with flowers beside it. Around it were the rooms of the best artists. Sometimes, at gala performances, the King came to see them; then the green-room filled with police agents who looked nastily at everybody, and with officers in gala uniform who followed the King.

Those visits were a great pleasure for Anselmi, who was an elegant gentleman, but they annoyed Titta Ruffo who was said to have been a carter. One night the police arrived and people kept saying: 'Now the King will come soon!' Everybody was cleared away except the chorus girls and visitors who were dukes or something of the kind and who all had top hats. Everyone kept very quiet, waiting for the King to arrive. And then Titta Ruffo went and began to sing, with that big voice of his and the door of his room half open: ' *Mierda—miiierda mieeerda-mierdaaaa!* ' [1]

Nobody dared to say anything to him and he went on singing ' *mierda* ' at the top of his voice. The King must have disliked it, because afterwards the Royal Commissioner of the theatre asked Titta Ruffo whether he could not have sung something else.

---

[1] *Mierda* means muck and is a very rude exclamation.

'You know,' said Titta Ruffo, 'that's a word which is very good for practising one's voice. It contains nearly all the vowels.'

From then onwards he filled the passages of the Royal Theatre with his *mierdas* before coming out to sing. And the more top hats were about, the more *mierdas* he let loose.

He liked pulling the legs of all those who wore a top hat. They crowded into his room, called him Maestro, brought him flowers, asked for his photograph and did not give him a moment's peace. He played a joke on them at that time. He lived in the Hotel de Rusia, but he did not like the hotel food; one day, the conductor of the chorus took him to the tavern of Eladio's father who was called Eladio too. His wife cooked very good meals for cab-drivers and Titta Ruffo sat down there and stuffed with their kind of stew. After that he ate all his meals there. Once the top-hatted gentlemen invited him to dine out at any place he liked, and he took the lot of them to Eladio's to eat *cocido*. There came many cars and coaches with the coronets of dukes and marquesses on their doors, and they all went into the tavern together with the coachmen and the members of the chorus. Eladio's father and mother did not know what to do with all the people. The whole quarter came and stood in a crowd outside the tavern and it was fun to see the great gentlemen eating *cocido*, turning up their noses, and the bottles of rough red wine standing on the tables.

When Titta Ruffo sang, we boys crept up in the wings, squatting on the floor and keeping quite still so that they should not chuck us out. And so we heard him sing Rigoletto, Pagliacco, and Hamlet. In *Rigoletto* he came on the stage as a hunchback, with a white wig and an old face, and nobody would have recognized him, he looked as if he had been a hunchback all his life. In *I Pagliacci* he sang with his face painted like a clown's, and in *Hamlet* he was a Prince of Denmark with a cloak of real ermine dotted with tiny black tails.

He had bought that cloak out of cussedness.

The first time he sang *I Pagliacci* in the Royal Theatre, he came out in a costume of cheap stuff, made up of coloured patches. The Director spoke to him about it: everybody dressed in splendid silks, and famous artists had no right to be stingy about their costumes. Titta Ruffo said to him:

'Those are village clowns, and I don't think they would wear silk. I'm not a fashion plate, but an artist, and I dress according to my role.'

Then everybody started saying that he was a tightwad and a miser. 'If all's said and done, he's a carter,' somebody said one day, and Titta Ruffo got angry.

When he sang Hamlet he hung up his fur cloak in the green-room and they all crowded round to see it and stroke the fur. Suddenly Titta Ruffo turned up and said:

'What—does the carter's cloak please you?' And he put it on over his velvet suit with lace and embroidery and a heavy gold chain. After that nobody said a word, and he continued to sing the clown in his patched calico dress.

It was a tremendous thing to hear singing close to you. When I was sitting in the wings, the singers sometimes came to sing what is called 'off stage'. I saw them from below, in their silk costumes, singing and watching the conductor of the orchestra through a slit in the scenery. The voice would vibrate so that you saw the singer's flesh quiver and go on palpitating during the high notes. There were two exceptions: Titta Ruffo and Massini Pieralli. When they sang it was not they who vibrated but everything near them. I vibrated myself, and when I put my hand on the wooden frame of the scenery I felt the wood vibrating. The air was sucked in and thrown out of their chests as though in a blacksmith's bellows, and only their throats made the sound. If you were standing beside them, you could look at their mouth and not hear any sound coming from it, but then everything else sounded; you saw them forming words with their lips, tongue, and teeth, but the words were pronounced by the stage, the scenery, the canvas, the orchestra, the public, the hall, the whole theatre. Even the footlights seemed to sound. That was what the theatre people called voice production.

Once Titta Ruffo was discussing this; he went to the very back of the stage and gave a cry, which they said was the cry of the shepherds in the Alps. We all saw him open his mouth wide for the yell, but we did not hear it. Then the whole theatre, which stood quite empty, began to yell, and it was as though the roof and the pillars were going to burst and the big chandelier in the centre to fall. When there was nothing more to hear, the whole theatre still resounded. Another time, in the Café Español, he took a coffee-spoon and drew it across a row of glasses, one after the other. He did it a second time, and as he passed the spoon over the glasses, in the way one passes a finger-nail over the teeth of a comb, he gave a cry. All the glasses repeated his cry, and broke off at their stems. The glass cups fell on to the marble of the counter and tinkled like bells.

Anselmi, the tenor, was the opposite of Titta Ruffo. Titta Ruffo was short and squat, with black, crisp hair and strong hands. Anselmi was rather tall and rounded like a woman. He had a sweet voice, so sweet and soft that sometimes you could not tell whether he was singing or the orchestra playing by itself. He was pretty like a woman, with curled hair; he rubbed creams and lotions into his face and wore clothes which looked like a lady's. People in the theatre said that aristocratic ladies used to send him letters and invitations, but they also said that he did not want to have anything to do with women, because it was not good for one's voice. He lived only for his throat; he went round wearing a scarf and gargling and spraying all the time. When he was singing on the stage everybody was on the lookout so that there should be no open doors and no draughts.

This was another curious thing. Inside the theatre there was not enough draught to move a hair. But when the curtain rose in front of a full house, a hurricane swept out of the stage's mouth. The cold of the stage, of the scenery, and of the four drops rushed into the house. On gala nights, when the stalls were filled with ladies in low-cut dresses, you saw them putting their hands on their chests because they were frozen. Through the doors at the back of the stage, which opened on to the Plaza Isabel II, the cold air of the night streamed in and the warm air from the hall streamed out. The poor people who slept there clustered round to have a share of the warmth.

On nights when there was a performance the beggars were waiting for the end to open carriage doors and beg for ten centimos. Then the fine gentlemen came out, in swallow-tails and top hat, their shirt fronts sparkling with diamond studs, and their women in fur coats and shoes of silver tissue and silk dresses with the train caught up in their left hand. A beggar with lice in his beard would open the door of their carriage with one hand and take off his rag of a cap or his greasy beret with the other, making a bow. When they stopped at the very carriage door and went on talking, the beggar, with his head uncovered and without an overcoat, almost died with cold and stamped on the paving stones with his canvas shoes. Later the beggars all met under the huge arches of the Plaza Isabel II, where they had prepared their beds of old newspapers and straw. They counted their coppers and sometimes gambled with them by the light of the square iron lamps outside the theatre.

One of the beggars was more famous than all the others. He was a spare old man with white hair and beard, wrapped in a frayed coat too large for him, with boots which had twisted points gaping like the mouth of a fish so that the toes stuck out. He never opened carriage doors. He took up his post in the dark away from the theatre doors, and waited for the couples who did not ride in a coach, because they lived near or because they wanted to have a snack in a café before going to bed. Nobody could see him. Suddenly he would come out of his dark corner where he had been hiding and grasp the arm of the man:

'Gentleman—give me a duro, because I've not eaten to-day.' He said it in a hollow voice which seemed to come out of an empty stomach, as if it were an empty box.

Sometimes, but very rarely, they gave him five pesetas or one peseta. When he got his duro, he made a deep reverence with his bowler hat, so that he almost swept the ground, and followed the couple for a good while, wishing them every kind of happiness. When he got one peseta, or, as happened much more often, ten centimos, he would stretch out his right hand, with the coin lying on his open palm, and say proudly:

'One peseta? Sir, you've made a mistake. A man can't feed on one peseta. You've spent twelve duros, sixty pesetas, for a stall and paid the agent's commission on top of it, and now you want me to get a meal for one peseta?'

Then he would thump his chest with his left hand, and since it was very bony, it would resound like a wooden partition wall. Sometimes people gave him more at that and sometimes they chased him away in a bad temper. Then he started shouting and explained to all the world what kind of gentlefolk they were:

'So that's what's called a gentleman! A fine topper and a fine lady and a peseta for me to eat a measly handful of beans and croak! But I'm a gentleman myself!'

If they still refused to let him have anything, he would follow them, plucking at the man's sleeves and coat-tails and reducing his price. From a duro he would go down to two pesetas, then to one, then to fifty centimos, then to twenty-five centimos, then to ten centimos. If everything failed and the man said nothing, or went on his way, or just said: 'Forgive me for God's sake, brother,'[1] the beggar would play his last card. After keeping silent for a moment or some distance from the theatre, he took off his hat and said:

'Gentleman, some time ago, I implored you to give me the smallest sum a man can ask for his meal. You did not think fit to give me anything, so what can I do? Have patience. It won't be my first night without a meal. But, sir—a cigarette—you won't refuse me a little cigarette!'

He usually got his cigarette and sometimes at this last moment he got the peseta he had not managed to get before. In their bedroom under the arches of the Royal Theatre they used to call him The Marquess, and he maintained that he really was a marquess. When he was drunk he told stories, and the beggars, the boys in the street,

[1] The traditional formula by which a Spaniard, when accosted by a beggar, acknowledged his religious duty to give alms and, simultaneously, excused himself as having nothing to spare.—*Translator's Note*.

and the passers-by listened. The firemen who were on duty in the theatre paid him wine or hot coffee, and sometimes they made him drunk so that he should tell stories.

The stone columns of the arches had broad bases and one could sit on the corners. There the Marquess sat down and started his tale. The firemen had given him the left-overs of their meal, he had drunk a few gulps of wine, a cup of coffee, and the coachmen had invited him to a glass of spirits. His eyes were rheumy and his nose red with the cold and the wine.

'When I married,' he said, 'I made my honeymoon trip to Venice. I married a fine woman. I won't tell you her name, because names don't come into the story. At that time we travelled in a diligence and it took us two months from Madrid to Italy. These mucky cars didn't exist yet, with their screech and stink. Good horses and bad roads— but it was life all right.'

He went on for hours telling about his travels in Italy and his love. The beggars were sitting at his feet and the coachmen standing behind him listened while they drank sips of coffee from the spouts of their coffee-pots.

To drink coffee as the coachmen did was an art, and their coffee had a taste of its own. The waiter brought them two coffee pots on a tray of white metal, one of black coffee and the other of milk, one big and the other small, and both boiling hot because otherwise it would not be right. They poured coffee into the milk and milk into the coffee, from one spout into the other, until both were the same colour. Then they drank in little sips from the spout, putting their lips to it, sucking and passing the pots from one to the other.

There was Señor Encinas. He was an old man with white hair and moustache and a round, red face covered with purple veins which seemed about to burst in his cheeks. Every night when there was a performance he arrived at nine o'clock at Señor Manolo's tavern, drank two glasses of red wine and went across to the Café Español, tripping between the tables with the short steps of a short, fat man. He was Number One in the theatre claque. He had still heard Gayarre and Patti sing, and he became excited whenever he spoke of them. He used often to tell the story of the wasp.

One night, Gayarre and Patti were singing a duet just beside the prompter's box and Gayarre had his mouth open, letting loose his notes. La Patti was looking at him and laughing, unable to stop her laughter, and the public were looking round to see what the singer was laughing about. Suddenly Gayarre pulled a funny sort of face, stopped in the middle of a note, coughed, spat on the stage and began to laugh too. The opera had to be interrupted, one half of the audience was laughing, the other half trampling. Then Patti came forward, and she explained to the public what had happened. A wasp had been flying round between the two of them, and every time Gayarre opened his mouth it looked as though the wasp was going to fly straight into it, until Gayarre drew in his breath and swallowed the wasp.

Señor Encina was so fond of music that, as he said, he had started learning his *sol-fa* when he was forty. Since he started his lessons he always went about with a roll of scores which he bought second-hand in the Calle de la Montera, and followed the operas with the score on his knees, waving his right hand as though he were conducting the orchestra.

The claque met round the table in the Café Español. The boss of the claque was an Italian, an old singer who had lost his voice because of his drinking and smoking. His name was Gurius. His face was wrinkled from all the make-up and people said that he could wring milk out of a brick, because he was able to get money out of anybody. Not only money, but everything he needed. He had a special way of asking for things. He would fasten on to a singer in the middle of the street, embrace him, and kiss him noisily: ' *Mio caro carissimo!* ' And he would go on talking Italian at top speed without letting the other even open his mouth. Suddenly he would step away from him, survey him from his crown to his feet and say: 'Do you know, old boy, that you and I are of exactly the same height and build? 'That's quite true,' the other would answer. 'Well, then you must have some suit at home that isn't too much worn and would fit me, because after all one has got to be decently dressed.' The next day he would have his suit, because he was the leader of the claque and could have ruined any artist. In the same way he supplied himself with shoes, shirts, and hats.

When he wanted a drink, it was much easier. There was always a number of young boys who waited day after day to be permitted to join the claque; Gurius, of course, knew them all, fastened on the most ingenuous among them and clapped him on the shoulder. 'Well, how are you, my lad?' The boy would be very proud of being singled out and answer, often with a blush: 'As you see, Señor Gurius, I was waiting to ask you if there wasn't any place free so that I could get in.' 'Well, well, we'll see if there isn't a ticket left over to-night. I'm just going over to Manolo's for a drink, and I'll be back in a jiffy.' Then he would take the boy by the arm and ask: 'Did you hear *Rigoletto* the night before last?' and drag him along to the bar. When he had had enough drinks he let the boy pay and never thought of him again for the rest of the evening. And yet he earned a lot of money. The singers paid him well so that he should not spoil their numbers. When they did not feel well or were afraid of a particular note, they got together with Gurius. Then Gurius placed one of his best men in a good spot, and when the singer was climbing up the scale and nearing the top note and the crack, the man leapt up from his seat and shouted 'Bravo', and the whole claque burst into a storm of applause. Then nobody ever knew whether the singer had held the high note or not.

People who had no money and loved music paid two pesetas a month to be a member of the claque. Gurius had worked out two lists for the two series of subscriptions. As all his seats were on subscription, he made two other series of 'candidates' who also had to pay their two pesetas and were called in turn to replace those of the regular members who failed to turn up. Moreover he had two more lists of auxiliary replacements, people who, too, paid their two pesetas and were called in when there were neither enough regular members nor candidates.

When a famous artist was going to sing, all the six sets turned up to see whether they could not get in; but then those who got in were the people who paid five duros, even if they did not belong to any of the claque sets. In Manolo's tavern one of Gurius's assistants cashed in the five duros and a tip for himself as well. Then he gave his customer a hand-written card and told him in a whisper what he had to do. He had to go to the Café Español and push his way through the hundred people crowding round Gurius.

'Señor Gurius?' he would ask.

Gurius would get up courteously behind the marble table on which he checked his lists and collected his fees.

'*Servitore.*'

'I have this card for you from Don Manuel.'

'Permit me—but do sit down. How is Don Manuel?'

If Gurius was thirsty, which he nearly always was, he added: 'Would you like a drink?' and turned to the waiter: 'Pepe, bring a glass of cognac for me, and for this gentleman—what's yours?'

He would adjust his spectacles and start reading the card, taking his time until the waiter came back. Then he stuck his hand in his pocket and kept fumbling for cash until the other had paid.

'Goodness, please don't, this one's on me. . . . I'm only sorry because I'm not sure whether I can be of service to Don Manuel. You see, you're the third person to come to me to-night for the same thing. Of course, on gala nights even Ministers send people to me with their recommendation. Oh well, I can't say no to Don Manuel.'

X. THE CHURCH

Once a month all those of us who had already been to their first Communion went to confession. The priests distributed themselves over the church and the thousand pupils distributed themselves among the priests just as they pleased because nobody could force us to confess to a priest we did not like. Some priests, such as Father Joaquín and Father Fidel, had very long queues waiting at their confessional; by looking at the size of the files you could see which of the priests were liked by the boys. Those who had confessed joined their form in the file in front of the High Altar, to say their penitential prayers, to hear Mass and to take Communion. Thus the Church was filled with the sound of coming and going, of mumbled prayers and the patter of shoe-soles. The Father Prefect went round to keep order.

Every month it was the same. Father Vesga was left with no more than the six or eight boys whom he had made promise that they would confess to him. Although he took longer over each confession than any of the other priests, he was always left alone before the others had finished. Then the Father Prefect would go from file to file and ask one or the other boy whether he would not go to Father Vesga for his confession. We liked him so much that he usually collected enough boys to form a queue. That day he had done the trick with me, and I went to Father Vesga because I did not really mind.

Father Vesga put his arm round my shoulder and neared his head to mine. The confession began. The questions about the Commandments came one by one, and I was proud to be able to answer them all.

'Do you love God? Do you go to Mass on Sundays? Do you love your parents? Do you speak the truth?'

We reached the Sixth Commandment. All the priests used to ask us whether we did dirty things or not; as we knew what they meant by that, we answered 'yes' or 'no', mostly 'yes', because we all did those things or thought we had been doing them. Then the priests said: 'Look here, my son, you mustn't do that. It's a sin and very bad for you. Children who do it become consumptive and die.' They told us to say a few penitential Paternosters, and that was that.

With Father Vesga it was different.

'You know what the Sixth Commandment says, my son?'

'Yes, Father. It says: Thou shalt not fornicate.'

'Tell me what "fornicate" means.'

131

I did not know and could not tell him. I knew that it was a bad thing which was done between men and women, but that was all I knew. Father Vesga turned very grave.

'You must not lie in the Holy Tribunal of Penance. First you tell me that you know the Sixth Commandment, and now you contradict yourself and tell me that you don't know what fornication means.'

'Fornication, Reverend Father, fornication is—well, things men and women do, which are a sin.'

'So, so. Things men and women do. And what is it men and women do, you shameless boy?'

'I don't know, Father. I've never fornicated.'

'And a nice thing it would be if you had, you shaver. I'm not asking if you have fornicated or not, I'm asking you what it means to fornicate.'

'I don't know. The boys say that fornication is when a man makes a woman be with child. When they're married it's not a sin, and when they're not married it is.'

'Now, come, what I want you to do is to tell me how men and women make children.'

'I wouldn't know. They get married and sleep together and then they get children. That's all I know.'

'So, that's all you know, eh? What a very innocent babe, it doesn't know more than that! But what you do know is how to play with your parts.'

'Sometimes, Father.'

'Well, that's fornication.' There followed a sermon of which I did not understand a word, or rather, which threw me into endless confusion. Woman is Sin. For the sake of Woman the human race fell from grace, and all the saints suffered the temptations of evil. They had apparitions of naked women with bare breasts and lewd movements. And nowadays Satan does not even spare the children. He comes to drive away their sleep and to show them naked women to sully the purity of their minds. And so on and on for half an hour. He spoke to me of flowing hair, quivering bosoms, lascivious hips, of King Solomon, of obscene dances, of women at street-corners, in a torrent of angry words which all went to say that Woman was a sack of uncleanliness and evil, and that men slept with women and therefore went to Hell.

When I got away from the priest to say my penitential prayers, I could not pray. My brain was full of naked women and of the curiosity to know what it was they did with men.

But nobody knew it. I asked my mother, my uncle, my aunt, and they answered my questions in an odd manner. What is fornicating? How are children made? Why do women get pregnant? Some people told me that children ought not to speak of such things, and others said that it was a sin, and a few said I was a shameless boy.

In one of the bookstalls of the Calle de Atocha I found a book which explained everything. It told of a man and a woman who went to bed together and of everything they did. The book made the round of my class and all the boys read it. So as not to be caught by the priests, the boys took it to the lavatory to read and to look at the pictures, which showed the man and the woman fornicating. I read the book many times and it excited me. The same happened to me whenever I saw picture postcards of naked women.

Now I understood why the Holy Virgin had the Child Jesus without doing dirty things with Saint Joseph. The Holy Ghost made her pregnant without their having to do them. But because my father and my mother slept together they had me, and therefore my mother was not a virgin. What I did not know, however, was why my uncle and aunt had no children, although ᵗhey did sleep together. Perhaps my aunt was so pious that they dᵢᵈ ᵑot do any dirty things and so could not have children. But theʸ ᵂᵒuld have liked to have some. On the other hand, God had said: 'ᶦncᵣease and multiply'.

I did not understand.

Father Vesga said it was ᵃ ˢⁱⁿ to ⁿear a woman. But Don Juan, a very kind priest in the chᵘᵣch of San Martín, was once in the sacristy together with a womaⁿ. ˢhe was sitting on his knees and he had his hands betweeⁿ her breaˢts. When I came in they both got very red. The priest came up to me and said I should go away, he was just hearing her confession. I told Uncle José about it and he said those were things young children should not discuss and I was on no account to tell my aunt.

Men said things to women in the streets, and women at street corners invited men to go and sleep with them, and the men gave them money.

I was in a terrible muddle about it all and did not know what was good and what was bad.

But there were many other things I found I did not understand. The church of San Martín had many collection boxes, like all churches; it said on them 'For the Poor Souls in Purgatory', 'For the Cult of the Faith', 'For the Poor'. The priests opened those boxes every evening, took out the money, made little piles of a duro out of the big coppers and piles of half a duro out of the small coppers, distributed the piles among themselves, and played cards in the sacristy. One day Don Tomás lost all the cash which had fallen to his

lot, as well as five duros out of his own cassock. When he got up from
the table, he said:

'To-day the Blessed Souls have done the dirty on me.'

He took the bottle with sweet strong wine, the sacramental wine,
and drank down a big glass.

'One must take life in gulps, as it comes,' he said and went away.

The dead are hallowed and the soil of the cemeteries is holy
ground. In the Cemetery of San Martín, the walls of the vaults had
crumbled and the coffins with the bones stuck out. The chaplain and
the keepers of the cemetery collected the rotten planks and used them
as firewood. Often they threw in the bones as well, because they were
so worm-eaten that they burnt like wood. But when people had
arranged for one of the dead to be dug out and transferred to another
cemetery, the priest put on his embroidered cope and carried the
aspergillum, and the grave-diggers dug most carefully so as not to
crush the coffins. They took out the bones, laid them tenderly on a
white sheet, the priest said his Latin and the sacristan gave the
responses. Then the priest sprinkled Holy Water over the bones and
they were carried off to be buried elsewhere, all because the family of
that particular corpse had the money to take it away. The other
corpses were only good enough for bonfires, and their bones were
broken up with a hammer before being thrown to the flames.

On some days more people died than on others. Two women
would come to the sacristy and order a Requiem Mass to be said for
their husbands, or fathers; their names were noted down on a list,
and they had to pay a stipend of three pesetas for the Mass. 'To-
morrow at eleven,' said the priest. Then other women would arrive
and ask for another Mass. The priest would note their names and
pocket his three pesetas. 'To-morrow at eleven,' he would say. Sometimes three or four families met in church, each in its corner, to listen
to a Mass each family had paid for its own departed. When the priest
read the oration for the deceased, he reeled off from a slip of paper
the names of the three or four people who had died, so that the dead
could share the Mass among themselves.

Once an Obsequial Mass was ordered costing two hundred and
fifty pesetas; three priests were to celebrate and a black catafalque
was to be set up in the middle of the church. It so happened that
three more Masses for the Dead were paid and registered for the same
day. 'To-morrow at ten,' said the priest to everybody. At ten the
church was full of people who listened to the Solemn Mass being
sung. But then, when no Requiem Mass was read, the three families
went into the sacristy one after the other to inquire about it. The
priest asked:

'Weren't you at the Solemn Mass?'

'Yes, Father,' they all answered.

'Well, that was the Mass for your dear departed. By a coincidence several families came together at the same hour, and as we have not so many priests as to be able to oblige everyone, we agreed to hold a Solemn Mass for the families together. So you have gained by it, really.'

The people walked away through the sacristy corridor and one said with great satisfaction: 'Who could have foretold this to poor Juanito? There you see, my girl, he was lucky all his life and even after his death they let him have a whole Solemn Mass for three pesetas.'

And mysteries: everything in religion was a mystery.

A Saint was walking by the sea shore when he saw a child sitting on the sand. The child held a shell in his hand and filled it with water from the sea and then poured the water into a hollow in the sands.

'What are you doing, child?' the Saint asked.

'I am emptying the sea into this hollow,' answered the child.

'That is impossible. How can you expect the water of the sea to find room in this little hollow? It is impossible.'

'It is more impossible to find out why God is One and Three,' replied the child, 'and yet you keep on trying to find out.'

At that the Saint realized that he was speaking to an Angel whom the Lord had sent him.

It did not interest me why God was One and Three at the same time. But I wondered why he had to be One and Three to be God. It only seemed to be so as to make things difficult for us.

'How many Gods are there?' asked the teacher.

'One.'

'Yes, but that's not the right answer.'

'Three.'

'Yes, but that's not the right answer either.'

The right answer was to say that there were three deities, Father, Son, and Holy Ghost, but only One True God. Then the teacher was satisfied; but I was not, because I still did not know which was the true God, nor did the teachers.

My aunt wanted to have the Pope's Benediction. For ten pesetas she got a Benediction which was for her personally, and she put it in a frame. Some years later they gave her another for one hundred pesetas, which was valid for her and all the members of her family down to the fifth generation. She took the old benediction out of the frame and threw it in the dustbin. Then she put the new Benediction in its place, and so I was blessed by Leo XIII.

The more I learnt about religion, the more problems arose. The worst of it was that I could not discuss them with anyone, because my teachers only grew angry and punished me. One day in the Scripture lesson we came to the story of Joshua, who stopped the sun in its course until the end of the battle. I asked Father Vesgá how that could be, for our geography teacher had told us that the sun stands still and the earth revolves, and therefore it would be impossible to stop the sun. Father Vesga answered grumpily:

'You should not ask forward questions. This is laid down in the Holy Scriptures and that ought to be enough for you. Faith moveth mountains and detaineth the sun. If you had the right faith you would understand these matters which are as clear as daylight.'

Then I asked Father Joaquín about it. He put his hand on my head and said with a great smile:

'Now, what shall I say to you, my boy? In olden times many odd things happened. As you know, there was a time when the animals spoke and everybody understood them. Doubtless in Joshua's time the sun moved.'

Father Fidel said more:

'Listen, my boy, what happened was that it was not the sun that stopped, but the earth, only it looked as though the sun had stopped. It's just like when you are in a train, you think the telegraph poles move and then stop. When the Bible was written, people didn't yet know that the earth moved, they only saw the sun moving just as we see it now. For that reason they put down that the sun stood still, although it was really the earth.'

'But, Father, according to what we learnt in Physics the earth could not stop because if it did we would all be thrown into space. Besides, the earth would burn if it suddenly stopped.'

He looked at me with great seriousness and said:

'But, my dear boy, who told you that it stopped suddenly? It stopped slowly, of course, like a tram stops. And now run away, I've got a lot of work to do.'

Little by little I realized that I was not alone in wanting to know the truth about God and Faith. The books I was reading raised the same questions. The Church put those books on the Index, but it did not answer them. The only person with whom I could speak about them was Father Joaquín, who neither grew angry nor took the books away from me. We had many discussions. Only once did he convince me. I sat at his desk and he stood in front of his music-stand, the oboe in his hand and the birds on the window-sill. He looked out into the courtyard, into the sky, as though he were seeing nobody, and he began to speak not to me but to himself.

'None of us knows anything about anything. The only certainty is that we exist. That the earth exists, and the sun, and the moon, and the stars, and the birds and fishes and plants and all things, and that everything lives and dies. There must have been a beginning once, the first hen or the first egg must have arrived, but I don't know which. The first tree and the first bird. Someone made them. After that everything carried on under a law. This is what I call God and in Him I believe, in Him who rules all this. Beyond God I only believe in goodness.'

He was silent, and then he gave me a book:

'Take it and read it. And believe in what you like. Even if you don't believe in God—as long as you're good, it is just as though you did.'

He gave me *The Life of Saint Francis of Assisi*.

I had a shoe-box with holes in the top so that the caterpillars inside could breathe. They were silkworms. I had the Chinese kind, with coffee-brown spots, and the white kind. When I threw mulberry leaves into the box, the silkworms first stayed hidden. Then they began to climb up and nibble the edges of the leaves; they cut out round bits with the two dark teeth at the point of their head, holding on to the edge of the leaf with their legs and moving their head up and down. As they went on eating they made tiny cylindrical droppings. From time to time they wrinkled their forehead between the two little black eyes, and the bluish band running along their body began to undulate from tail to head, as though a blood stream were passing through it. Then they changed their position and found themselves another part of the leaf to nibble. Sometimes two of them came nose to nose while they were gnawing their way through; then they lifted their heads and seemed to be looking and saying something to one another. One of them would wrinkle its forehead and they would change places.

I picked them up in my fingers. They were soft and warm, they twisted their bodies round my finger with their hairy little legs and seemed to sample its skin, quite astonished that there existed such a kind of leaf. Then they noticed the box beneath them, rolled up into a tight ball and let themselves drop to start eating again.

If I put the leaf of any other tree among the mulberry leaves they did not touch it. They stepped across and went to the other leaves. They knew, smelt, and saw it. I wondered if they knew and smelt and saw me. Did they know who I was and what I was like? When I watched them in their box and they lifted their heads, they seemed to look at me. Then I took one, laid it along one finger and passed the tip of another of my fingers over the soft, tender body. It stretched, and raised its head and front legs. Suddenly it wrinkled its forehead. I dropped it into the box, and it resumed eating. But now and again it lifted its head to look at me.

Later on they crept into a corner of the box, fastened their legs to the cardboard and started swivelling their heads round, and a thin thread of spittle dripped out of their mouths. Their bodies became very small and the silk thread wrapped itself round them, until the only thing to be seen was a little shadow still moving its head in the shell of the cocoon. In the end the cocoon-egg lay there, yellow or white, fastened to a corner of the box. Every day I opened another cocoon to see what was inside. The skin of the silkworms had turned hard, as if made of horn, dark as an olive stone, ringed all round, with the snout and the two black teeth left. They were fast asleep and did not waken, and the only thing that moved gently were the rings. Later on they grew real legs, a head, and wings, they turned white and developed two shaggy horns formed like silken half-moons. In the end they bored a hole through the cocoon and crept out on the white cloth I had prepared for them at the bottom of the box. The females fluttered their wings very quickly and flew round and round. Then the male came and they fastened on to each other by their tails. They stuck together for hours. The belly of the female swelled to a ball and she sprinkled the white cloth with minute yellow eggs which looked first golden and later turned black. And then the moths died. They stayed in the box, dried up, their wings sticking to their small bodies as though they had sweated in death.

I kept the white cloth under a stack of sheets. It was full of thousands of eggs. My aunt put apples between the linen, which dried and crumpled like the face of an old woman. Next year the white cloth smelt of apples and out of every little egg came a black thread which turned into a silkworm.

I was sitting on the balcony with the shoe-box standing in the sun so that the silkworms should be warm. Beside me I had a heap of books which I picked up one by one to go through them. It was almost June, and I had to pass the examinations for two matriculation courses at the same time, and then to compete for an honours certificate. They were all pushing me: the priests of the school crammed me and occupied themselves with hardly anyone else in the form, examining me about the same things in a thousand different forms. My uncle promised me that I could study engineering if I got through the exams with honours. My poor mother stroked my hair and asked me to make an effort; she could do nothing for me, but **my** uncle and aunt would do everything if I was a good boy. My aunt dressed me up in my best clothes and took me visiting; she showed me off to her friends as a phenomenon, and bald gentlemen and old ladies, rather like my aunt herself, plied me with silly questions.

'Very nice, Arturito, very nice! And now tell me, how are you getting on with your studies?'

Once Doña Isabel made me so furious with that kind of question that I began to speak at great speed about logarithms, the binomial theory, parabolic curves, and produced a spate of nonsensical algebraic formulas with lots of 'a.s' and 'x.s' and symbols and phantastic figures. Doña Isabel stared at me and her chin sagged until I stopped short and said solemnly: 'And that's all I know.'

'What a marvel, Doña Baldomera, what a marvel of a child! Just like my husband. When poor Juan sat down to work with figures he was simply marvellous. D'you know that he did sums in his head? In his head! This boy will go far. Just as my poor Juan would have gone far if he had only lived.'

I felt like calling her idiot, old sow, bitch, beast, and all sorts of things. I would have liked to tear the false plait out of her top-knot and scour her face, covered in butter-yellow face-cream mixed with powder as it was, with a swab soaked in dish-water.

My future! I was going to be an engineer so as to make everybody happy, but above all so that my mother no longer needed to go on washing and to be somebody's servant. They were all very good to me. They all dished out charity to me. Yet I felt tired and did not want to eat or play. I only wanted to see: to see things and beings as Saint Francis had seen them.

The cat settled down on my knees. He looked at the box with the silkworms and at the books; he looked at me with his golden eyes. Then he turned those eyes inwards, curled up into a ball, his body folded between his legs and his tail stroking his nose, and purred. I thought that he understood me and knew about things. I too understood him. But when he sat there looking at me and looking at things, I did not know what he wanted to say. He said nothing, but I could see in his eyes that his head was as full of thoughts as my own. He slept so as to avoid thinking. The same happened to me. Often I was suddenly so overwhelmingly sleepy that I lay down on the carpet of our dining-room, or on the floor of the balcony, and slept.

The two dogs of the coach-yard were white and lively. I had seen them when they were just born and small as a fist; they knew me and liked me. When I went out into the street they came up, wagging their tails, barking and jumping. I used to collect lumps of sugar in the café and they always begged for them. I squatted down on my haunches and they thrust their black noses into the pocket of my blouse to get at the sugar. The cat looked down from the balcony through the bars of the railing and saw me playing with the dogs. Then, when I went upstairs, the cat refused to play with me; he was angry. I opened the cupboard and produced a bag of biscuits. We both ate, I sitting on the floor and he sitting between my knees, and made it up. Later on my aunt was annoyed, but she was wrong. The cat and I were right.

People were astonished at the things Malleu could do with his lions in the Buen Retiro Gardens. I was not astonished. He had a large round iron cage which he filled with wooden stools. The lions came filing out, and one after the other jumped on a stool, sat down, its head high, and watched Malleu. He was a tall, lean, green-eyed man with frizzy hair like a Cuban's. He talked to the lions and they understood. They roared, and people thought they were going to attack him, but Malleu knew that the lions were only answering him, and I knew too. After that they did their tricks, leaping and running through the cage. The biggest lion opened its jaws wide and Malleu stuck his head inside. The others leapt at him and stretched out their paws with thick toes and curved claws, as though they wanted to devour him. But they only wanted to play, because Malleu never beat them.

I watched him while he was feeding them. He did it himself. An assistant brought a wheel-barrow loaded with chunks of meat and Malleu went into the cages. He speared each lump of meat on a big, long fork and fed it to them. Then he scratched their manes just above the eyes and patted them gently on the head. The lions would growl softly and sometimes one of them would throw itself on the floor on its back, waving its paws in the air. I once saw a lion whom he had not patted come growling after him, grumbling because it had been forgotten.

When Malleu left the cage he petted the children outside and asked us boys if we liked lions. He took us to see lion-cubs like woolly poodles. They nibbled his hands and scratched him. Some of us stuck our hands through the bars and petted them too. They did not mind us, but when a grown-up man tried to touch them they got angry. They showed their teeth, growled, and put out their claws.

'Brother Wolf—Brother Stone!' said Saint Francis.

I had sown string-beans in an empty pimento tin and chick-peas in another. I wanted to see them grow. Every day I dug up the earth to take the seeds out, and afterwards I put them back. They sprouted; each threw up a shoot like a little white horn; then they grew small roots; and in the end they had leaves. They grew as if they had understood me and wanted to give me pleasure, by showing me how they were and how they grew.

I hammered a piece of iron and it grew warm as if it felt pain.

Then the examinations were over and I had been entered for the matriculation course with honours. They took me to a doctor. I was very thin and had no appetite. I only wanted to read, to sleep, and to watch animals. The doctor examined my chest and said:

'There's nothing wrong with him. It's his age. He's growing. The best thing is to send him to the country and give him a tonic.'

I went to Méntrida to run about by the river and to take spoonfuls of cod-liver oil, black and thick; it made me so sick that they had to stop giving it me.

I had a prospectus of my school with me; it said that tuition there was so good that in the final examinations of the year the Institute had obtained so-and-so many honours and matriculation certificates. My Aunt Aquilina showed it to all the women in the village: 'That's my nephew, you know, Leonor's son. He's very clever.' Then the women stuffed me with cake and gave me small glasses of strong wine to strengthen me.

The best physicians were my Uncle Luis, the school-master of the village, and Saint Francis.

When they told Uncle Luis about my studies, he put his heavy hand on my shoulder and said:

'So what? Have you come to pull the bellows-chain for a bit? What you need is good food and exercise. Come along to-morrow and I'll teach you the craft.'

So I pulled the bellows-chain, and hammered and filed lumps of iron in the vice at the workshop. I stained my face and hands black with soot. I went shooting with my uncle at dusk. He filled me with food and wine, but I was angry and almost in tears when I was not able to lift the smallest of the hammers with my thin arms.

'Damnation,' said my uncle, 'what the boy needs is less school and more play. As it is he'll get T.B. and then we'll see what comes of all that bloody school-learning.'

He set out to shoot partridges and rabbits for me and when he did not get any he killed a pigeon. Aunt Rogelia made a broth of it for me alone. I developed an appetite and Uncle Luis was happy when he saw me eat. The rabbits and partridges tasted of the herbs of the hills.

Aunt Aquilina took me to the village school teacher. He was a small, friendly, gay old man. My aunt started explaining, he listened and read the school prospectus. Then he put his hand on my head.

'My poor little fellow—and tell me, what would you really like to do?'

I told him that I was going to be an engineer and that I liked animals and plants. I told him about Saint Francis, and he smiled. I spoke to him with all confidence because he listened very attentively, without saying a word, and looked at me all the time as though he wanted to know what was inside me.

When I had finished, he said:

'Come and fetch me to-morrow morning, we'll go and catch butterflies together.'

There we were in the meadow by the river, the schoolmaster and I. I didn't know how to catch butterflies, but he ran after them with a gauze net on the end of a long stick and caught them in their flight. Then he took them very carefully between the tips of his fingers and put them into a round tin box. He showed me lizards, little tortoises, and chameleons. We watched green cicadas dry themselves in the sun, escape from their jacket, and fly off, while the old sheath which showed the outlines of legs, wings, and head was left lying on the ground.

He explained the animals to me one by one. He took a lizard and told me what lizards were like, how they ate, how they lived. Then, when I thought he would put it into his tin box too, he stroked its head with one finger. The lizard shut its tiny eyes as though it liked the touch. Then he opened his hand and set it free. The lizard stayed there on the hand, green and glittering in the sun, and instead of leaping to the ground it climbed up the sleeve and rested on the schoolmaster's shoulder, waving its long tail like a whip. The schoolmaster walked on with the lizard, which poked its head into the hair on his neck from time to time.

When we returned to the village and reached the edge of the meadow, the schoolmaster picked up the lizard, put it on the ground, scratched its back, and said:

'Now be off with you, we're going. You go home.'

The lizard stayed quietly in the grass and then went slowly away, its head swaying above its forelegs.

I ate a meagre *cocido* in the schoolmaster's house, with only one piece of meat and one piece of bacon, no sausage and no other dish to go with it, served in old, yellow-and-green pottery bowls. It was very well cooked. The school had a farmyard and there the schoolmaster's wife, a quiet, clean old woman, shook out the crumbs. The hens and the sparrows came for them; they knew that they got them every day at that hour.

The village priest gave a lecture on Religious Doctrine for young

142

girls and lads every Sunday afternoon. Everybody had to go, because otherwise the priest would have been angry and there would have been trouble with the Mayor and with the farms which employed labour during the wheat and grape harvests. The school teacher had tried to hold daily evening classes for the young people, where they could learn to read and write, which hardly any of them knew how to do. But the priest was furious and the Mayor forbade the classes.

The school teacher stayed on for nothing except to teach the small children how to read. That was all he could do, because after they were seven to nine years old, the children were used for work in the fields. In the summer they even used the little boys of five and six to glean wheat-ears and to pull up onions. So the schoolmaster devoted his time to collecting animals in the meadow. He had a collection of cases full of butterflies, moths, and beetles and a few stuffed birds. The neighbours brought him their canaries and their decoy partridges when they were sick or had broken a leg, and he cured them.

I brought him the *Life of Saint Francis*. He had read it already. He merely said that Saint Francis was made a Saint because he had been that kind of man. But nowadays there were no Saints any more.

When I went alone to the meadow I sat down in the grass and watched. After I had kept still for a while, all the animals moved as though I did not exist, and I looked at them playing and working while I thought.

Up till then I had believed in God as everybody, the priests and my family, had taught me to believe in Him: as a very kind man who saw everything and put everything right. The Virgin and the Saints commended to Him all those who prayed to them in their need, and begged God to grant them the things they wanted.

But now I could not help comparing everything I saw with this idea of an absolutely just God, and I was frightened, for I could not discover His justice anywhere.

Certainly, it was very good that I could stay with my uncle and aunt and become an engineer. But my mother had to go washing down by the river and be the servant of my uncle and aunt, and she had to leave my sister with Señora Segunda and my brother as a boarder in a charity school, because if she had not done that, she would not have been able to support us all, even working as she did. It would have been much easier if my father had not died. They were giving me the chance to study for a career, but I had to pay for it by going crazy with all the books and obtaining honours in the matriculation course so that the school could put it into their prospectus, otherwise they would not give me free education. Then I would be just like all the other boys.

God rewarded those who were good.

Poor Angel got up at five in the morning to sell newspapers in his torn canvas shoes and then, when the sales hours were over at midnight, he went to sleep in the entrance of the Royal Theatre so as to be able to sell the first place in the queue. He and his mother together hardly earned enough for their meals, and they worked the whole day long. But Don Luis Bahía owned half Brunete by driving the poor people to whom he had lent money from the land which belonged to them. Not only did God not punish him, but when he came to San Martín, the priests there made much of him and took him to be an excellent man, because he paid for Masses and Novenas. What happened with me at school happened everywhere. The only good people were those who had money, all the others were bad. When they protested, they were told to be patient because they would go to Heaven; therefore all the evil that happened to them in this world did not matter; on the contrary, it was really a merit and their lot was enviable. But I did not notice rich people making themselves into poor people so as to go to Heaven.

I wanted to know things, to know much, because this was the only way to become rich, and if you were rich you had everything, you even went to Heaven.

For money the priests said Mass and gave indulgences for millions and millions of days. If a poor man died and God condemned him to a hundred thousand years in Purgatory, and if his widow could not spare more than three pesetas for a Mass, only two or three thousand days would be taken off his time in Purgatory. But when a rich man died and his people paid for a first-class funeral, it did not matter if God condemned him to millions of years in Purgatory; three priests would celebrate Mass; there would be a choir and the organ and everything, and he would be granted a plenary indulgence. If somebody was lame and had a thousand pesetas so that he could go to Lourdes, he had a chance of coming back on straight legs. But if he was poor and could not go to Lourdes, he had to stay lame all his life, because the Virgin worked miracles only for those who went there.

When the poor people had to go in ragged clothes and one saw their naked skin, just because they had nothing else to wear, they were not allowed into church to pray, and if they insisted the police were fetched and detained them. But the big chests in the sacristy were filled with good clothes and jewels for the Saints, and the wooden images were clothed and decked with diamonds and velvet.

Then all the priests would come out, just as in the Royal Theatre, in silver and golden robes, while the candles were lit and the organ played and the choir sang; and during the singing the sacristans would pass round the collection boxes. When everything was over they locked up the church and the poor people stayed under the porch to sleep in their nakedness. Inside was the Virgin, still in her golden crown and velvet mantle, very snug and warm, because the church was carpeted and the stoves burning. The Child Jesus was dressed in gold-embroidered little pants and he also had a velvet cloak and a crown of diamonds. Under the porch was a poor woman for whom my mother had once bought ten centimos' worth of hot milk because she showed us her wrinkled, dried-up breasts, while her baby was crying, half naked. She sat in the porch of the church of Santiago, on a litter of waste paper, and said to my mother:

'May God reward you, my dear.'

My mother went home and came back with an old shawl which she used to wrap round her waist when she was washing by the river in winter, and the woman bundled her child up in the shawl, for they were going to sleep there in the open all night. The woman said she would cover herself with old theatre bills.

On the following day my aunt took me to the Novena and said how beautiful the Virgin was with her mantle and crown and all the candles. I remembered the poor woman of the night before. When we came out of church I told my aunt about her.

'My boy,' she said, 'there are many unfortunate people, but God knows what He is doing. Maybe she was a bad woman, because, you see, all the women who walk about in the streets are lost creatures. I suppose she has no milk because she drinks too much.'

The Novena was in honour of Our Lady, the Most Holy Virgin of Mothers' Milk and Good Delivery.

The meadow by the river was alive with animals which had been coming up softly and slowly while I was thinking. They took no notice of me. Two lizards were playing between the grasses in the sun, moving their tails and flicking their tongues. Frogs were leaping in the stream and chasing each other. There was a black patch of ants which were coming and going with loads of grains for their ant-heap. Dung-beetles had surrounded a heap of droppings and were fabricating little balls out of it. They worked in couples, a male and female together, each pushing their ball, which sometimes toppled and rolled over them. They were all playing and all working, both things alike.

I wished to be like them, I wished all people to be like them. I tried to speak of those matters to Uncle Luis and he listened, trying to follow. After I had explained, he said:

'Now look here, all that's just a lot of rubbish they've put into your head. God once set out to create the world. Every time he had made a little ball, like our earth, and taken it out of his oven still red-hot, he gave it a flick and sent it spinning through the air. From time to time he amused himself making people and beasts, and so he let one of the little balls cool and let all the people and animals on top of it grow. He watched the creatures growing and taught them how to live. One day he got tired of all the worlds, among them our earth, took the lot and kicked them into space. Then he went to sleep and nobody has heard a word from him since.'

Of course he said it to tease me. But I was unhappy because he would not understand that I needed God.

I went back to Madrid, I continued to go to Church, at school and with my aunt. But I could not pray.

PART II

I. DEATH

Every morning, when my uncle was going to shave, he hung his mirror on a nail in the balcony frame, tied the loop of his razor strop to the window catch and ranged his bowl of hot water, his brush, cut-throat razor, and the little squares of paper he used to wipe off the lather, on the dining-room table. His razors were German; the mark engraved on their blades showed three little men holding hands, as if they were dancing and singing. The blades were honed so that they curved inwards from back to edge, sat loosely in their horn grip, and were so thin that they looked as though they were going to snap. They had a little curved tail like a dog's tail, where you put your thumb, and the handle stuck our stiffly.

He smeared his face with the soap which he used to grate himself off a big cake, set the blade at an angle and started to shave. The razor rasped on the hard hairs of his throat, and curly white waves of lather, flecked with fine black lines of cut hair, collected in the hollow of the blade. Whenever the heap grew too big, he wiped it off with a piece of paper. The sun shone through our balcony in the mornings, and when it fell on the paper, the tiny bubbles of the lather turned from white to mother-of-pearl.

I had torn off yesterday's pages from the three calendars in our house, and as the sun shone on the lather, I twisted a page into a tube, dipped its end into the foam and blew softly. The bubbles grew into a bunch of grapes, they swelled and quivered, and I caught one on the tip of my tube. In the sunlight it turned blue, red, purple, and orange, until it burst and spat little drops on my nose. Sometimes there was a hair on the top of the little globe, and it slid softly downwards as if it was falling.

I watched him while he gravely shaved his throat before the mirror. His hairs puzzled me. Why has he got hairs? Why haven't women any? I shall have hairs like his one day, but my sister never. Girls don't grow hairs. Old women often have some on their upperlip or on their chin. When my uncle stands there in his vest, his shirt sleeves rolled up, he has a smell. It is the smell of a man. When people begin to smell like that they grow hair on their faces.

Uncle José stood with his head thrown back, his throat taut, and

147

looked in the mirror out of the corner of his eyes. The up-stroke of the blade cut his hairs with a rasping sound—riss, riss! The noise stopped. Blood splashed bright over the white lather, ran down his throat and painted a river with all its streams on his vest. My uncle stayed with his arm hanging down, the razor dangling as though it were broken, his other hand dabbing at the wound, a cut like a small mouth. You could see the sound of the gurgle, as little blobs of blood came out of the lips of the wound and became a trickle which ran down between the grey hair on his chest and his vest. Uncle José put the razor on the table and sat down in the rocking chair. He let himself drop, and then for the first time I saw how heavy he was. His face was yellow as the wax of a church candle, his hair glued to his temples, his bald head covered with little sweat drops, his moustache limp, his lips purple.

'Call your mother,' he said.

My mother had a shock when she saw his yellow face and the red stream which had made trickles all over his vest. My aunt was at Mass.

'Don't be scared, Leonor, it's nothing really. I've cut myself, and the sight of the blood made me feel sick.'

My mother washed him. She drew his under-vest over his limp arms and left his grey-haired chest bare. In the groove of his chest, the sweat collected in glistening drops. A glass of cognac. My uncle rested in the rocking-chair, breathing slowly, his mouth half open, and stroked my head. I was sitting on the curved chair-arm. Rocking-chairs like ours were made in Vienna; they dipped branches in boiling water, and when the wood got soft, they bent it into any form they wanted.

The steaming hot tea and the cognac revived him, and I could see the drops of blood coming back into his face and his bald pate so that the skin reddened. The cut was no longer bleeding, it was covered with a strip of taffeta and one could not see anything. When my aunt came back, my uncle told her that he had cut himself, as if it were of no importance.

I went into the kitchen and asked my mother in a low voice: 'Mother, is Uncle going to die?'

'Silly, don't you see it was nothing serious? Many people feel sick when they see blood, and so your uncle was a bit sick.'

But I knew he was dead. I didn't know what it was to die. But I knew he was dead. 'Rabbit', my cat, also knew that Uncle was dead. I had told him so. He mewed very softly, plaintively, opening his mouth slowly, as if he wanted to yawn. I hugged his head and he looked at me with his yellow eyes. Then he went out on the balcony, sat down on his haunches, and began to stare into the darkness, rigid, with his eyes turned inwards.

My uncle had gone to the office as he did every day, and I stayed on the balcony, for it was a holiday and I was not going to school. The cat was with me, curled up on his little mat. From time to time, he lifted his head, scented the air, and looked as if he were waiting. Inside the house, my mother and my aunt were cleaning up and clattering with their pots. The smell of food seeped out to the balcony.

A carriage turned the street corner, and the cat and I got up to look. The horse came up the short slope and stopped before our house door. A man and a priest got out, they entered our house in a hurry, and came out again with Señor Gumersindo, our concierge. The coachman climbed down from his seat. Between the four of them they lifted Uncle José out of the carriage. The black roof of the coach tilted under their weight, and in the sun it looked like a black mirror throwing its glints up into my face. The four carried him into the house, and I ran out of the room and hurtled myself down the stairs.

Watching them, and walking backwards, I climbed the stairs again in front of them. How heavy my uncle was! His legs doubled up against his stomach, head lolling, arms hanging down, shirt open and damp with sweat, foam on his half-open lips. He was breathing hard and blowing out the foam, as if it were he who had to carry the four upstairs, not they him. His eyes were half-closed, the whites showing, and the pupils hidden in the inside of his head.

Upstairs, they dropped him on the bed—how heavy he was! My aunt shrieked and wept, my mother ran to the kitchen to fetch tea, to fetch hot water, to fetch I don't know what. I took one of his hands, it folded up in mine like an empty glove. The cat was restlessly weaving in and out between my feet. Together they dragged off his boots and opened his trousers, his coat, his waistcoat, his shirt. After they had taken off his socks, they lifted him up to take away his clothes from under him, and left him there on the under-sheet in his pants and vest. Then they covered him up to his throat, and there his head remained, like Saint Peter's, with a fringe of grey hair round a bald skull, sweating and snoring. The cat jumped on to the foot of the bed and sat down to look at him with serious eyes. He stayed there because nobody dared to chase him away. I wanted to chase him off, and he looked at me. I left him. My mother wanted to chase him away, and without turning round, he bristled his fur and growled softly, as though not wanting to wake my uncle. He showed his fangs and his red tongue.

149

What is angina pectoris? They didn't know, or they didn't want to tell.

In the evening, when the sun had gone and the lamps were not yet lit, the neighbouring women came together and sat in a circle, in silence.

'God give him back his health, or whatever may be best for him,' said one of them.

'Our Father which art in Heaven . . .'

We all prayed, very low, so that he should not hear us, while my aunt pressed herself into the arm-chair and let her tears run over her face. I prayed—oh, how I prayed! God and the Virgin and all the Saints must hear me! When the old women stopped, I went on praying, very softly and secretly so that they could not see me. God must hear me!

The bedroom was full of strong apothecary smells, of the patter of feet on tiptoe, of the clatter of cups and bottles on the marble top of the night table. Don Tomás, the doctor, came out and said in a low voice to all of us and to nobody in particular:

'What a man. He is made of iron. Anyone else would have been dead by now.'

Then he stayed in the bedroom clutching my uncle's wrist, and felt his pulse. My uncle slowly opened his eyes, looked at us, and he stretched out a hand and stroked my neck. Thus we passed the night, _____ d I fight-
_____ uld not
get me away, my _____ coffee with a drop of brandy. When I woke up I found myself on my feet, half lying on the pillows, with a blanket wrapped round me and my uncle's hand on my neck. My mother was sitting on a stool at the foot of the bed and my aunt was sleeping in the arm-chair. The light of dawn came through the balcony. All my bones were aching. Mother lifted me up as I was, wrapped in the blanket, and carried me to my bed. She began to untie my shoes, but I never knew whether she got them off, for I sank down into blackness.

Then came better days. Uncle José left his bed and wandered slowly round the house, in slippers. But we three, the cat, he, and I, we knew it, he was dead.

One day he started looking for things in the chest of drawers, and called me:

'Take this,' he said. 'My silver watch with the two little keys. I've tied them with a bit of string so that they shouldn't get lost. My cuff-links. The walking-stick with the golden handle. My signet ring.' He took it off his finger where it sat loosely; he had become much

thinner. 'Give it all to your mother and tell her to keep it for you.'
He kissed me.

I took the things to my mother.

'Why did your uncle give you all this?' she asked.

'I don't know. He told me you would keep them for me until I'm
older.' I did not want to tell her that he was dead. She went to my
uncle.

'Why did you give the boy all this?'

'Listen, Leonor, you're somebody to whom I can tell the truth. I'll
never wear them again. I know it. I'm dead.' And he said it serenely,
his grey eyes looking at my mother, at me, and the cat, as if he were
ashamed of his dying.

'Don't talk such nonsense, you'll soon be well again. You're very
strong and healthy.'

'Maybe you want to deceive me, or maybe you don't see it, just
like the doctor. But it's true. I know that I've very few days left. I feel
it inside here.' He gently tapped his chest. 'Look, the boy knows it
too, don't you?' And he looked at me. When the cat lifted his head,
watching him, he added: 'And the cat too. Children and animals
feel what we others can't feel.'

At night I went down to fetch the milk, and in the stables a dog
was howling, as dogs do when there is death in the house. Señor
Pedro held its muzzle. 'Keep still, blasted dog.'

I went back with my milk can and thought of what my uncle had
said. The dogs knew it too. My uncle was already in bed. He took a
glass of hot milk with some drops of the medicine that smelt so
strongly. I sat down on his bed and he spoke to me, but I did not
know what he was saying. He had his meal all by himself; then he
turned down the wick of the lamp which was mirrored on the oilcloth of the table like a little yellow sun. They sent me to sleep, but
first I kissed his face many times; it was prickly. They had given him
my bed so that he should have quiet, and I slept in the back room
next door on a camp bed.

The cat came with me, crept under the sheet where it folded over
the blanket, and fell asleep, purring. We both slept.

The cat woke me. He sat up on the bed and mewed softly. A strip
of light shone from under the door of Uncle's bedroom and all was
quiet. The cat and I listened. And suddenly the house was full of
cries.

The blood relatives were sitting round the dining-room table. My
aunt sat at the head, and I by her side. There they were: Uncle
Hilario with his bald mahogany-coloured skull, and the wen like a

151

ripe tomato on top of it. Aunt Braulia in the fourteen green, yellow, and black petticoats of her Sunday dress. Uncle Basilio, another brother of my uncle's, with a big square head on a massive body, squeezed into a suit of thick, black cloth which smelt of moth balls. Aunt Basilisa, sister of my aunt, a very small, wrinkled, grumpy old woman with a moustache of sparse grey hairs like the clipped whiskers of a cat. Her husband, Uncle Anastasio, very impressive in his black suit, like a retired Captain, with black-lacquered moustache and beetling, shoe-polish-black eyebrows. My Grandmother Inés, who was here because my aunt had asked her to come and help her, as Grandmother understood about this sort of thing, being the trustee of Señor Molina's Estate. And then there was Father Dimas, my aunt's spiritual adviser, who had heard my uncle's last confession.

My grandmother and the priest sat next to each other. The two big fat ones together. The priest belonged to the class of flabby fat people who are made of rolls of lard; he was all fat: his many chins, the pouches under his eyes, his wrists, his chest, his stomach and the enormous belly which stretched his cassock and made it look like a shiny balloon. My grandmother belonged to the other class of fat people, who have big solid bones never quite buried in flesh. She had a heavy jawbone, a big, broad nose; the knobs of her bones stuck out of her skin at the wrists and elbows of her colossal arms. The priest was unctuous, Grandmother was sharp and prickly like a hedgehog. Don Dimas did not yet know her, and he would never have imagined that there existed in such a Christian family as ours so deadly an enemy as she was.

Uncle Hilario put his heavy hand, racked by the plough, on the table and asked:

'Well, Baldomera, and what do you intend to do now?'

'That's why I asked you to come. So that you can advise me. I—I've an idea.'

'I'm surprised to hear it,' said my grandmother who was put out of gear by the presence of the priest and only waited for an occasion to explode.

'Let me speak, Inés,' my aunt went on. 'As my poor Pepe fortunately left enough for my modest needs, and as I've nobody in the world except the child'—she gave me four kisses wet with tears—'I'd thought of retiring into a Holy Establishment where the Sisters take ladies like myself as boarders; and the child would go to a boarding-school.'

Father Dimas tenderly contemplated the nails on his hands which he held folded over his paunch. The country cousins looked at one another without quite taking in what she had said. Uncle Anastasio

and the family. The family wants to separate you from the boy and from other relatives, and all—now get this straight—all of them want to get at your money.'

There was a chorus of protests:

'But, Inés, the only thing we want is her welfare.'

'What you want is her money. If the departed had left her with one old rag in front and another behind, I'd like to see who would be the perfect gentleman and take her into his house, old, bigoted, and touchy as she is. Of all of us who are here, maybe the only one to take her in would be me, because I've enough bread left to give her a piece of mine. Listen,' she added and turned to my aunt, 'stop asking the family for advice. Families and old junk are all right—at a distance. Ask advice from people who have nothing to do with you, and you'll see that they tell you that you ought to stay at home and tie the strings of your purse tight to keep off the spongers who will come over you like flies after honey. Do you realize what it means to be a good soul like you, who is foolish out of sheer goodness, with a hundred and fifty thousand pesetas in a family of starvelings? You'll know in time, only wait.'

Uncle Hilario made a dignified protest:

'There is nobody here who wants to take anything away from her.'

'Is that so? How much did you owe Pepe? Must have been more than five hundred pesetas. And of course, when you heard that your brother had died you came here with the cash in case Baldomera needed some at once, didn't you? Yes, and that's why I had to give her a thousand pesetas yesterday so that she could pay for things without having to worry.'

Uncle Hilario sat down in confusion and grunted:

'That's no way of discussing things.'

'Of course not. The only thing one can do if one's got any decency is to open the door and go.'

'That would be rude,' objected Uncle Hilario.

'Well, then swallow your pill. Truth is always painful. And the truth is that you've all come here like carrion crows at the smell of death, to see which bit you can carry off for yourselves.'

Aunt Baldomera had begun to weep and to cry, and Grandmother cut short the discussion with a simple recipe:

'Well, the matter is closed. And you stop crying, the departed will not come back for all your tears. Let's say a Paternoster, perhaps it will do him good—I'll pray too, though I don't believe in it—and afterwards every owl back to its own olive-tree!'

My aunt began the Paternoster, half smiling, half crying. When the two old women were left alone, they fell into each other's arms, both weeping. Suddenly Grandmother broke away, opened the balcony doors wide, and said:

'Let's have some air. It smells of rot in here.'

The gusts of fresh air carried off the smell of many sweaty people, and the clouds of cold cigar smoke, blue in the light of the lamp, drifted out in long thin ribbons.

The days became monotonous. Early in the mornings, my aunt, more pious than ever, used to go to church and did not return before eleven or so. My mother put the house in order and in the afternoons went home to the attic. My aunt and I stayed alone, I reading at the dining-room table, she slumbering in the rocking-chair, the cat on her lap. At eleven or twelve at night she woke up with a start, looked at the clock, and we went to bed, my aunt, the cat, and I.

Her affection for me and her jealousy of my mother had sharpened. She would not leave us alone for a minute. On Thursdays and Sundays, when I was free, she would not have me go with my mother, but went out with me herself, to the Plaza de Oriente or the Plaza de Palacio. There she sat on a seat, and every time she would find another old woman to whom she could tell the story of my uncle, and shed some tears. In one of the attics of the house lived Señora Manuela who had a refreshment stand in the Plaza de Oriente; we often went there, my aunt took some refreshment and exchanged with Señora Manuela memories of their respective husbands.

Since my uncle had died, the family showed a fervent love for my aunt. The Brunete family came to town nearly every month. Aunt Baldomera had torn up all the receipts of their debts to Uncle José, because they had had such a bad year. When they arrived they used to bring a couple of chickens and some dozens of big, fresh eggs. When they went, they would take with them 50 or 100 duros. My aunt's sister, Aunt Basilisa, often came to keep her company in the afternoon; at other times, Baldomerita, my aunt's godchild, would come and be received with a shower of kisses and hugs. My aunt gave her things, because she herself would not wear them again in her mourning which she intended to wear 'until God took her home to her Pepe'. One day she gave Baldomerita her gold and diamond earrings; another, her golden chain; another, her brooch; another, her rings. All the valuable things disappeared one by one, the high tortoiseshell combs, the waving mantillas with their dense lace, the Manila shawl with its ivory Chinese figures, the embroidered silk dresses. Every time the day of a patron saint or another holiday arrived, the family was short of money and unable to celebrate it. And my aunt took a big banknote, folded it quite small and put it in the bodice of her niece's dress. Late in the afternoon, when my mother had gone or was about to go, Aunt Eulogia would arrive together with her daughter Carmen; they were relatives of my aunt in just the same degree as my mother and I. Each time they found something to do in the house, something to sew or to iron. Between flattery and caresses they got one hundred peseta note after the other out of my aunt.

They all did the same things; they spoilt me and made much of me, and they ran down my mother, fanning my aunt's dislike of her. The situation between my mother, my aunt, and myself became increasingly tense, the smallest causes produced discussions which stung like needles. My aunt wept in the dining-room and my mother in the kitchen. Then the end came; my mother said:

'Listen, Aunt, things can't go on like this. You and I don't understand each other. You've been very kind to us, but there has to be an end somewhere. I will go back to my attic, you have others who will serve you gladly, and we'll all live in peace.'

'And the child, what will you do with the child?'

'You will have to decide what you want to do about him.'

I was a mere nothing in their discussion, neither of them asked me what I wanted.

'If you don't want to stay in my house,' said my aunt, 'I won't force you. The child can stay until he has finished school and then we shall see to it, if God gives me good health, that he makes his career as his uncle wished.'

'Agreed,' said my mother. 'You find somebody to help you and as soon as you say the word, I'll leave the house.'

In the afternoon, Aunt Eulogia and Carmen promised to come from the next day onwards.

'Of course, of course, Baldomera, you'll see how well we'll look after you. You and the boy will have everything you need.'

Aunt Basilisa spoke seriously to my aunt:

'What in the world is this? You're jumping from the frying-pan into the fire; you chuck out Leonor and take in Eulogia. Haven't you burnt your fingers often enough? These women are coming here to sponge. What you ought to do is to live with us—after all, I am your sister. If you are worried for the boy's sake because our house is not big enough to have him there, why, we could come here and live with you; this flat is very big.'

But my aunt had no wish to have Uncle Anastasio in her house and decided for Aunt Eulogia. Carmen would sleep in the flat, her mother would come in the morning and leave at night.

All these conversations went on in my presence. Nobody restrained himself in what he said. Why should they? My aunt was going to make me an engineer. What more could I want? Moreover, they were not concerned about me. Once inside my aunt's home, they would arrange to get rid of me, sooner or later.

My mother packed her clothes and Señor Manuel came to fetch the big and heavy box. While he went down the stairs, my mother entered the dining-room.

'Well, Aunt, I'm going. I hope you'll keep well. When you need anything from me, send me a message through the boy.'

And then I said—and the tears choked me:

'She can't send you messages through me, because I'm coming with you.' I turned to my aunt and said in a white fury: 'My mother won't stay here and I won't either. I'm going with her to the attic and you can keep your money and your career for yourself. I can work. If you've had no children, that's your bad luck. I won't desert my mother. You can stay here with your Baldomerita and your Carmencita and give them what you like, the mantillas and the money, because you're a selfish woman. My mother has been your servant for twelve years. That's what she was, but you talk big and say you've kept her and me out of charity, because we were starving. And now these filthy women come and you give them the money, I've seen it, and the jewels and the dresses and everything, because they flatter you and kiss you all over.'

I was filled with anger and rage at seeing my mother scorned, rage at losing my career, rage at seeing strangers loot the house, and nobody could have made me shut my mouth.

'Just count your money. . . . Yes,' I was glaring at my aunt, 'the money you keep in the notecase in the cupboard. Where you've got your five thousand pesetas and the bank receipts. Just count it, and you'll see what's missing. Later on they'll say my mother took it, but I know who filched the money.'

Aunt Eulogia and her daughter were clattering with the pots and pans in the kitchen. My aunt, deeply disturbed, went to the cupboard; five hundred pesetas were missing.

'There you see. My grandmother was right when she said you were a fool. Do you know who took them?'

I dragged Carmen out of the kitchen.

'It was her, she took them yesterday. I saw it, yes, I saw it. I was hiding here'—I hid behind the curtain—'and her mother was on the lookout in case you moved out of the arm-chair. Go on, now, say it's a lie.'

Carmen, who was hardly older than I, a child herself, started to cry.

158

'Was it you?' demanded my aunt.

'Yes, Señora. I don't know anything about it. My mother told me to.'

I took my mother by the arm.

'Let's go. Now you know.'

We went, my mother shocked, I trembling with rage and excitement and with tears running down my face. When we were down in the street, my mother kissed me. From the balcony my aunt called out:

'Leonor, Leonor! Arturito!'

We turned the first corner of the Calle de la Amnistia and then walked slowly, without speaking, through the sun-filled streets, until we were up in the attic. There my mother began to unpack the clothes from the box. I watched her, without saying a word. She stopped and said gently:

'We must fetch your clothes from your aunt's.'

'Let her go to hell with them,' I gave back furiously.

And I threw myself on to my mother's big iron bed, weeping into the pillows so that they got wet, shaken by spasms. My mother had to lift me and slap my face, because I could not speak. Señora Pascuala, the concierge, made me drink a cup of lime-blossom tea with brandy. I lay there like a trussed bundle.

'We'd better put him to bed properly,' said Señora Pascuala.

Between them they undressed me, and I let them. I watched the little square of sunlight under the window. Afterwards I fell asleep.

Mother went to my school with me to say good-bye to the Fathers. One after another came and spoke to her. At last, the Father Rector came and joined the Father Prefect and us.

'It's a pity,' he said. 'He's a particularly gifted boy. Now look. We quite understand your position. We'll give the boy free tuition and food, because it suits us to, and it would be a pity to lose him.'

'But the clothes, Father,' said my mother.

'Don't worry, we'll see to that. The boy will not go without clothes.'

My mother was inclined to leave me in the school. She had borne with my aunt for so many years. What would she not have done for me? The Father Rector ended the discussion:

'Well, we're going to take the boy as another boarder. Where one hundred are fed, there's enough for a hundred and one. As to clothing and books, we'll arrange for them. Don't you worry.'

And I? Was I nothing? Was the whole world to dispose of me at its pleasure? Everyone wanted to give me charity and then to exploit it. I had to stay in the school, shut up there, always hearing people say

159

that I was there on charity, studying like a mule, so that later on the priests could use my successes in their advertisements in order to attract fathers like Nieto's who would call me son of a washerwoman.

'I want to go to work,' I said suddenly.

'All right, all right,' said the Father Rector. 'Don't you worry about anything, you will have what you need.'

'I don't want any more charity. D'you believe I don't know it?' Through my tears the words came tumbling out: I know very well what it means to be the son of a washerwoman—I know what it means to be told about the charity you've received—I know all about the school prospectus—I know what it means that my mother has to scrub floors in my aunt's house without being paid for it. I know about the rich and the poor. I know I am one of the poor and I don't want anything from the rich.'

They brought me a cup of tea from the College kitchen and the Father Rector kept on patting me on the shoulder. Finally, they had to leave me for a long time on one of the plush-covered sofas in the visitors' hall. The Fathers came one by one to see me and be kind. Father Joaquín sat down beside me, lifted my head and asked me what was the matter with me. I answered him hysterically, but he rapped me over the fingers and said:

'No, no, slowly, as if you were making your Confession.'

The Father Rector pushed my mother to the other end of the hall, and we two stayed alone. I told the priest everything; he was holding my hands in his own big hands and squeezed them gently to encourage me.

When I had finished, he said:

'You're right.' He went up to the Father Rector and my mother, and said gravely:

'You can't do anything. Between the lot of them they have smashed the boy. The best thing is to let him have a taste of life.'

When we left, he crushed my hand in his, in a handshake as between men, and said:

'Now you must be brave. You're a man now.'

We walked up the slope of Mesón de Paredas, my mother thoughtful and I proud: I was right. Father Joaquín had said so.

That afternoon, Aunt Basilisa came up to the attic to speak to my mother.

'Baldomera wants to see the boy,' she told her.

Before she could answer, I replied:

'Tell her I don't want to. And what's more, you've no business to come here to the attic. You've managed to get rid of us anyhow. This here is not Aunt's place. This is my place, and I don't want you or

160

anybody else to come here. Tell Aunt Baldomera that I won't come because I don't want to. It's as far from us to her as from her to us. If only poor Uncle José could see it!' Again rage blinded me, and I caught her by the arm.

'Off with you, off, out in the street, you old hag, tale-bearer, lick-spittle! Out with you, go back and steal your sister's jewels and money and clothes until she's left naked! Thief!'

She attempted to shout back. But Señora Pascuala, who knew the whole story and had arrived because of the noise, caught hold of her

'Go away. The boy's right, yes, Señora, he's absolutely right. The best thing you can do is to hop it. And don't give me any of your back-chat! I'm the door-keeper here, and I won't stand for any scandals. D'you understand, you beggar? What you've got, you toffs, is hunger and greed. And that's enough of it. Out with you. Out of this house!'

She shoved her along the corridor of the attics, and Aunt Basilisa never dared to say a word. If she had opened her mouth, Señora Pascuala would have beaten her up, what with her old wish to get square with one of these fine ladies.

My mother and Señora Pascuala agreed that I would have to enter a good shop as an errand boy. With my schooling I would make a good salesman and get on quickly once I had served my apprenticeship. Two days later, my mother took me to a fancy goods shop in the Calle del Carmen. It was called the 'Gold Mine'. The owner, Don Arsenio, kindly, short, and pot-bellied, laid down the conditions to my mother.

'As to work, there's plenty of it. But the boy will eat like a prince. In my house there's better food than in many a duke's. He'll get food, washing, and bed. Ten pesetas a month, and the tips.'

II. INITIATION TO MANHOOD

When the night-watchman was about to go off to bed at half-past six in the morning, he rapped a few times on the iron shutters with his pike. Then Arnulfo and I woke up. We slipped into our trousers in the gangway between our two beds, crouching, because otherwise we would have bumped our heads against the ceiling, and washed in turn in the bowl standing at the foot of our beds. We went down to the shop, opened the front door and swept shop and back room. Then I took a bucket of water and a step-ladder. I had to wash the glass panes one by one: five shop windows with glass in front and at the back; five mirrors inside the shop and two in the entrance; a pillar panelled with mirrors; a counter which was a showcase with plate glass for its six walls. The glass outside the shop windows was full of finger marks, blotches where shortsighted people had pressed their noses against it, dust, streaks, and all the dirt the street had thrown on to the panes in the course of a day. The glass panels of the counter had the same stains, and in addition blobs of sticking-gum from the labels, scratches from pencils and sleeve buttons, coloured marks from boxes standing on the counter.

Everything had to be made to sparkle like a diamond. At eight Don Arsenio came down, wiping the breakfast grease off his lips and having just lit his first cigar, and inspected the glass panes one after the other without ever finding them done as he wanted them. Then I started to sponge down the varnished woodwork of the entrance under his supervision, while he stood there on the sidewalk, puffing away at his cigar and contemplating his shop. In the meantime Rafael, the oldest shop-assistant, arrived, and as soon as I had finished washing the front door Don Arsenio sent us away to have our breakfast.

Arnulfo and I went up to the top floor where Don Arsenio had his flat. His wife, Doña Emilia, and a servant-girl gave us our breakfast, on the roof terrace when the weather was fine, and in the dining-room when it was bad. Usually we got a couple of fried eggs or a cutlet or a sausage with a fried egg, and a big cup of white coffee.

It was Don Arsenio's pride to have good food, and it was his compensation for the hunger he had suffered all his life until he had made himself independent. We all knew his history, for he told it nearly every day.

When he was five years old he herded sheep in the mountains of Leon and lived on garlic soup and sour milk. When he was eleven he walked to Madrid, tramping the high roads hand in hand with his brother; they were both to become unpaid shop assistants in the establishment called La Palma, the best novelty shop in Madrid, the owner of which was a countryman from Leon who recruited all his assistants from his old village.

He exchanged the garlic soup for hard chick-peas with bacon or potatoes with dried cod, the staple food of the staff of La Palma, and the freedom of the hills for the confinement of the back room from which he emerged for a Sunday afternoon once every two months, with a single peseta in his pocket, which was all the boss allowed the lads for their expenses.

He was shut up there for twenty years. Then, following the patriarchal tradition still alive in the trade, his master paid out his savings and granted him credit. So he set up his own shop, justified its high-sounding name, and turned it into a veritable gold mine. He married Doña Emilia, a cook whom he had come to know across the counter of La Palma, and the two devoted themselves to the task of getting fat, cramming themselves with the tastiest morsels his wife's experience helped her to find in the markets.

Every meal in their house was a surprise, and the only certain thing was that it would not contain either chick-peas, nor beans, nor dried cod. There were plenty of cutlets heaped with golden fried potatoes, fat fillets of hake, rabbits in thick sauce, roast lamb and sucking-pig, slices of smoked, cooked, or fried ham, chicken, and lobster. Every meal consisted of three courses and two desserts. Sometimes Doña Emilia came down to the shop in the middle of the morning or the middle of the afternoon and whispered something into her husband's ear. His round face lit up, and when she had gone, he turned to me:

'To-day you'll feast,' he said. 'Let's see if you can't stop being as thin as a lizard. I won't tell you what you're going to get, but you must tell me afterwards what you think of it.'

Just before the meal he returned to the subject, unable to keep still.

'Do you know what you're going to eat to-day?'

'No, sir, I don't.'

'You'll find out, boy, you'll find out. You must have patience. Are you hungry yet?'

'Well, just a bit, Don Arsenio.'

'All right, be prepared for something! But you know, the main thing is not to drink water now, because that fills up your tummy and takes away your appetite. Now get going, tidy up those boxes over there. Work makes you hungry.'

After his meal he came down with his little eyes glittering and his face flushed.

'Now, boys, get your meal, don't let it get cold. And later you'll tell me what you think.' He winked at us and patted his round belly. 'It's good stuff, you'll see.'

Upstairs a whole chicken, half a lobster, a platter with costly fruit and half an enormous cream-filled tart were waiting for Arnulfo and me, together with a bottle of wine and a cup of coffee. Arnulfo, who had come half-starved from a tiny village in Valladolid province, and I, who possessed a sound appetite, ate up everything and came back to the shop quite congested. The rule of the house was that you did not speak to the master, except on business matters, unless he spoke to you himself. So we went behind the counter without saying a word.

At that hour when there were hardly any customers, Don Arsenio sat in a chair wrapped in a smoke cloud from his cigar, which kept dwindling at both ends: at the burning end which was like a live coal, so constantly did he suck it, and at the end in his mouth which his teeth worried into shreds he would then spit out together with coffee-brown spittle. Don Arsenio peered into our faces to see in them the effect of the meal.

'Now, you little leech'—I was 'the boy', the 'little leech' or the 'little lizard' to him—'how did you like your meal?'

'Very much, Don Arsenio.'

'Very much—very much. And so that's all, is it? To eat a chicken as you've just done, nice and brown and stuffed with minced ham, and half a lobster with a bowl of mayonnaise, and then the fruit, and the hell of a lot more—and you just say you like it very much? Let's see now, where have you ever eaten like that before you came to my house?'

'Nowhere, sir.'

'There you see. My word! If you've never eaten like this in your life, why don't you say so?'

One day Don Arsenio's brother, who had a similar shop in the Calle del Pez, came for a visit and inquired about me.

'He's a wee bit thin,' said Don Arsenio, 'but that's something we'll soon change. Just let him tell you how he's fed, because in spite of being as thin as he is, he's a great glutton and eats more than I myself, I do believe.'

As words came easily to me and I was just in the right mood, I gave an extravagant description of the meals, such as Don Arsenio had never heard and would never have been able to give himself. First he listened with bewilderment and then with enthusiasm.

'That boy's got a golden throat. You listen to him and you feel like starting to eat. I'm going to enter a duro in your pay-book, as a present from me.'

Solemnly he got out the pay-book where he entered my wages and tips, and noted down five pesetas. For days afterwards he made me recite my speech to his friends, whom he seemed to bring home for that very purpose. Rafael, the shop-assistant, had to listen to it ten or twelve times, always with the same rider:

'There you see what you've missed, Rafael. It's no good falling in love. It's a fairy-tale that "bread and onion together with you" are just as good. Next Sunday you must come with your wife and eat with us. I'll tell Emilia to prepare something nice for you.'

That Sunday, Rafael and his wife, a pretty little woman, ate with us. They ate with real hunger and since we were alone on the terrace, the woman stuffed everything she could get hold of into an empty bag she had brought along: chunks of meat and fried fish, fruit, cheese, biscuits. After the meal, Doña Emilia sailed forth with a parcel.

'Maria, I've got a few little things for supper in here for you.'

On Monday, Rafael had to sit still under Don Arsenio's comments. When the three of us employees were alone, he complained:

'If only that man had increased my pay by what he spends on meals for us, he would have solved all our problems.'

For Rafael, the senior shop-assistant, earned 125 pesetas a month as a living for himself, his wife, and two children, and a third already on the way. To save money, he let his beard grow—it was black and very handsome—and wore his hair long, like a mane. His wife trimmed his hair and beard for him and he did not go to the barber more than once every two or three months. He was a smoker; we kept the cigarette stubs lying about in the shop for him, and he rinsed them in vinegar and dried them in the sun. Yet he was very affection-ate and friendly to everyone. Only his eyes were sad.

The main business of the shop was in veils and hair apparel. Then we also sold drapers' goods and haberdashery such as buttons, safety-pins, pins, cuff-links, silk ribbons, and a great many other things. The best-selling goods were veils and the new sort of buttons people called press buttons; you sewed one half of them on each side of the fastening and joined them by pressing one into the other. We sold them in thousands, but Don Arsenio was very annoyed because he had a large stock of hooks-and-eyes which nobody wanted to buy any more.

Veils caused the greatest trouble. They were kept in huge boxes with thirty to forty rolls in each, classified according to their pattern, and you spent the whole day taking down and lifting up heavy boxes, almost as high as I was, and rolling up veils. For the women were a nuisance; we had sample books with metal edges, which showed a sample of a veil on each page, but those women did not want to look at the veils in sample bits. We had to take down the boxes, unroll a good bit of every roll and let it hang down from the counter. They fingered all the veils, took the roll they liked best and held the veil to their face in front of a mirror to see whether the colour and pattern suited them. And then they did the same with another roll, and with still another. Many of them went shopping, as they called it, and looked at one thing or another, only to buy nothing in the end.

Don Arsenio and Rafael knew most of that breed; they served them as badly as they could, and left them without attention, until they got bored and walked out. Most of the customers for veils were rich people of the Salamanca district, who had the veils sent to their houses. I had to deliver them, and I got plenty of tips that way, which Don Arsenio collected from me and entered in my pay-book. I bought all the clothing I needed on my pay-book, and on Sundays, when I went for a walk, Don Arsenio let me have two pesetas to spend as I liked.

The customers for hair apparel were all the women of the quarter, most of them women who were street-walkers in the Calle del Carmen, the Calle de Mesonero Romanos, de la Abada, and de Preciados, where they stood at the corners during the night and sometimes even during the day. When the police came, they ran away and warned each other so as not to get arrested. So it happened quite often that you suddenly saw twelve to fifteen women running and hiding in the house doors because 'the cops' were near. But it seemed to me that the police were not keen on catching them, because it was usually quite a while after the women had started running, before a pair of policemen on their round together with a plain-clothes man came walking along calmly, without troubling to hurry.

These women never entered the shop in the late afternoon, when most of the other customers came to buy, because Don Arsenio would have turned them out mercilessly. So they came in the morning or after their midday meal, sometimes in a dressing-gown with nothing underneath. Don Arsenio, who at that time of the day stayed on the other side of the counter, patted their bottoms and pinched them. Rafael touched their breasts and sometimes pushed his hand into the neck of their dress; when there was more than one of them, Arnulfo took his share. The women let them, because Don Arsenio let them buy at a reduced price. But they did not know that he always began by asking a higher price. If Doña Emilia came down and caught us out, Don Arsenio gave her a few noisy kisses and told her not to get angry, that was the way to do business.

Arnulfo, who was seventeen, was crazy about women. When we went to bed he told me all his adventures with the bad girls of the quarter and then he masturbated most nights. His face was yellow and he had a dry little cough; sometimes, when he was coughing, Don Arsenio gave him a look and said that he would become consumptive from 'so much bell-ringing'.

Don Arsenio's other passion besides food was the gramophone. Once he and Doña Emilia had been to Paris; from there he had brought a Pathé gramophone with a huge wooden trumpet and another of metal, and a box decorated with columns and bronze garlands. It was the biggest gramophone I had seen in my life, and it could be used for records half a yard wide, which contained whole operas. At ten o'clock in the evening, when we had closed the shop, he put the gramophone on the counter and brought out his box of records. He had hundreds of records of all kinds. Doña Emilia went to bed early and did not stay to listen, but he left the door of the shop standing open and his friends of the neighbourhood dropped in, the owner of the carpet store, the grocer, the watchmaker, the toymaker. They sat down and listened, and towards eleven, when there were few people about, the tarts started gathering in the doorway to hear the music. From under the door they called out to men who passed by, and sometimes one of them told a man to wait for her until the end of the piece.

I liked listening to the gramophone, although it meant going to bed late, but it was bad on Saturdays. As we did not open the shop on Sundays, Don Arsenio's friends met to play cards. Arnulfo and I stayed behind the counter and watched them. They sent me out to fetch tobacco, or coffee, or sandwiches, or cakes, or beer, or brandy. They stayed on till five or six in the morning. After one o'clock I could no longer stand on my feet for sleepiness. At dawn the night-watchman and the police used to come in to have a cup of coffee or a glass of brandy; and the street-girls who were customers of the shop also came in to have a joke with all the men, let themselves be mauled about and in return ate the remainder of the cakes and sandwiches. On Sundays we could stay in bed until lunch-time, and afterwards go out until nine o'clock, when we came back to have our supper and go to bed.

On Sundays I went to the attic to stay with my mother. Rafael was working at a grocer's close to our house, and Concha was in service in the same street; so we spent many Sundays all together and went picnicking to the country. On other Sundays mother stayed at home and Rafael and I went to the cinema or the theatre together. Rafael had begun to smoke and when I was with him I smoked an occasional cigarette, but I did not like tobacco and I was afraid that it would be bad for my chest, as I was so thin.

A few days after I had started working, Aunt Baldomera came to the attic. When she heard that I was working in a shop she began to weep. Then she and my mother made it up and she often came to the attic on Sundays. When she did not turn up, Rafael and I went to her place, Rafael stayed downstairs, because my aunt did not like my going about with him; I stayed with her for a while and always got a duro out of her to go to the pictures, on the condition that I would not go out with Rafael. Every time she wept and asked me to leave the shop and come to live with her again. But I told her I did not want anything, that was all finished and done with, and anyhow I liked working. She did not want me to work in a shop, cleaning windows, but I was not going back as long as Aunt Eulogia was with her.

Then there was a Sunday afternoon when I came home and heard news. Aunt had been to tell my mother that she had thrown out Aunt Eulogia because she was fed up with being robbed, and that she wanted my mother and myself to come back to her. My mother had told her that she would come every day to do the housework and the cooking as before, but as to me, she was not going to interfere and I was free to do as I liked. We spent the whole afternoon talking it over, my mother and I, and I did not go to see my aunt because I did not know what to say to her.

On Monday morning my aunt turned up at the shop. Don Arsenio thought she was a customer, because he did not know the whole story; he asked what he could do for her, but she burst into tears, sat down on a chair, and said:

'I've come for the child.'

Don Arsenio stood there as though turned to stone and must have thought she was quite mad.

'For the child?' he asked.

'Yes, for the child. The whole thing was just crazy, you know. Fortunately, the child doesn't need it, because he gets everything he wants at home.'

'Yes, yes, madam, you're quite right. Don't be upset, it's a simple affair, we'll settle everything as nicely as possible.'

'Where is the child? Have you sent him out?'

Don Arsenio lost his patience.

'But what child d'you mean, madam, for Heaven's sake?'

When I came down from breakfast I found Don Arsenio in a rage, listening to my aunt's story, and my aunt sobbing and weeping big tears. Rafael and Arnulfo had their fun with both, looking on from behind the counter, and I felt a fool. I gave her a kiss.

'Why are you here, Aunt?' I asked.

'So this lady is your aunt?' asked Don Arsenio.

'Yes, sir.' I started telling him the outline of the story, but he stopped me.

'Yes, yes, I know, she's told me everything at least three times over. And now, what does it all mean? You know, visits to the staff' —he said it pompously—'are prohibited during working hours, except in a case of emergency.'

'What do you want me to do with her, sir? She's like that. I don't know why she's come.'

At that my aunt calmed down.

'Look here, child, I've come to fetch you. Your mother surely has told you that we have made it up. Eulogia's gone, and high time too, I was fed up with her. You can't imagine what she's stolen from me, child. If they had stayed on at home they wouldn't have left the nails in the wall. Now you come along with me, and if you want to work we'll find something fitting for you. Only not as a shopkeeper. Now go and get your things, say good-bye to these gentlemen, and let's leave this place. Lord, Lord—what you must have suffered, my poor child!'

Don Arsenio had an outburst when he saw himself treated with contempt.

'Now, listen, madam—whatever you are. To be a shopkeeper, as you call it, is a very respectable trade. And we don't eat boys alive in this place. I'm sure that with all your lah-di-dah you won't give him the food he got here with me.'

'I can imagine what meals you give your staff.'

'Better ones than you would give them, madam. That's all there is to say about it. But listen carefully to what I'm going to say now. This boy was brought to me here by his mother, and I'm not at all interested in family rows. The boy won't leave here unless his mother comes to fetch him and he wants to go. I don't know you and I don't want to, but this boy is a minor entrusted to me, and my word goes here. And so, madam, here's the door, you know the way out.'

There followed hugs, sobs, and kisses. My aunt fumbled in her pocket and pulled out a twenty-five-peseta note.

'Here, my boy, and buy anything you need.'

Don Arsenio handed her back the note.

'The boy doesn't want anything, madam. He's got the money he's saved and doesn't need alms to bribe him. And now will you go, madam, for I don't want customers to come and find wailing women here.'

When she had gone, I managed to pacify Don Arsenio by telling him over and over again that my aunt was nuts and that I didn't want to leave the shop to go back to her. When I assured him there was better food in his house than in my aunt's he was perfectly satisfied. On the following Sunday I told my aunt that I would stay on in the shop because I was all right there and liked it.

There followed a few crazy weeks. When I came out of the shop in the morning to clean the windows I found my aunt there, with a couple of buns in her hand, and very much afraid of meeting Don Arsenio. She kissed me over and over, kept on worrying me about coming back to her, and planted herself at the foot of the step-ladder, crying out that I would fall and kill myself, that I would get chilblains from the cold water, that I could have slept peacefully in my bed at that hour, that I got little food and went late to bed, and so on and so forth. As all the boys of all the shops were cleaning windows at that hour just as I did, they all pulled my leg about it. In the end I spoke to Don Arsenio, and he came down early one morning, made a row and chased her off. She did not return, but a few days later I met her in the street when I was carrying a parcel with a veil to a place in the Calle de Ferraz. After that she spent her days lurking behind corners and when I least expected her I found her at my side. It became a nightmare. At the same time I felt sorry for her; and I would have liked to give up the shop for a better job. The people at the shop found out that she was tracking me down and they all teased me about it, even the tarts, who began to know her because they spent their time at street corners.

The gramophone settled the matter.

Don Arsenio arranged an evening concert on his roof terrace and told Arnulfo and me after dinner:

'Carry the gramophone upstairs. You take the box, Arnulfo, and you there take the trumpet. But take great care not to drop anything on the stairs.'

When I walked through the narrow door of the shop, the trumpet banged against the plate-glass of the showcase. Nothing happened, but Don Arsenio, who for some reason was in a filthy temper, pounced on me like a wild beast, struck me hard in the back of my neck and screamed:

'Idiot, son of a bitch,' He often used that word. 'Have you no eyes in that blockhead of yours?'

At the blow and the insult I wheeled round. I went back into the shop and shouted furiously into his face:

'Don't touch me, you stuffed pig. It's you who's the son of a bitch, you and your family. Shove your old gramophone where you've got room for it.' And I chucked the trumpet on the floor.

Five minutes later I found myself in the street, pursued by Don Arsenio's screams.

I had to choose between two courses; to go home to our attic, tell my mother all that had happened, and find work in another shop. Or to go home to my aunt. But that would have meant giving in.

It was half-past three in the afternoon. At that hour my mother was working at my aunt's flat. I went there. My aunt was very happy when she saw me; she believed that I had been on an errand somewhere near by and had come up to see her. I told her nothing. I stayed in the kitchen with my mother and told her everything.

'All right. Don't worry. We'll find another shop.'

But, of course, my mother had to tell the story to my aunt.

That night I stayed at my aunt's to sleep. I was lying in my gilt bedstead and looked up into the even, shining stucco ceiling high above my head. In the attic, the foot of my bed scraped against the sloped roof and plaster flakes stained its dirty green bars.

III. RETURN TO SCHOOL

The tall oak wardrobe was still full of the clothes which belonged to someone else: the two sailor suits, the blue and the white one, on their curved clothes-hangers. The short knickers with the elastic band over the knee, which left a red welt on one's skin. The row of striped drill blouses, each stripe a chain of tiny checks. The cream-coloured piqué shirt-fronts. The silk neckties. The flat, starched collars. The round sailor caps with their gold lettering and dangling strings. The tartan caps and the beret for the street. The red school folder.

My aunt took out piece after piece and laid everything out on the bed. I recognized them all, one by one, as one recognizes what one has worn on one's own body, but they seemed foreign things, things that belonged to someone else.

'What shall we do with them?' she asked me.

With the pride of the possessor of a man's suit made to measure, with no more wrinkles than those round the bulge of my uncle's silver watch anchored to its plaited gold chain, I answered:

'It doesn't matter, we'll find some boy who can make use of them.'

My aunt folded up each piece of clothing and stored it away in the bottom drawer of the wardrobe, with moth balls between the folds.

'Well, I think we will keep the things. They may come in handy,' she said.

Did she think that I would ever put on those clothes again? I glanced at myself in the big looking-glass of the sitting-room, a looking-glass in a gilt frame which reached up to the ceiling and was slightly inclined as though bowing to the floor. In my soft hat I was as tall as and taller than many men, only I was very thin and the face was the face of a boy.

'I'm going out,' I told my aunt.

'Take care of yourself and be careful where you go and what you do and don't be late.'

'I'm going to see my friends, and I'll be back soon.'

When I started walking down the stairs I whistled loudly, as I always did. At the next landing I fell silent. Was it right to whistle and jump down stairs as I did when I went down to play in the street, with my packet of sandwiches in my hand? Señor Gumersindo, the concierge, saw me in the doorway and stopped me:

'You're looking very smart, young sir.'

He no longer called me Arturito. I was 'young sir'. I walked up the street and looked for my friends. The gang was playing at hopscotch in the Plaza de Ramales and having an argument as to whether Pablito, the plasterer's son, had touched the line or not. My arrival stopped their dispute. I had to tell them all my adventures in the shop, and all about my soon entering a bank as an employee. The boys were thrilled. When they had enough of listening to me, the boy whose turn it was picked up a pebble, put his hands behind his back, made a few secretive movements, and then held his two closed fists under my nose.

'Come on, say which. Are you going to play?'

I would have liked to be in the game. But how could I play in a grown-up suit, with a silver watch in my pocket, and a gold chain across my waistcoat?

'No,' I said, and added, to tone down my refusal: 'You can't jump in this sort of suit.'

For a while I stayed there, watching their jumps, somewhat shame-faced, for I felt a fool, and then I left with a 'See you later' which really meant 'never'. I walked down to the sunlit Plaza de Oriente, across the wide yard of the Plaza de la Armería to the balconies which opened on to the Casa de Campo. Boys much bigger than I were playing in the square with bare legs, in blouses and smocks. But I could no longer play. I was a man, I had to be serious. In a few months' time I would work in the Bank. For I was certain to win the competition for the job.

Everything was settled. Don Julian, the man from the Bank who always came to the Café Español, was going to recommend me to the directors. He was one of the heads of their Stock Exchange Department and had worked in the bank for thirty years. The directors thought much of him, and with his recommendation it would be quite enough if I passed the entrance test. For this I had to learn simple book-keeping, which was easy and also arranged for. The *Escuela Pía*, my old school, had a commercial class for poor pupils, and I was going to take it.

Matters with my aunt were settled as though nothing had ever happened. My mother went there in the mornings and left late in the evenings. She could have slept at my aunt's, because Concha and Rafael got bed and board where they worked, but she did not want to. She said she had her own home and would not leave it a second time, and I thought she was right.

It was as though nothing had ever happened; but many things had happened. When I wanted to go out, I no longer had to ask if I could go and play. I simply took my hat and said: 'I'm going out now.' I no longer had any need to open the sideboard in secret to get at the biscuits, and then to leave the door open and crumbs on the carpet so that my aunt should think that it had been the cat. Now I opened the sideboard, put three or four biscuits on a plate and ate them. Then I poured myself out a glass of strong wine and drank it. My aunt looked on and beamed. When I was going out she asked me if I had any cash with me in case I wanted to buy something, and I always carried two or three pesetas in my waistcoat pocket. Before, it had always been necessary to tell her a long tale before I could get a single peseta out of her.

I had to see Angel. Here on the balcony of the Palace there was nothing for me to do, except to stare at the Campo del Moro and the Casa de Campo like an idiot. It was quiet at the café about that time. I found Angel sitting by himself in the corner of the entrance lobby, making parcels of the papers he had not sold the day before and had to return to the distribution agents. When he saw me I thought his face turned sad.

'Hullo, Arturo, and how are you?'

I quickly told him the story of the last few changes in my life: the shop, my aunt, the bank, Don Julian. He listened in silence, with his old man's face wrinkled. When I had finished he patted me on the shoulder with a hand blackened by coppers and printers' ink.

'Now we won't cry out the *Heraldo* at night any more.'

He dragged a bundle of cheap novels out of the bottom of the cupboard and offered them to me.

'Take all the ones you haven't read yet.'

I went through the series of the *Illustrated Novel* and picked out those I did not know. Angel only watched me.

'Well, look, I'm taking these here. Come up to us later on and take all you want of my books.'

'I'm not going up to your place because your aunt won't like it.'

'You're silly,' I said. 'Now look here. From to-night on you simply bring us the paper upstairs, because I told you to. And then you stay with me for a bit. I'll arrange everything with my aunt.'

173

Pepe, the waiter, came out. When he saw me he was surprised.

'Well, well, Arturito, it's a long time since I saw you last. And now you're a young man.' He gave me a long look. 'And how's Doña Baldomera?'

'All right. Poor woman, she thinks of my uncle's death all the time.'

'Poor Don José. Your uncle was a very good man. How time passes. When you came to the café the first time you were still in swaddling clothes and I hadn't any grey hairs yet. Of course you and your family won't come here now, but I do hope you'll come from time to time to see your old friends. Manuel, my boy—you know him —is a young man too by now. He does everything at our little wine-shop, together with his mother.'

'But, Pepe,' I said, half amused and half ashamed, 'you speak to me so solemnly. Now, are you going to address me as "Arturo" or as "sir" in future?'

'I don't know, it's just that I'm used to it, you know. Of course, there it is, you're used to seeing young Arturo and so you can't get into a new habit overnight.'

'But I'm what I was, and I want you to go on as before, Pepe.'

The old man embraced me and kissed me on my mouth with his grey moustache, far more affectionately than he had done on the nights I had come with my uncle. Then he sat down on Angel's stool and wiped his eyes with the white napkin hanging over his sleeve.

I went away with my bunch of books under my arm. I did not want to go home. I wanted to see the quarter, and the boys, and— well, I wanted to play.

In the Plaza de Isabel II, I turned round on my heels and walked slowly home.

'What's the matter with you, my boy? You look irritated,' said my aunt.

'Nothing's the matter. Nothing.'

I sat down in a chair to read one of the new novels. The cat was sitting on his square of rug, watching me. There was nothing else on the balcony. But I could not go on reading. I got up and went into the bedroom. There I took a pair of shorts from the bottom drawer of the wardrobe, undressed, and put them on. In shirt sleeves I went back to the dining-room, and I noted the coolness of the air on my bare legs.

'I've changed, because I didn't want to crumple my suit,' I told my aunt.

And I threw myself down full length on the balcony floor, an open book between me and the cat. My hair touched the cat's head and

174

every time I turned a page he stretched out his paw and gave the paper a lightning rap. He wanted to play and turned over on his back, his white belly stretched. I stuck my head into the hollow between his four legs, and he mussed my hair because it tickled him.

Doña Emilia called from the balcony opposite me:

'Arturito, sweetie, so you've come back?'

The cat jumped up and ran off. I was ashamed of my childish games. I gave her a brief answer, went inside and shut the balcony door. Then I changed slowly back into the grown-up suit and resumed my reading, sitting at the dining-room table and not taking in a word of what the book said.

The Commercial Class started at ten and lasted till half-past eleven in the morning, and there was a shorthand class in the afternoon. Father Joaquín took the morning class and a parliamentary stenographer of the Senate took the afternoon class.

I went before ten o'clock and called on Father Joaquín in his room. It was open to the four winds as always, there was his music stand, there were his birds fluttering round the window. He was reading a book and said mechanically: 'Come in,' when I knocked softly. 'Ah, it's you.' He stood up and hugged me. 'So you want very much to start studying again? It won't be difficult for you. In a few months you'll have caught up. You will go to the lectures downstairs with all the others, so that you keep in step with them, but I'm going to explain things to you outside class hours, much more quickly and simply than I could do it with the other boys. And then it will be work and earning a living for you, because you're a man now, aren't you, boy?'

We went downstairs to the class together. All the boys rose.

'Sit down,' said Father Joaquín.

He went with me to the platform, turned round, and said:

'From to-day you're going to have a new class-mate who's known to a good many of you anyhow. He won't stay with us long, only long enough to study book-keeping which he needs because he's already working. Now, all move down and make room for him. As you know there isn't a first or last pupil in this class, but we'll have to give him the first place because he's earned it.'

There I stayed, at the beginning of the first row, and he began with the lesson. It seemed intended to give me an outline of the matters already studied by the class, so that I should be able to follow. I found it easy to pick up the main threads with the help of the syllabus Father Joaquín had given me. The boys watched me and whispered among themselves. Many of them stared at my hat which was hanging on a peg among their caps and berets. None of them spoke to me. They were all poor boys from the quarter. I knew some of them, but when I tried to speak with them they shut up like clams and answered me with a 'huh', a 'yes', or a 'no'.

After the end of the lesson I followed Father Joaquín back to his room. 'What do you think of it?' he asked me.

'It's difficult to say.' I found it hard to speak. With my hat between my fingers, I was standing on the other side of the desk, facing him. Father Joaquín rose, walked round the desk, put his hand on my shoulder and drew me gently nearer.

'Now come, tell me. What's the matter with you?'

'I don't know. It's very funny. Everything seems changed. Even the stones of the cloisters, which I know by heart, one by one. Everybody seems changed to me, the boys, you, the school. Even Mesón de Paredes Street. When I walked through it this morning I found it changed. To me, the men, the women, the kids, the houses, everything—absolutely everything—seems changed. I don't know how, and I can't explain it.'

Father Joaquín looked straight into my eyes for a short while.

'Of course you see everything changed. But everything is just the same as before, only you have changed. Let's see what you've got in your pockets—show me.' I was bewildered, but he insisted. 'Yes, I mean it, show me everything you carry in your pockets.'

In confusion, I pulled a silk handkerchief out of my breast pocket, then my smart, new leather wallet, the silver watch, the folded handkerchief, two pesetas, a self-propelling pencil, a small notebook. There was nothing else.

'Haven't you anything else?'

'No, sir.'

'Well, well. And what have you done with your marbles and your spinning-top? Don't you carry brass chips, or match-boxes, or printed pictures, or string for playing thieves and robbers? Haven't you a single torn pocket, isn't there a button missing somewhere, haven't you got ink-stains on your fingers?'

I must have made a very silly face. He took the things piece by piece, mockingly, and stowed them back into my pockets.

'Here's the nice silk handkerchief, to look elegant. So you ogle the girls already, do you? The nice wallet to keep the money safe. There aren't any banknotes in it yet, but they'll come, never mind. Everything takes time. Here's the silver watch so you know the time, and you don't have to look at the clocks in shops any more and then sprint through the streets because it's getting late. And you don't have to wait for the clock in the bell-tower to strike any more.'

176

He put both hands on my shoulders, the two big hands of a man, and again looked straight into my face.

'Do you understand now what has happened to you?'

'Yes, sir,' I said.

'If you go now to see Father Vesga,' he added quizzically, 'he'll tell you that you have lost the condition of purity. I tell you simply that you're no longer a child.'

I met nobody but my aunt and my mother, and Father Joaquín was the only person with whom I could talk and have discussions. Least of all we spoke of book-keeping, which came to me very easily indeed. Sometimes we went together to hunt for books in the Prado, or to go to a Museum, and we talked. We talked as though we had been father and son in the flesh. Then one day Father Joaquín said:

'It's Communion to-day. Have you already dropped the practice of going to Communion once a month?'

'Yes, sir.'

'Of course, it's quite natural. Anyhow, if you feel like it you can come to Communion to-morrow.'

On the following day I went to school and accompanied Father Joaquín into church.

'Now what do you intend doing?'

'I'm going to take Communion,' I answered.

'If you like, stay here and wait for me, and then I'll hear your Confession.'

When I was in the confessional, in front of him, he said: 'Now tell me your sins.'

'But what could I tell you, Father?'

What could I have told the man who knew my innermost thoughts, as my mother did not know them, as I did not know them myself, since it was often he who had explained them to me?

'That's true enough,' he answered. 'Let's pray a Paternoster together for the soul of your uncle.'

We broke fast in his room, with a cup of thick chocolate, buns, and a glass of lemonade.

When I walked home, there was light everywhere.

I was separated from everybody else, except Father Joaquín. I saw this very clearly. The people I knew stopped treating me as a child, but nobody thought of treating me as a man. I realized that there were many things of which they could not talk to me. Yet I needed to talk, I needed people to talk to me, I needed to understand things. The grown-up people never realized that their behaviour to me was ridiculous. If they were talking of women when I happened to come in, they stopped and changed the conversation, so that I should not hear that kind of thing, since I was still a child. They did not realize that I knew everything they could have told me. When we were together in the backroom of the shop, Arnulfo had told me all about his affairs with the tarts of the quarter, down to the very last detail. I knew more about it than many of the people who shut up as soon as I was near. They were hypocrites and fools, all of them. Didn't they see that I was lonely?

I needed to play. I bought a heap of tools and started to construct a small steam-engine. I made the drawings and cut out the pieces from sheet-brass. I had bought a treatise on steam engines and copied its drawings. The book was old and described engines of thirty years ago, but it suited me. I wanted to make a very simple engine. My aunt was annoyed because I stained my hands and made a mess in the flat.

On Sundays I went down to the *Rastro*, the Junk Market, to buy the pieces I could not make myself. It was in El Avapies, near my school.

The steep slope which leads from the Plaza de Cascorro down to the *New World* is called *Ribera de Curtidores*, Curriers' Bank. From the near-by slaughterhouses the hides of all the cattle which Madrid consumes wander into the tanners' workshops. On both sides of the sloping street are the tan-yards with timber structures of four or five tiers, where the hides hang from rafters to dry in the air and sun which enter freely from all sides. The skins carry an acrid smell of rotting flesh, which fills the whole quarter and clutches at your throat. On that slope, the street-hawkers set up their junk stalls and you can buy everything, except what you set out to buy.

There they sell every used thing people get rid of. There are old clothes worn out fifty years ago, skirts still spread on crumbling wicker hoops, uniforms from the time of Ferdinand VII. There are paintings, furniture, carpets, tapestries, dented musical instruments, pots and pans of all sizes, rusty surgical knives, old bicycles with twisted wheels, absurd clocks, iron railings, tombstones with blurred names, old carriages with broken spokes or a hole in the roof through which the sun shines onto the tattered velvet of the seat. Stuffed cats, dogs and parrots with tow sticking out of their bellies, spy-glasses, a yard long, which fold up like an accordion, ships' compasses, weapons from the Philippines, old medals and crosses from some general's chest, books, papers, inkpots of stout glass or glazed pottery, and old iron. A great deal of old iron: twisted bars, of which nobody could guess the purpose, hoops, pipes, heavy pieces of machinery, monstrous cog-wheels which make you think with a shudder of hands crushed between their teeth, anvils with blunted noses, coils of wire covered in ochre rust, and tools. Outworn files with iron dust choking their ridges, fantastically shaped hammers, pincers with chipped jaws, tongs with a broken limb, beheaded chisels, gimlets, and angle irons. Then there are victuals: mouldy peppered sausages, maggotty biscuits, raw ham, sweetish cheese, dried up like parchment but sweating honey in large drops like pus, tripe fried in tallow, stale crisps, squashed chocolate grown soft in the heat, shell-fish, river crayfish wriggling in dripping mud, buns with a shiny crust, apples dipped in blood-red caramel. There are hundreds of stalls and thousands of people, looking and buying. All Madrid walks about the Rastro on Sunday mornings.

Down in the Ronda, between the *Americas* and the *New World*, were the poorest stalls where the poorest people came to buy. One of the stalls called itself *The Flower of Cuba*. In the centre of its planks, two yards long and a yard wide, there was a pile of tobacco, black and evil-smelling, taken from the fag-ends of Madrid streets. To the right there were rows of packets of cigarettes, rolled in coarse paper and tied together with gaudy green ribbon. To the left, in neat, symmetrical files, were cigar-butts in dozens, sorted according to size and quality and with cigar bands to show it. Prices varied. A good stump of a Caruncho cigar, with its band to prove its authenticity, fetched as much as fifty centimos. The owner of the stalls was an eighty-year-old gipsy, with curving silver side-whiskers. Beside him squatted three women who rolled cigarettes with bewildering speed. The loose tobacco was sold by weight: fifty centimos the quarter pound. The establishment was always crowded, with buyers in front and sellers behind the counter. The sellers were street-urchins who came with a tin or a sack full of cigarette stubs, already freed from paper, to offer them to the old gipsy. He weighed out quarter-pounds to those in front and those at the back, with hands the colour of tobacco, and he took fifty centimos from the ones and paid twenty-five centimos to the others for the same quantity. The tins were emptied on top of the tobacco pile, and the pile never diminished.

Among all that filth I felt happy, for the Junk Market was a huge museum of absurd things and absurd people. Little by little, my steam engine was born out of it.

On Thursday I went alone to the pictures, on Sundays I went with Rafael. Books, the cinema, the steam engine, Father Joaquín, and the classes at school made up my world. Sometimes I went for a walk with my aunt, and once a month she took me in a carriage to the cemetery to put fresh flowers on my uncle's grave and say a rosary.

179

There were no more quarrels with my mother, but slowly my aunt began to lose her memory and her mind. She was becoming foolish.

I was going to enter the examinations for the Bank at the end of the summer. Don Julian came from time to time and explained things about which I would be asked. It turned out that what I learnt in the school would not help me. At the Bank they had different, shorter methods of book-keeping; everything was done with tricks and combinations of figures which had nothing to do with the rule-of-three and the rules of interest. Yet I found it easy and felt that if everything was of the same kind, they would pay me a good salary as soon as I was working in the Bank and they found out how good I was with figures. Then my mother would no longer go down to wash clothes by the river.

At half-past six I presented myself at the Bank. An old commissionaire who was sitting there went to fetch Don Julian. Behind him I walked up a stairway with a red carpet held in place by gilded rods. Upstairs was a passage covered with waxed linoleum on which one's shoes slipped, and stout wooden rails on both sides. Behind the rails were clerks such as I had not seen in my life. One of them was very fair, with almost ashen hair, a pipe hanging from his lips, which smelt of English tobacco, and a monocle screwed into his right eye so that the right brow was higher than the left. Another was short and grizzled, with a bald spot above his forehead, a black moustache which looked dyed, and a French goatee. There was a thin old lady with very slender wrists who used a typewriter at incredible speed. A spick-and-span orderly with the initials C.E. embroidered in gold on his blue uniform led us into one of the enclosures behind the wooden rails, which had six or seven tables, each with its typewriter.

Then came a gentleman in a coffee-brown frock-coat, gold-rimmed spectacles hanging from a silk ribbon tied to his buttonhole, a grey French goatee and a long amber holder with a burning cigarette. Don Julian greeted him, and the two conversed in rapid French. The gentleman came up to me and asked me which of the typewriters in the place I knew best. I selected an Underwood. He seized the edge of the table, gave a tug, and the typewriter wheeled over, fell back and downwards. At the same time a slab was pushed forward and the desk was smooth and flat, the typewriter had disappeared as if by magic. Below the table was nothing but a sloping board, and the typewriter was invisible.

After this I came to learn my first word of French, destined to follow me throughout my life: *Dossier*. The man with the goatee and the gold-rimmed lenses took a yellow folder with a great number of sheets and said in bad Spanish:

'We shall now start your dossier.'

Christian name, surnames, father, mother, studies, date of birth, and so forth. Then I was given sheets, with the problems I had to answer typed out on top, and space for the calculations left below. I stayed alone and worked out the figures. Don Julian and the Frenchman, whom I later learnt to know as the Chief of the Personal Credits' Department, walked up and down in the linoleum-covered gangway. When I had finished, the Frenchman dictated a passage which I had to type, and another passage which I had to write out in longhand. Then they gave me a page of notes referring to the commercial report of a Lugos firm. From the notes I had to work out a complete report.

When the test was over, Don Julian accompanied me home. On the way he patted my shoulder.

'They liked you very much, only your handwriting is not so good. But that's something you can quickly improve.'

In the Puerta del Sol we each drank a glass of vermouth. The seltzer-water tickled. I drank it greedily, for my mouth was dry and I still felt dazzled by those wide halls and globes of milky light. And I was going to work there? I was full of pride.

When we came home, Don Julian told my aunt that she could count on my having obtained the job.

Three days later I received a letter—the first letter of my life—in which the board of directors of the Crédit Etranger, 250,000,000 Frcs. Capital, informed me that Don Arturo Barea Ogazón would start in their service as from the 1st of August 1911.

I had still three months to go until I was fourteen years old, but I was already an employee of one of the biggest banks in the world.

IV. WORK

Standing round the table, we were rapidly classifying the mail according to the initials in red ink with which each department marked the letters it had dealt with. Every now and again, Medrano went to the desk where the heads of the department sat, and brought back a new heap of letters in place of those we had already classified. Talking was forbidden, but the three of us, Gros,

Medrano, and I, were talking in a whisper all the same. Nobody could tell whether we were speaking about our work or about something else.

'Who got you in here?' asked Medrano.

'The Head of the Stock Exchange Department.'

'And me the Cashier, who's an old friend of our family's. What's your school?'

'The Escuela Pía—and yours?'

'The Salesians in the Ronda—more or less the same thing. Here we're at least not bothered with those eternal Masses and Rosaries. That's to say, Señor Zabala, the Head of Correspondence—the one who's sitting in the middle over there—is a Jesuit. He wears a scapulary under his shirt and goes every Sunday to hear Mass in the Calle de Cedaceros at the Jesuits' Residence. The one next to him—Señor Riñon, the little man to his right—is just the same. He's Head of Spanish Correspondence. The only one who's all right is the third one, the Head of Foreign Correspondence, Señor Berzotas. You see, he's done a lot of travelling and so he doesn't give a fig for priests and friars any more.'

'What did you say his name was?'

'Berzotas.[1] He plays tennis. On Saturdays and Sundays he goes to play in the sports' ground the English have got somewhere in town. And he wants to set up a sports' club for our whole staff.'

Just then, Señor Berzotas called me: 'Hello, boy—the new one, I mean—come over here.'

'At your service, Señor Berzotas,' I said politely.

He flushed and gave me a very sour look. All the clerks sitting near by grinned, and I felt bewildered.

'So my name is Berzotas, is it? And pray who told you so?'

I had learnt at school not to give anyone away, and answered quickly:

'Nobody, I just thought I'd heard somebody saying it.'

'We haven't got any fat cabbage-head here, because if there were one, we would throw him out into the street and that would be that. My name is Manuel Berzosa.'

He had spoken severely, but when he saw that I was embarrassed to the verge of tears, he patted me on the shoulder.

'All right, never mind. There is something rather cauliflowery about the name of Berzosa. Look, the British gentleman over there, Mr. Clemans, has been calling me Birchosas ever since his first day here, and he won't change his ways for anything.'

[1] This name sounds ridiculous in Spanish, as it means Big Cabbages, from *berza*, cabbage.—*Translator's Note*.

He gave me a bundle of letters to distribute and I went back to our table, furious with Medrano.

'Don't take it so seriously, we make jokes the whole day round here. You'll see. And if anyone gets all het-up about it, so much the worse for him.'

The second practical joke came in the middle of the afternoon. Gros, who was manipulating a copying-press and a heap of damp cloths, said to me:

'Go to the w.c. and fetch two buckets full of water.'

I came back with two buckets which were so heavy that they kept brimming over and splashing my trousers. Gros washed his hands with meticulous care in one of them, and Medrano in the other. Then Gros said:

'Now you can take them back.' And they both spluttered with laughter.

I swallowed the pill, took the two buckets and in passing Gros made one of them rock. The water wetted his trousers the whole way down from above his knees. He turned round in a fury.

'Can't you look out?'

'Sorry, it was a joke. And if you get all het-up, so much the worse for you.'

In the end the three of us were roaring with laughter, so that Señor Zabala, with his nasty beard fluttering, came up and scolded us in his womanish voice. After that they showed me how letters were to be copied. You first spread out a moistened sheet of thick, close-woven cloth, then you placed a sheet of copying tissue-paper on it, and on top you put the letter which had to be copied. The moisture passed through the tissue-paper under the pressure of the hand-press with gilt balls on its handle, and the letter was copied. Once you had mastered the technique it was easy. If the cloth was too moist, the print was turned into a single big blob, but if it was too dry, it did not copy at all. Moreover, typewritten letters had to be treated differently from handwritten ones.

And that was all I learned in the course of a fortnight: the correct degree of moisture required for copying a letter.

I was profoundly disappointed. The first day I came to work and was waiting for the Staff Manager to assign my duties to me, I believed that in a few minutes I would be sitting at one of those desks and using a typewriter or making calculations, those miraculous calculations which were being made in a bank. To be prepared for anything of the kind, I had brought along half a dozen of the nibs we called cock's spur nibs; I wrote best with them, although they sometimes spluttered. While I was waiting, Don Julian came and told me:

183

'They're going to send you into Correspondence. It's a very useful section for you. Now do your work well and behave.'

The Correspondence Section—writing letters for the Bank! They would surely give me a typewriter to handle. Most of those I saw in use were Underwoods or Yosts, and I had worked with both types. They would soon see what a good typist I was. I had won Yost's championship for speed on a typewriter with invisible writing and a double keyboard.

When the Staff Manager came, an imposing gentleman in a braided frock-coat, white cloth spats, a greying beard, and gold pince-nez, I followed him proudly. He introduced me to Señor Zabala. 'Here's your new boy,' he said. Señor Zabala called Gros: 'You there, boy, show him things so that he can help you with your work.'

Gros and Medrano took me between them, and there we stood armed with paper-knives, at a deal table the black paint of which came off in flakes and which was covered with scratches and stains from ink or gum; we slit open envelopes, took out the letters and put them in a carrier which was sent over to Señor Zabala's desk.

'Take care you don't tear one of the letters while you slit an envelope,' Gros warned me. 'If you do, Whiskers gets simply livid.'

'So you call him Whiskers?'

'Everybody does, and what's more, it annoys him more than if he were called a bastard.'

After that I was always paired with either Gros or Medrano and spent my day running up and down stairs. We distributed the mail to various sections and collected letters which had already been answered. We ran up and down the stairs four steps at a time, because everything was urgent. In the evening we copied the hundreds of letters written by all the departments in the course of the day. After that we put the letters in their envelopes, closed them, sealed the registered letters and went to supper. By then it was a quarter to ten. I ate hardly anything and fell on my bed like a piece of lead. My aunt said:

'How tired you are, my poor little boy! Do go to bed quickly.'

The fortnight that followed turned me into a past-master in copying, the cleverest copyist in the bank.

There were sixty boys like myself employed in the bank, who had no wages and were called learners. We were supposed to work a year without pay, after which we might be made employees. But to become an employee we had to collect good marks. No more than two or three vacancies a year turned up among a staff of three hundred employees. This meant that in the course of a year, fifty-seven of the learners were thrown out and replaced by new boys, while three stayed on and were given a permanent job.

The only way in which I could collect good marks was to be the quickest of the sixty learners, which was easy for me with my long legs, and to make myself liked by everybody. And besides, I copied letters particularly well. The three heads of the Correspondence Department noted it. Whenever there was an important letter to copy they called for me, because I did it without a blot and without the slightest stain from the damp cloth. The sheets came out of the hand-press as though they had been printed. It was a talent Gros and Medrano envied me.

Yet all the time it was impossible to let your mind stray for a single moment. Anybody, even simple employees of some standing, had the power to throw out a learner. As fifty-seven had to be weeded out in the course of the year, the Staff Manager, Señor Corachán, stalked the boys, as he did the other staff while they had a smoke in the lavatory. He haunted the place, he skulked behind corners, he hid in the w.c. and suddenly appeared to trap the employees. He used rubber-soled boots, and would come up silently behind you, listening. Suddenly he would put his hand on your shoulder and say:

'Please come upstairs to my office and report to me.'

We called him *The Fly*, and when he turned up in one of the passages, the employees passed on the warning in a whisper:

''Ware The Fly!'

Those who were talking shut up and started writing at great speed. Those who were secretly reading a newspaper under the cover of a folder coughed, shut the folder with a casual gesture, pushed it into a drawer and began to write. As the sections were separated only by wooden rails some three feet high, and by glass panels, he could spy on people everywhere. Sometimes he came to the Correspondence Department which was on the first floor and had a rail directly overlooking the big central hall of the ground-floor departments, and from there he watched the employees one by one. Afterwards he went down, took the hidden newspapers out of the drawers and dealt out rows. While he was leaning over the balustrade, you felt like pushing him so that he would fall down, head first.

But there was one man whom he persecuted cruelly: poor Plá. As soon as he saw from the first floor that Plá's chair stood empty, he hurried downstairs, sat down on it, took out his gold watch and placed it on the desk. When Plá came back, he had to face Señor Corachán who said:

'Señor Plá'—and he said it in a ringing voice so that everybody should hear—'exactly twelve minutes by this watch I've been waiting for you in this chair. And you alone will know how long you have been absent from your post in all.'

'But, sir, I only went for a moment to the w.c.'

'Do you call this a moment? A quarter of an hour of your working hours wasted! Moreover, you are supposed to arrive at this place with your needs already attended to. But you use the lavatory as your pleasure ground. You simply stink of tobacco!' Then he rose, straightened his frock-coat, shut the lid of the gold watch with a dry click and added: 'Sit down, and don't let it happen another time. This is insufferable!'

Plá looked at him with his short-sighted little eyes glinting behind his huge spectacles and stuttered something, because Plá was not only short-sighted but also a bad stammerer as soon as he was angry or embarrassed. His hands, which did not know what to do with themselves, but dangled like round lumps of fat from the ends of his short arms, resting on his paunch, for Plá was altogether a sweaty round ball, and his excuses dripped spittle over the papers on his desk. When one of those raindrops fell on a letter done in copying-ink it made a purple blob.

Although Plá stayed every night until nine or ten, befogged with work because it was his job to deal with people all over the world who wanted to play in the Spanish Lottery, Señor Corachán specially checked his hour of arrival in the morning, shoved his watch under Plá's nose and was rude to him. Most of the other employees never took notice of Plá except to crack jokes about his blindness and his stutter; but we boys were friends with him. I had to hear the speech which he made to any new boy:

'You're new here, aren't you? What's your name?' (He did not wait for an answer.) 'Well, well, I hope you're going to learn something. Your future is here in this place. Just think of it. A year without wages—sixty boys like you—three vacancies a year, and after twelve years' work in the place ninety pesetas a month, which is what I earn now.'

At other times he made fantastic calculations.

'There are twenty banks in Madrid, with fifty learners each, which makes a thousand altogether. In Spain there are—let's say—two hundred banks with an average of twenty learners each, which makes four thousand boys. There are thousands of commercial firms which have learners without wages, so there are thousands of boys who work for nothing, but rob the grown-up men of their jobs.'

'But, Plá,' I told him, 'it's apprenticeship.'

'Apprenticeship? It's a systematic exploitation of young boys. It's very cleverly worked out, mind you. When you have been here seven or eight months, they chuck you out some fine day. If you then go to another bank and tell them that you have been here eight months and been given the sack, they won't take you. If you keep your mouth shut, you may be taken on as a learner for another year, but then you run the risk of again being dismissed after eight months. And you'll find yourself in the same situation as now all over again. If you try to take a job in an office, they'll tell you that their business is quite different from that of a bank, but that you can join them as a learner so as to get acquainted with their special requirements. The only chance to break out of this vicious circle is to make use of the time you are still working in the bank to find another job. In that way it's quite possible that you'll find a firm which will pay you twenty-five to thirty pesetas a month.'

'But I want to be a bank clerk.'

'All right then, but you will have to be very patient.'

We all cherished the hope of becoming members of the staff of the Bank and being promoted to a good post. After all, we saw something of the higher officials and knew their history. There was Don Julian, now Head of the Stock Exchange Department, with an income of a thousand pesetas a month. He had entered the Bank as a learner, like myself. The same applied to the cashier, who had been an employee for thirty years, and to some of the others. It was true that most of the officials with high salaries had never been learners, and had joined the Bank as employees, but they all had some kind of special knowledge. Some of them knew languages, and others were experts at investing the Bank's money so that it produced interest and profit. One of those was Señor Tejada. He had the Bank's Power of Attorney at the Stock Exchange and was above Don Julian; he was the only man who had the right to place orders at the Exchange, and Don Julian did nothing but carry them out and conduct the correspondence with the clients. Señor Tejada made millions for the Bank and was paid very well for it. He was one of the people with the highest income, almost as high as the Directors. And I knew I might get where he was, because it was all rather simple; Don Julian once explained to me how Stock Exchange speculation worked.

The Bank could never lose. Those who lost were stockbrokers with little capital, and the clients themselves. Moreover, the Bank got wind of things before anybody else knew about them, by means of code telegrams which Don Julian had to translate. Gambling on the Stock Exchange consisted in betting whether stocks and shares were going to rise or fall in value by the end of the month. If the Bank had many shares of a company in its safe, this was easy; then it was bound to gain either way. It accepted any offers, whether based on a rise or a fall, and at the end of the month it took stock of its purchases. If it found it more useful to raise the value, it offered to buy more of the shares at a higher price. Since the Bank already possessed the majority of the shares or else had bought them, there were few of them left on the market and the brokers themselves had to buy them so as to sell them back to the Bank. In this way the price was much higher by the end of the next month. But then the brokers who had sold shares to the Bank at the beginning of the month were forced to deliver them at a price much lower than the current one, or else to pay the difference. Later the value of the shares went down, but the Bank had sold them at the top price and cashed in on the difference. Thus many people were ruined, but the Bank made money.

There was another business which brought in still more. It was the great business of the Banco Urquijo, which belonged to the Jesuits, and of the Banco de Vizcaya, which was said to belong to them too. Suppose some industrialists wanted to establish a factory which would cost them five millions, but had not got the capital. In that case, and if the transaction sounded good to the Bank, it lent them the money, and issued shares, which it offered to the public. If the public bought all the shares of the Issue, the Bank got its commission on the loan and on the handling of the shares. If the public did not absorb the entire issue the Bank kept the unsold shares and launched them on the market later on, when the factory was already working and the shares fetched a higher price; and then the people bought them. The Bank pocketed the difference. It happened frequently that the undertaking was not sound and collapsed after the Bank had sold out its shares; then the shareholders never saw a red cent, as all the Banks knew that it was better not to touch these shares. In a similar manner the Banco de Urquijo and the Banco de Vizcaya had made themselves masters of the Public Utilities of Madrid, and of almost all the industries of Bilbao.

Another important branch of the business was the deposit accounts. Many people did not want to keep their money at home but took it to the Bank which kept it safe and paid a small annual rate of interest. This money, which did not belong to the Bank, was used for loans to business men who took all their drafts to the Bank. The Bank undertook to collect them and charged a commission for it. But as it did not pay them before it had collected the amount, and as the business man often needed the money at once, they asked for drafts to be discounted when they handed them in. The Bank charged the discount rate and brokerage commission. The discount rate was four per cent. The money advanced on the drafts belonged to the people who had deposit accounts and received an annual interest of three per cent for them. The Bank cashed in four pesetas on each draft of 100 pesetas it discounted—and it discounted many thousands a year.

For this purpose, they had a special reference department and knew exactly every customer's credit. In this department girls were typing out copies of all the information collected, and filing them by the hundred every day. The girls were paid two pesetas daily, and many days they had to work twelve hours without looking up from their typewriters. In the Securities' Department there were girls too, but they were much worse off than those in Reference, although they had the same pay. I saw them every day, because I had to take round the correspondence to the various sections; sometimes the girls gave me sweets.

Down in the basement there were some rooms all in steel, roof, walls, and floor, tables, and chairs. The doors were steel grilles, and during the night the rooms were protected by another thick door of steel with many bolts and knobs bearing numbers which had to be arranged in certain combinations so as to open the door. There were no windows, and everything had to be done by artificial light. It was there that the girls worked. They had to file the bonds deposited by the clients of the Bank, to cut off the coupons of every bond due for payment, and to prepare the invoices for all coupons to be paid inside Spain. They spent the day, scissors in hand or counting packets of a hundred coupons each, and listing them one by one in the invoices for cashing. There was no ventilation and the air was suffocating. All the girls looked pale, and Señorita Magdalena, who was the senior in the service, had to be given three or four days' leave every month. The only man down there was the head of the department, Señor Perahita, a fat man, very fat and very jolly. He seemed not to be affected by working there, for he grew fatter and redder every day. Near the door of the section there was the engine of one of the lifts, and the smell of the grease came into the room and stuck in your throat.

Then there was the Safe Deposit, yet another steel room with a very stout steel door. It was entirely filled with safes like wardrobes with drawers inside, and every client had a key to one of the drawers. Most of them were jewellers of the district, for the Bank stood in the jewellers' quarter. In the evenings they would come with their cases full of jewellery and lock them up. Other clients, too, kept their jewels, bonds and cash in the safes. One of them had a lot of gold in bars and gold coins; when he opened his safe, it was all shining yellow. The coins and the bars were arranged in piles. One day he showed us a bar which had come from China and was covered with Chinese characters stamped in relief. It weighed at least half a pound.

There was an old lady who kept all her bank notes in the safe and used to come there every morning to take out the money she needed for the day's shopping. She opened her safe and looked round in all directions to make sure that nobody could see how much money she had. When another client was just opening another safe near by, she waited until he had gone. Once the cashier of the Bank asked her why she did not open a deposit account, so that she could draw whatever she needed each time, while saving the rent of the safe and receiving an annual interest on top of it. She replied that every bank went bankrupt sooner or later, and it was impossible to convince her. She always asked Antonio, the chief commissionaire, to accompany her down to the basement, because she was afraid of somebody hiding there to rob and kill her when she opened her safe.

This Antonio was worse than Señor Corachán. He was always spying on the messenger boys and on us, and reported us to Señor Corachán. Thus everybody loathed him, including those of the staff who had started as learners, because they knew he was a lick-spittle. Nobody spoke when he was near and he hated the whole clerical staff. Sometimes it happened that one of the commissionaires or one of the collectors passed his examination and became a clerk in the Bank. Then Antonio never spoke to him any more. He lived in the building itself and supervised the night-watchmen until midnight or one o'clock, walking silently through the corridors on rubber soles like Señor Corachán. The night watchmen hated him so much that they played him a trick once which made him nearly die of fright.

One of the night watchmen, Señor Juan, hid in a corner and when Antonio had passed by, on tiptoe so that they should not hear him, he suddenly rang all the alarm bells and pointed his revolver at Antonio who was at the bottom of a dark passage. Señor Juan shouted: 'Stop or I shoot—hands up!' Antonio was standing with his back to him and wanted to turn round, but the other said: 'Don't turn round, or I shoot.' 'But, Juan,' cried Antonio, very scared, 'it's me—Antonio!' 'Shut up or I'll put a bullet through you.' As all the night watchmen were in the plot, they kept him for half an hour standing there, face to the wall and hands up, until some of them came back with the policeman posted in the Calle de Alcalá, who also carried their revolvers in their hands. We were watching, and had great fun seeing Antonio coming out with a frightened face in the midst of people pointing revolvers at him. Then Señor Juan said very seriously: 'Well, it's a pure miracle you haven't been shot. I see a black shadow creeping about very softly, without making any noise, so I think it's a thief. If you'd started to run or to make any funny kind of movement, I can tell you, I'd have laid you out.'

The next day the whole Bank had a laugh at him, even the directors. Señor Carreras, the assistant director, who liked a joke, cross-examined him in front of us all to get his laugh.

One after the other the boys who had entered at the same time as I had disappeared, until the three of us were left, Medrano, Gros, and I. It was peculiar that we were again three, just as in the Escuela Pía, and I had a hunch that we all would become regular employees. Christmas was drawing near, and then we would learn which way things were going. We were full of hope, because they attached two new boys to us so that we should train them. That meant that we were five and that two of us would be transferred to another section. If they had intended to throw us out they would have done so before and not kept us on to teach two newcomers. But on the other hand the fact that we had only two boys to train meant that one of us three was either to stay on in the section or was going to be dismissed, and so we were all afraid. Each one of us had gone to the person who had recommended him to the Bank, and each had been given good hopes, but you never knew what those people were going to do.

On Christmas Eve we were all waiting for the envelopes which had been put on the desk of the Heads of Departments. They were yellow envelopes which contained the Christmas bonus and the month's salary; in some cases the slip of paper that gave the two sums also carried a handwritten remark which could mean promotion, or else a warning that the directors were not satisfied with the employee's work. Thus everybody was impatient and nervous, waiting to know his fate.

Señor Zabala called the employees one by one in a loud, sharp voice. Some of them he congratulated even before they had had time to open their envelope. They all thanked him and wished him a Merry Christmas. Then they started to open their envelopes and stood around in groups talking them over, some happy because they had been given a fat Christmas bonus or a promotion, and others very annoyed.

Recalde was banging his fist on the table and cursing. Señor Zabala rose from his chair and called out:

'What's the matter, Señor Recalde? Come here.'

Recalde came up, his hat pulled down over his forehead, and began to thump on Zabala's desk.

'It's a bloody trick! That's the third year they've done the same thing to me. I won't stand for it any more. The whole Bank and all those Jesuit swine like yourself can go to bloody hell! I've been working here and nobody can say anything against my work, but of course, the Reverend Father Capuchin's made up his filthy mind that I mustn't have a mistress. I've got one because I bloody well want to.'

Señor Zabala, scarlet with fury and tugging at his beard, cried:

'Hold your tongue or it will be the worse for you. Hold your tongue, I'm telling you!'

'I don't want to. I'm shouting because it suits me and because I'm leaving this pigsty anyhow.'

He strode out of the room and slammed all the doors along the corridor. A group of clerks clustered round Señor Zabala and consoled him with a lot of flatteries. But another group, those who were discontented, stood round another desk and said that Recalde was in the right.

We three boys were the last to be called. They had given each of us a bonus of twenty-five pesetas and the slip of paper said that Gros and I should transfer to the Records Department and that Medrano was to act as auxiliary correspondent. We were crazy with joy because these transfers meant that our promotion to real employees was a certainty. We decided to have a glass of vermouth together at the bar of the Portuguese in the Calle de la Cruz.

There we found Plá, a Plá who was a stranger to us. He spluttered worse than ever and his little eyes were watering behind his lenses, he invited everybody to have a drink on him, and he showed everybody his slip of paper and the banknotes he had received. It was a happy Plá, who hugged the three of us.

'Have whatever you like, it's on me. Boy'—he shouted at the lad behind the counter—'give those three a drink, and anybody else who wants one too.'

Then he started once again on the story of his good fortune so that the three of us should know it.

'Granny will go crazy with joy.' Granny was his mother, a tiny old lady, very kind, who sometimes came to fetch him. 'You see, I was tearing the envelope open in a bad temper, as every year, and thinking it will be the same old story, they'll have forgotten me. And then there it was, I found a heap of banknotes and a note saying: "As from January the 1st, Head of the Records Department with a monthly salary of 175 pesetas." Double what I've been earning, less five pesetas.'

'Then Gros and I'll be with you in Records,' I said, and we showed him our slips.

He hugged us again and invited us to another round. Then we invited him to have drinks on us. More employees of our Bank came into the bar and a long row of glasses was lined up in front of Plá.

Everybody invited him for a drink, and he invited everybody. He was going to be dead drunk in the end and out of pure joy. We went home. Plá had touched me. I too wanted to see the happiness in the face of my own 'Granny' and of my aunt, when they heard the news.

All of us in Records had our hopes and illusions. Plá was happy. Gros and I were happy. Antonio Álvarez, the third boy in Records, was also happy, because they had given him 100 pesetas for a Christmas bonus and he was earning 75 pesetas. He had been no more than four years in the Bank. The future was ours. We worked like donkeys day and night.

The former head of the department had been dismissed because he had made 'nests'. That is to say, he took bundles of letters, and instead of classifying them and putting each letter in its file, he hid them away in corners. Then the letters were missing. One day they discovered one of those nests of his and gave him the sack on the spot. When we took over the work there were thousands of letters waiting to be classified. Every day we found a new nest. All this had to be cleared up even while the daily correspondence was being filed. We worked from seven in the morning to one at night. The Bank paid us a coffee every night. When we came home our fingers were rasped by paper dust and streaked with dry ink in microscopically small grains.

Who was it who had hit upon the idea of making Plá Head of the Records Department? It must have been Corachán. There the poor short-sighted man was, his thick slabs of lenses a-glitter with round specks of light from the lamp which burned day and night just above his head; he was crouched over the counter, his nose almost bumping against the heap of papers in his effort to decipher signatures and letter-heads, for hours and hours. Afterwards he suffered from terrible headaches. At midnight they brought us the coffee and Plá drank it greedily. It was thick black coffee with a lot of chicory and fish-glue in it, and it left black stains on the filing-counter. Plá took a small bottle filled with cheap brandy from his pocket; it cured his headache. Afterwards he could not sleep and in the mornings he ran round in circles, like a dazed owl, until the snack at eleven, fifteen centimos' worth of cheese sandwich and a drink of wine, brought him to life again.

We all worked ceaselessly, and Plá was fond of us as though we had been his sons. We had to take a bite of his cheese and a sip of his wine and a whiff from the cigarette he always kept lighted beneath the filing-counter. His little round body hid there; he took a long pull at his cigarette, flapped his hands to disperse the tobacco smoke and keep it from curling upwards, and then emerged with the grave face of a boy who has been naughty.

The counter ran the whole length of the records room, some thirty yards and the whole day long employees of other sections came there to find out about things in the old files. This meant that we had not only to do the filing, but also to answer the queries. When the directors or the Guarantees Department wanted information we had to take the files up to them, which we did for nobody else.

The Guarantees Department was the most aristocratic section of the Bank. It was the place dealing with all the rich foreigners who brought letters of credit, and with millionaires, who never had to stand in a queue to cash a cheque like tradesmen and other people with current accounts. The Department had a staircase of its own with a gilt railing and a thick carpet instead of the linoleum all the others had. All its employees wore frock-coats. Its big waiting-room, with enormous leather arm-chairs and plenty of foreign magazines, was sometimes quite full of millionaires. One of the employees was an Englishman, with a monocle stuck in his eye, who always smoked a light brand of tobacco with a peculiar scent. For in that Department they allowed the employees to smoke; most of them were foreigners who would not have stayed on working in Madrid if they had been forbidden to smoke, but would have gone back to Paris or London.

Everything showed that there were different categories even among the people who had money. It was not as though none of the people with a current account had much money. It was simply because of their social standing. There was an ordinary Juan Perez who owned two million pesetas, but had to wait in the queue downstairs in the central hall, and there was His Grace the Marquess of Something-or-other, with hardly 100,000 pesetas to his credit in the account, who dealt directly with the Guarantees Department and came with great airs to cash a cheque for 500 pesetas and to smoke the cigars supplied in the waiting-room. While everybody addressed him as Your Grace this and Your Grace that, Juan Perez was sitting on the wooden bench downstairs, waiting until the cashier sang out his number, No. 524.

But there were still more influential clients, the directors of the great industrial concerns in Spain and abroad. They were received in the board-room by the director, Monsieur Michaud himself, or by Señor Carreras. One of those men, Don Carlos Mazorra, was one of the greatest men on the Spanish Stock Exchange. He always won. For a long time the Bank tried to fleece him like all the others, but when it was found that this was not only impossible, but that he sometimes tricked the Bank, they came to an agreement with him.

Since then the Bank informed him of good business in hand, and Don Carlos passed on information to the Bank. Sometimes Señor Tejada and he went in together for a deal worth millions and shared the profits.

They did so over the Banco Hispano deal. That bank captured within a short time a great part of all the other banks' customers. One day all the banks, including those abroad, got together and agreed to wreck the Banco Hispano by making its shares fall and producing a run on the bank. They did create a panic; people stood in a queue all along the Calle de Sevilla to withdraw their money. When the Bank had no more ready cash to pay them out, it applied to the other banks; they, however, refused to lend money on the securities the Banco Hispano had in its safes. Even the Bank of Spain refused help, and on the following morning the Banco Hispano had to suspend payment. Most of the people who had been able to withdraw their money came to our Bank and opened an account with us. But in the end it turned out that the Banco Hispano had more than sufficient funds to continue payments and it did not go bankrupt. During the slump of the shares many people were ruined, but Don Carlos and our Bank made fat profits, because they had bought up shares when they were at their lowest.

On August the 1st, exactly a year after I had entered the Bank, they made me a paid employee, with a monthly salary of twenty-five pesetas. It was very little. But at least I was no longer afraid of being thrown out. At the same time I was transferred to the Coupons Section of the Securities Department, with Perahita as my chief. It was going to be all right. The Bank had just decided that it was impossible to go on working in the steel room, because everyone fell ill there; one of the inner courtyards was being covered with a glass roof and turned into a room. There the Coupons Section was going to work with all the girls, three clerks, and Perahita as the Head.

While the courtyard was being converted, I went to work in the steel room. The little staircase which led up from there ended just by the door of the courtyard where the builders were setting up the roof of steel and glass and painting the walls a cream colour. When we came upstairs from that cold steel cellar which was always lit by electric lamps, we looked at the new quarters which were our hope. With their roof and floor of glass, the light-coloured walls, the sun shining down at noon, it made a violent contrast to our cellar and we were happy thinking that we would work there. We kept on asking the masons and painters:

'Will it be much longer?'

'Two or three days, and the time it takes for the paint to dry,' they told us.

Everybody was content, but I wasn't. The two rooms had made me think. If they had sent me to the Coupons Section a year earlier, I should have passed that year between steel walls. I should not have stood it. Even in the few days I worked there I felt a pressure on my chest, and every time I came out into the Calle de Alcalá, the air seemed different; sometimes I was almost sick. Red sparks from the electric light seemed to stay before my eyes for a long time and I saw dancing spots when I came out into the daylight. If I had worked in the steel room for that year, I would not have been paid and if I had fallen ill they would have sacked me. Now, after a year as a learner, swallowing the dust of the files and running up and down stairs, I earned twenty-five pesetas per month, less than a peseta per day. This would go on for another year, and then I would follow the career of all the others. After the second year they would raise my salary to 37·50 pesetas a month, and after the third year to fifty pesetas. At twenty years I would earn 100 pesetas a month, if I was lucky, and then I would be called up for the Army. In the meantime my mother would have to go on washing clothes by the river to earn her living.

On one of the first days after my transfer to the new department a commissionaire came and told me:

'Señor Barea, you are to go up to the board-room. To Señor Corachán.'

They all looked at me with scared faces and I, too, was scared. Such a summons always boded ill. I climbed the stairs to the top floor with hollow legs and a beating heart. The worst that could happen was that they would dismiss me for some reason, but I could not imagine for what. Still, I wouldn't lose so very much—twenty-five pesetas a month.

I went into the room with its deep leather chairs and conference tables, with leather folders and agate ink-stands. Señor Corachán was sitting near one of the windows, reading some papers. He let me stand there in front of him for a few minutes. I saw clearly that he was doing nothing, not even reading; he was only showing off. In the end he raised his head, mustered me, took a dossier, turned its leaves and asked me pompously:

'You're the employee Arturo Barea Ogazón of the Coupons Section?'

'Yes, sir.'

'Good. Now look here (pause) the Management have agreed (pause) in view of the positive reports in your dossier (pause) not-to-throw-you-into-the-street.' (He stressed each syllable, tapping the pencil on the palm of his hand.)

'But why, sir?' I asked.

'You have——' and now he burst out in anger, 'an infernal handwriting! This cannot be tolerated. Do you think you can work in a bank, be employed by a bank, with a hand like yours which looks like spiders' legs? You ought to be ashamed of yourself! The Management cannot stand for this a single day longer. Take note of this: you are being given a month's time—one month!—to improve your handwriting. If you don't, you'll be dismissed. It is understood that in view of the fact that I am giving you a month's warning the Bank is entitled to consider itself free from any obligation to pay you the month's salary on dismissal, stipulated by the law. You may go now.'

'But Don Antonio——'

'Not a single word more! The Management cannot enter into discussion with you. Be quiet and go.'

I should have liked to hit the whiskered beast in front of me, his chin quivering with rage and his eyes protruding behind the gold-rimmed lenses which danced on the bridge of his nose.

I told the story to my mother while she peeled the potatoes for supper in the kitchen; my aunt had gone to church to say her Rosary. I cried with rage.

Her gentle fingers stopped peeling potatoes and strayed through my hair.

V. THE WILL

Don Primo, the notary, had chambers panelled in carved wood, which impressed all the country relations as they sat down, one after the other, in a circle round the huge table. Many of them were sitting on the very edges of their chairs. The men held their round hats on their knees and fingered them, the women put both hands in their laps and kept plucking at the cloth. I had been so often in the room and had spoken so frequently to Don Primo that I was intimidated neither by the place nor by the severe figure of the notary with his black suit, gold-rimmed spectacles, and aristocratic head. When I arrived with my mother and Grandmother Inés, he patted me.

I did not know why all the people who had come to hear the reading of my aunt's will were looking at me with such resentment. They had split up into groups: Uncle Hilario with his wife and daughters —Uncle Basilio with his wife, sons, and daughters—Aunt Basilisa with Uncle Anastasio, who dared not smoke but was chewing a stinking cigarette-stub, and Baldomera whose face was like a daft nun's—Aunt Eulogia with her Carmen—Uncle Julian, like myself a nephew once removed, with his wife and three small children clutching at her skirts. Why did they all bring their children?

While Don Primo read the will, they stretched out their necks better to listen. Every time a name occurred the named person's face changed and shone with pleasure at not having been forgotten, and all the others looked at him, annoyed that there was still another with whom to share.

I was the main target of their anger.

Apparently, my uncle and aunt had made their wills at the same time and in agreement. They left the fortune to whichever of them should survive, for free use during his or her lifetime, but whatever remained after the death of both was divided into two equal parts. Uncle and Aunt had disposed of one part each in favour of their own relations. I was the only one who figured in both wills and had a share in both parts. Otherwise my uncle's blood relatives inherited from his part, and my aunt's blood relatives from her part.

They all thought that they, who were either brothers or sisters or direct nephews or nieces of the deceased, had more rights than I, who was only a nephew once removed. When my name turned up in the second will, a general murmur interrupted the reading. Don Primo stopped and looked at them, questioning:

'Would you like to make any comment?'

Uncle Hilario stood up.

'If I've got it right, the kid inherits double.'

'Just so,' answered Don Primo, 'once under José's will and once under Baldomera's will.'

'But that's all wrong, damn it all. Because I'm the brother of the deceased, his own flesh and blood, and I say it's all wrong that a stranger should just walk in and carry off the cash.'

Uncle Anastasio, twisting his cigar stub between his lips, intervened:

'That's just it. And we won't stand for it. We shall go to law about it.'

Don Primo smiled.

'I think Pepe knew you all very well indeed. When these two wills were drafted, he asked me to add the clause which I'm now going to read to you:

'"It is our will that any of the heirs who may attempt to enter into

198

a law-suit concerning our wills shall by this selfsame act lose any right to his or her inheritance which shall thereupon be distributed among all the other heirs in proportion to their inheritance.'"

Grandmother Inés rose gravely from her chair, turned to face the two men and said:

'Well—are we going to law?'

'Nobody asked you to carry a candle in this procession,' said Uncle Anastasio severely.

'Of course not, my lad. But you see, the kid here has been given two big tapers to carry, and as I happen to be his grandmother, I'm here to support his weak arms so that he doesn't drop them. Has anybody anything against it?'

All but myself were upset about the will. The only heirs were the nearest relatives—brothers and sisters—and I. Beyond that, they had left various legacies to all nephews and nieces, which meant that those with the greatest number of children came off best. Uncle Anastasio, who had only his Baldomera, and Aunt Eulogia, with Carmen and Esperanza, were angry with Uncle Hilario who had three children, and they were all angry with Uncle Julian who was no heir but received legacies for himself, his wife, and his five children, so that he got more than any of the heirs. When we left the notary's house, we were all enemies.

My mother had the keys of my aunt's flat, and out of fear that she might take something, the others came after us so that in the end we were all assembled in the flat. The door stayed open and they came in in small groups.

The room in which my aunt's body had been lying was empty, but it still smelt of flowers and of death, a faint, insidious, clammy smell. A few wax blobs were left on the tiles. It was as though at any moment her slight porcelain figure might come out of the bedroom with short little steps.

They all took seats round the table. All of them. As though anybody who had not taken his place there would forfeit his rights. Grandmother Inés squeezed herself into the rocking-chair below the clock. She had to force the two curved arm-rests apart to get room for her behind. When she had succeeded in sitting down on the plaited cane seat she heaved a sigh of contentment. My mother sat down beside her on the low stool on which my aunt used to sew beside the balcony until the daylight failed her. I threw myself on the floor, on the carpet. I could not have sat down at the table with the others. Stretched on the carpet and watching them all upside down, I felt better. Don Julian had spoken with Señor Corachán and I had been given ten days' leave from the Bank.

The Bank seemed no longer to exist. Lying there on the floor I was again a child, and in the end I rested my head on my mother's lap, between her knees. She had a black skirt which smelt of starch and new cloth and rustled at every movement of my head. One of the legal executors was speaking and explaining what had to be done. It was necessary to make an inventory of everything in the flat, to agree on the value of each item and then to make lots which would be distributed among the heirs. There were eleven lots: nine heirs with one lot each, and two lots for me. Now the disputes started. The lots had to be fixed by value in money, but it was difficult to agree on the big pieces of furniture. As nobody knew who would get each thing, the prices were fixed ridiculously low so as to pay as little as possible in death duties. But suddenly Fuencisla, one of Uncle Hilario's daughters, said:

'I've taken a fancy to the Virgin.'

Carmen gave back at once: 'And I too.'

'There is no difficulty about that,' said the Executor. 'If all those present agree, we shall put a value to the Virgin and allot it to one of you, deducting the price from the corresponding lot.'

The Virgin was placed on the dining-room table. The figure stood in a wooden case with glass in front and a door, with a little silver key at the back. The statue was eighteen inches high. The Virgin held the Child Jesus in her arms and both had little gilt flames stuck into their hair. She had an embroidered mantle and the Child a little velvet cape flecked with gold.

'Well,' said the Executor, 'what value shall we put on this?'

Nobody spoke.

'Shall we say fifty pesetas?'

They all hesitated in giving their agreement, as though it were a serious problem. Uncle Anastasio, his cigar-stub lit at last, said nothing, went up to the statue, opened the door at the back of the case and touched the wooden face of the Virgin with one finger. He went on sucking at his cigar while he closed the door, and the others looked at him in astonishment. He addressed the Executor with gravity:

'You say, then, that the value of this Virgin will be deducted from the lot of one of those two girls?'

'Certainly. That is to say, if all those present are agreeable that one of them should get it.'

'I've no objection to the Virgin's being allotted to one of them,' said Uncle Anastasio in a throaty voice, 'but I cannot permit a carving of the twelfth century—well, or whatever century it is,' he added hastily when he saw the Executor's dumbfounded face, 'to be given away for fifty pesetas. This Virgin is worth at least five hundred pesetas, and that's modest. Because you won't deny that it's carved wood!' He opened the little door once again and rapped a few times with his knuckles on the Virgin's face, which sounded like a block of wood.

'Wood, you see, gentlemen, authentic polychrome wood carving. It's rare nowadays to find one of these Virgins.'

Grandmother Inés grunted from the depth of her rocking-chair:

'And of other virgins, too.'

'I've no objection,' said the Executor. 'If you think that the Virgin should be put down at a value of 500 pesetas, or at 1,000 pesetas, it's all the same to me. Only, we'll have to establish first which of the two . . .' he stammered a little before he decided on his way of address, '. . . of the two young ladies is going to get it.'

Both answered at the same time, each claiming the Virgin for herself, but protesting against the price. Five hundred pesetas were five hundred pesetas. For a while there was a medley of voices. In the end the Executor imposed silence and suggested a solution:

'Let us put the Virgin up to auction between these two young ladies.' This time it came pat. 'When the bidding is over, the winner will keep the Virgin, provided you all agree to that. If not, it will be added to one of the lots and whoever gets that lot will keep the Virgin.'

'I'm willing to give fifty pesetas, as you said before, if only in memory of poor Aunt who was so fond of it.'

'Of course, that's what you think, you'd get it for fifty pesetas,' retorted Carmen. 'I'd give one hundred pesetas, sir.'

The two of them were hopping round the table like a pair of fighting cats, and between them stood the Virgin with her empty smile. They threw figures at each other as though they were chucking stones. Flushed red with rage, Carmen dealt the final blow:

'Eight hundred pesetas!' she bellowed.

Fuencisla burst into tears. Aunt Braulia angrily pinched her arm to stop her from bidding higher. Carmen looked at the lot of them arrogantly. 'Yes, sir. Eight hundred pesetas—and I'm not going back on my word.' She screamed it, arms akimbo, just like one of the shameless girls of El Avapies—which indeed she was.

Grandmother Inés broke out into loud laughter so that her breasts and her belly, which flowed over from the chair, shook and heaved. Carmen turned round and faced her:

'What's that? Do you mind? Because I can do with my own money what I jolly well please!'

Grandmother went off into gales of laughter, unable to speak. She coughed, sputtered, and her eyes ran over. When she calmed down, she said between chuckles:

'No, my dear girl, no, I'm not getting angry with you. You can take your Virgin away and read Masses to her. Anyhow, you'll spit on her more often than you pray to her. And as a consolation, I'm going to tell you that before you were born, Pepe bought it on the Junk Market for ten pesetas one Sunday, and they carried it home for him into the bargain.'

Next day they began breaking up the flat. The relatives from Brunete turned up with their farm carts, the mules harnessed to a wooden yoke on their necks, with the pole sticking out between them. There were still bits of straw clinging to the bottom of the carts and in the esparto ropes which had been used to bundle up the straw. They moved down furniture and broke china in carting it down the stairs. Uncle Julian arrived with his children and two push-carts. When they had loaded them and dragged them away, the carts almost toppled over. We were the last. We had sold the big pieces of furniture which had fallen to our lot, because there was no room for them in the garret, but we had kept my bed, three wool mattresses, some cutlery, and all the clothes which had come to us. Beyond that there were a few banknotes which my mother had pushed into her black shopping bag. Uncle Anastasio had sold his whole lot. He kept the money and told his wife and Baldomerita: 'Now let's go.' But at the next corner he left them alone and the two came with us, trotting alongside the handcart which Señor Manuel was pushing for us. They lived close by in the Plaza del Angel.

Aunt Basilisa began to talk: 'It's a burning shame, my dear, a burning shame, that's what it is. Those men! And there's nothing one can do. I would have loved to keep a few of my poor sister's things, but you see what happened. He put the money in his pocket and off he went. Later he'll tell us it's all in the way of business and we shan't even see a copper. The only good thing is that I was able to save a few things before Baldomera died, because if it hadn't been for that . . . Of course, when we get the real money we've inherited it won't happen that way, it'll have to go into the bank for our girl when she marries, whether he wants it or not.' She stopped for a time while we crossed the Plaza Mayor, walking round it the wrong way because they were repairing the asphalt.

Then she started again: 'I tell you, my dear, life is hell. A good thing I've got that post as a concierge, it's a steady two hundred to two hundred and fifty pesetas a month. But him—since they retired him with sixty pesetas a month he's made himself a very comfortable life. In the mornings he reads the paper and rolls his cigarettes. After dinner he goes to the café. In the evening he comes home for supper, and then he goes to the tavern and gambles away his cash. At the beginning of the month I've got to keep my eyes skinned to see that he doesn't get away with the rent the tenants pay. We wouldn't see the shadow of a farthing otherwise. And it's no good protesting, because if I do he goes mad and starts knocking furniture about and shouting: "After thirty years of honest toil those women won't let me have a glass of vermouth with my friends. But it's me who's master here!" Well, you know him, Leonor. And then he runs about with those servant wenches. He's an old man now, but he still goes to bed with any one he can get. It's a shame, my dear, it's a real shame, I tell you. He makes up to them on the stairs and then he takes them into the lift and stays with them, because he says they don't know how to work it. My foot . . . it's because he can squeeze them as much as he likes in there.'

When we said good-bye to her, she called out:

'Well, come and see me some time!' and walked away on Baldomerita's arm, limping because of her rheumatics.

Señor Manuel stacked up the pieces of the bedstead, the mattresses, the clothing, and the small bundles in the garret, and it was quite filled. Señora Pascuala had come up to see everything and pushed her fists into the wool filling of the mattresses, fingered the sheets, and weighed the silver cutlery. I started to set up my own bed. Its gilt rails mocked the two other beds with their green-painted iron bars and creaking springs. Then, only then, did I dismantle my little old bed and unscrew all its rusty screws. The pieces leaned like a green skeleton in a corner where the sloping roof and the floor met. We put the two big mattresses on my mother's bed, her double bed with curved iron rails at the head and the foot and with two flat panels which had saints painted on them. My bed had its own mattress. And in the angle between roof and floor the two old flock mattresses were left lying, patched and faded.

'What are you going to do with them?' asked Señora Pascuala.

'I don't know. We'll have to give them away to somebody.'

Señor Manuel scratched his bald pate and rolled one of his fat cigarettes made of stubs and twisted like a tree-trunk.

'Are you going to give them away as a gift, Leonor?' he asked.

'Well, of course, they're not good enough to sell.'

He scratched his head again and sucked his cigarette which he had lit with his tinder rope.

'It's just . . . you see . . . it's like this . . .' The words strangled him. 'It's years since . . . Well—you know I've got a landlady who lets me have a room. But for two and a half pesetas a month you can't ask for much. I've got a pallet, fixed it up myself, but it isn't like a mattress.

Not to speak of a bed. I don't get a bed even when I go home to my village; there I've got a good-sized heap of maize straw and that's a fine thing to sleep on. But if you're going to chuck it away, well, give it away, then it's better I should get it. Don't you think that's right, Leonor? And then'—he had grown sure of himself in speaking—'let's make a bargain. You let me take the bed and the mattresses away, and I'll carry your washing up for you at half price for three weeks. I won't say that I'll do it for nothing, because if I lose that fixed amount I couldn't really manage. What do you think of it?'

He gazed anxiously at my mother and waited for her answer. My mother smiled as she sometimes knew how to smile. Then she turned to me.

'Here you've got the heir, he can do as he likes.'

Señor Manuel looked at me with the eyes of a dog who fears that his master is going to abandon him. I was now a young gentleman employed in a bank. For months he had never dared to kiss me or to talk to me as he used to talk before. I filled him with awe and I knew that he talked about me to all the washerwomen as though I were a wonder: 'Leonor's son, you know, he's working in a bank, he's become a real young gentleman!' Now he sucked at his foul cigarette and looked at me—looked at me—God, how he looked at me!

'Señor Manuel,' I said gravely. 'We're going to make a deal. I give you the bed and the mattresses, but on the condition that——'

He did not let me finish: 'Whatever you like, master, anything you wish. I've been working with your mother fifteen years—as many years as you have, master—and she can tell you——'

'I'll give you the bed, but you must stop calling me master.'

At first he seemed not to understand what I meant. Then he seized me, shook me with his big, strong hands, crushed me in his arms, kissed my face noisily, after flinging away the cigarette he had in his mouth, put his two hands on my shoulders, stood me in front of him, and began to cry.

We had to give him a glass of spirits. Afterwards he made two trips to carry home the old green-painted bedrails and the patched and re-patched flock mattresses. When my mother and I were left alone, we put the room in order; from time to time one of the neighbouring women came in to see what was going on and to inspect the bed which shone like a jewel in the garret, with its gleaming bars and its heavy crocheted bedspread. At nightfall Señora Segunda arrived.

My mother sorted out the clothes for which she had no use and gave them to her, one after another. Señora Segunda took them, held them to the light of the oil-lamp and exclaimed with pleasure. There were my aunt's chemises, bodices, skirts, under-skirts, and petticoats.

My mother kept the best pieces for herself and gave her all the rest. She picked up a dark brown winter jacket of thick cloth with a huge tear right across the front.

'I can't imagine that this could be of any use to you, Segunda.' She pushed her hand through the rent. 'Aunt could never bring herself to throw anything away.'

Señora Segunda held up the jacket and the light fell through the tear. 'It'll do for Toby, my dear. The poor thing suffers so much from cold in the winter when we are out begging. I'm going to make a coat for him. Toby! Toby!'

Lazily, the dog got up from beside the brazier where he was lying, sniffed at the jacket and wagged his tail. Señora Segunda insisted on fitting it on Toby's back, while the sleeves dragged on the floor, and he stood quite still, wagging his tail under the folds. Then he licked her hands and went back to his place in the warmth under the table.

Our life in the garret settled down. My mother was still doing her washing on Mondays and Tuesdays. I went to the Bank. On Sundays, my brother and sister came to see us. On weekdays, I read in the evenings and my mother did her sewing by the light of the oil-lamp. Sometimes we all went to the pictures on Sundays, in the afternoons, because Rafael had to be back in his shop and Concha in the house where she was in service by eight o'clock. I had become somebody. Señora Pascuala addressed me in the old familiar way but she looked at me with a respect mixed with a touch of envy, because her son Pepe was getting nowhere. Everybody else said 'Sir' to me.

From time to time I drank a glass of vermouth and smoked a cigarette. Soon I would be getting a few thousand pesetas as the heir of my uncle and aunt. I was the master of the house and of my people and I knew it.

We kept on hearing stories about the other heirs.

In Brunete, the two families, Uncle Hilario's and Uncle Basilio's, seemed to have quarrelled. After my Uncle José's death, both had wanted to assume the command of the small community he had created, Uncle Hilario because he was older, Uncle Basilio because he was younger and had sons. Their quarrel started on account of the furniture they had taken out of the estate. Although everything had been distributed by lot, and they themselves had fixed the value of each piece, they were now throwing in each other's teeth that one piece of furniture was worth more than the other and that both of them had been cheated. The people of the village went to both their houses, and in each said that it had got the better furniture. In the

205

end, they agreed no longer to work their land jointly. Yet when they came to divide the land they had bought under Uncle José's management, to distribute the mules, the farming implements, the crops stored in the barn, and even the pitchers which were used to bring drinking-water to the farm-hands, the row broke out in earnest. The women pulled each other's hair, and the men hit at each other with their sticks. In the end, they went to law to establish their claims to the land, and sought out Don Luis Bahía to advance them money on their inheritance from Uncle José, so that they could cover the expenses of the lawsuit.

Uncle Julian, too, was an odd case. His whole life he had worked as a wheelwright in a workshop, in the Ronda del Toledo. He had learnt his craft from my grandfather, and had then come to Madrid as a master in partnership with the owner of the workshop. He and his five children lived in a tenement house in the Calle del Tribulete. When the furniture was allotted, he got the sideboard and the dining-room table. Both were big, heavy pieces of carved oak. He took them home to a flat which had only four small rooms—a dining-room, two bedrooms, and a kitchen, while the lavatory was in the passage and used by all the tenants on the same floor—and naturally neither the sideboard nor the table fitted into the flat. But they pushed them in, and then had to squeeze themselves sideways between the table and the wall whenever they wanted to walk about the room. They took the sideboard to pieces. The lower part went into the parents' bedroom, and the upper part, where the glasses, cups, and platters had been, was hung on a few hooks in the kitchen. Uncle Julian had two grown-up daughters, one of them just about to marry. She asked for the two pieces for her new room. The other sister protested, because she too was engaged, and in the end Uncle Julian had to box both their ears and keep the furniture himself.

Uncle Anastasio's story was simple. He took the money from the sale of the furniture and went to gamble in El Bilbaino Club in the Calle de Peligros. And he won. He won a few thousand pesetas. He came home with presents for Aunt Basilisa and Baldomerita. For a month or so, they all lived in great luxury, and everything went well. They went to the theatre and cinema, they had their fancies and bought cheap trinkets. After that, Uncle Anastasio began to be short of money. He pawned the jewellery he had given to the two women, then the jewellery my aunt had given to Baldomerita, then the Manila shawl, the mantillas and whatever there was. When everything else had given out, he began to pawn household goods, and in the end Aunt Basilisa came in tears to my mother to ask her for twenty-five pesetas.

Carmen's father, Aunt Eulogia's husband, had come from Galicia as a young boy. He was a giant. When he was young, he earned money which he used to establish himself as a coal vendor in the *New World*. He earned a lot, but then he began to drink. He was so strong that he never got really drunk, but as he was ashamed of not getting drunk like his friends, he tried to make himself drunk too, and drank whole bottles of spirits. He ruined himself and had to close down his shop. Then, when he was no longer young, he took on a job as a porter in the most expensive furniture shop in Madrid and carried furniture to the customers' houses. He had a mate who was as big as himself, and the shop had bought them a very showy livery. They carried the furniture in a kind of litter covered in red plush, with broad leather straps slung across their shoulders. People in the streets turned round and stared at the two enormous men who carried the heaviest furniture as though it were a feather. Once, they carried a piano in this way, and people stopped on the sidewalks. They walked in step, and the piano rocked in its litter like in a cradle. He had good wages and good tips, but he spent everything on drink. One day they carried him home with an attack of delirium tremens. He didn't die because he was so strong, but he had to stay in bed, a useless invalid, his hands trembling ceaselessly. The doctor let him drink three glasses of spirits a day, for he said that he was bound to die if his alcohol were suddenly cut off.

After he saw all the furniture and clothing which had come to his wife from the inheritance, he dragged himself out of bed one morning when Aunt Eulogia had left the house and he was alone. As he lived in the Calle del Peñón, just behind the Junk Market, he called for a neighbour who was a dealer there and sold him all the inherited furniture and clothes, and some of the things from his own household as well. Then he called a boy and sent him for a two-litre bottle of spirits, got back into bed, and poured it all down. He went mad. The first person to come home was Carmen's younger sister, Esperancita. She found her father stark naked, smashing up furniture with a knobstick. He tried to kill her, and the girl ran shrieking through the corridors of the house. At that moment, Aunt Eulogia came home, and he struck her on the shoulder. He nearly broke her arm; if the blow had landed on her head, he would have killed her. All the neighbours had to come and truss him up between them with ropes, like a bundle. For three days he had to be kept in a strait jacket, tied to the bed and foaming at the mouth.

My mother went to see him the day before he died, and I went to the funeral. The room was smashed to pieces. The only thing that was left unharmed was the Virgin on top of the chest of drawers, with the little oil lamp inside, which filmed the glass and made soot stains on the top of the case.

It was a radiant Sunday, and I had gone to the Escuela Pía to see Father Joaquín. We had been chatting till lunch-time, and I had my meal with the Father in the Refectory. In the afternoon, walking up the Calle de Mesón de Paredes, I went into the house where Señora Segunda lived.

Toby welcomed me in the doorway with his dirty paws, shedding white hairs off his grey, woolly fur all over my trousers. He looked very funny in his cloth coat edged with green braid, which was tied round his neck and under his belly. Señora Segunda was getting ready to go out begging and showed me with pride what she had done with the clothes.

From a short jacket of my aunt's she had taken off the jet spangles and turned it into a coat for herself. Where the small disks had been there were dark regular spots which looked like embroidery. She had put on an old silk skirt, bright flowers on a dull ground, all greyed over by age. She had made an old mantilla into a loose veil which fell over her forehead and hid part of her dreadful nose. She was about to take her folding stool and Toby in his coat, and go to her regular place in the Plaza del Progreso. In her new costume she looked like a lady who had come down in the world; surely, now that the gaping holes of her nose were hardly visible, people would give her far more alms than before! One by one she showed me her things and explained.

'Thanks to your mother, everybody looks at me in a different way now. With my veil and the silk dress, and my face hidden away, people are sorry for me, much more so than before, and I don't make them shudder now. I've been teaching Toby to hold a plate between his teeth and to sit on his hind legs. He does keep still for a while but then he gets tired, poor darling. It's a pity. Now I always take my coffee without sugar at the café and keep the lump so that I can give it to Toby in small bits to make him stick it out longer. But he's old, poor thing, and gets tired of holding the plate between his teeth. It's a pity, though, because while he holds it people give us much more alms. Even men put a copper into the plate and pat the dog.'

She showed me four new sheets which she had made out of pieces of linen my mother had given her. She had sewn them together with tiny little stitches, and everything was white and well ironed.

'Just feel it,' she said. 'First I put them in lye for bleaching, because some pieces were whiter than others. But now thanks to the

208

bleaching and the blueing they're all alike and so fine that it is a pleasure to sleep in them.'

Out of old stockings she had made new ones; she had cut out pieces and knitted them together. Out of bits and snippets of material she had made a blanket for the dog, sewing them on to a length of burlap like loose flower petals.

And since it was necessary to brighten up her home, now that she had new clothes and was earning more money, she had painted her room—that little box shaped like a wedge of cheese—a chalky blue. It made stains on my sleeves, to complete the work Toby had started with my trousers.

On Mondays and Tuesdays I took the tram just outside the Bank and went down to the river to have my meal there. I was proud when the washerwomen saw me, and my mother was glad and proud too. She made me put on one of the white smocks of the Municipal Laboratory, so that my suit should not get dirty. She did the washing for Dr. Chicote and all the doctors of the Laboratory. So I could sit down on the grass, with the washing-board upside down as a table, and feed the duck with worms. I was no longer afraid of its bill; sometimes I caught it and held it tight. Then the duck grunted like a pig and flapped its wings in rage. It ran away, waddling and waggling its bottom like a fat woman with bow legs.

Señor Manuel pressed me to visit him in his house. It was a wooden shack which belonged to a widowed woman. She lived there, and he had a small bedroom with walls made of planks. The chinks were pasted over with paper. He had tacked up pictures of politicians, toreros, and dancers cut out of magazines. The floor was beaten earth, but he had covered it with bits of tiles he had found in rubbish heaps and laid out in a mosaic of many colours. There were white lavatory tiles, blue tiles, black-and-white marble tiles, and hydraulic cement tiles, red, or with little flowers, or with coloured disks of all sizes.

'That's what made me sweat most,' said Señor Manuel, 'getting this floor even. Well, it looks all right now. The only thing that's still missing is two big bits of glass for my window.'

The 'window' was a rectangular opening in the boards of one of the walls, where he had put a gilt picture frame with discoloured flowers and leaves. Half the frame was filled with two pieces of glass stuck together with putty, the other half was covered with greased paper. The frame was mounted on two hinges and closed by a hook. When it was open, the sunlight entered freely. When it was closed the light could only come in through the glazed half, and Señor Manuel wanted a pane for the second half so that he could have sun without having to open his window. He was very sensitive to cold.

'Look at the bed—your bed,' he said.

I did not recognize my old bed. Señor Manuel had painted it yellow, a gaudy yellow with a greenish tinge; he had put on the colour in thick blobs and it screamed against the background of the multi-coloured tiles. On the head panel of the bed he had stuck a print of Our Lady of Perpetual Help, which was full of flames from which the damned souls stretched their arms towards the Virgin, imploring Her to rescue them from Hell. A packing-case covered with white cloth was his night-table; it had a door, which was really the lid of the case, swinging on two leather straps and fastened with a hook like the window. Inside was a huge chamber-pot with a broken handle and in its bottom a painted eye and the mis-spelt words: 'I see you'.

On top of the bed he had put a thick mattress, two sheets, a patched-up blanket and a yellow bedspread.,

'Don't you like it?' Señor Manuel asked me. 'When I'm out, Señora Paca (she was the owner of the shack) comes in here and lies down on the bed for her siesta. The poor woman's got rheumatics, what with living here by the river twenty years and sleeping on a heap of sacking on the ground, and so she's quite envious of me. I told her she can have the bed when I die. But I'm sure she'll die before me, and then I'll be left with the shack. I'm still going strong, I am, apart from this accursed rupture. But I haven't the heart to let them operate on me. It's all very well if you die when your hour's come, but not in the hands of a saw-bones.'

He stooped and stroked the bedspread lovingly.

'Do you know, I've been doing more work since I've been sleeping in a gentleman's bed. I've got something for you.'

From the depth of a chest filled with rags, old newspapers, and books without covers, with pages missing, picked up God knows where, he fished out a white rag rolled up like a dirty bandage. He unrolled it on the night-table and from its last fold produced a minute gold coin. It was a ten-peseta piece from the time when the King was a little boy, a *centén*, as small and bright as a new centimo.

'For your watch-chain. It's the only thing I've got left from better times when we earned a lot, and the money wasn't called pesetas. I've kept it as a fancy, but after all, what good is it to me?'

I had to take it away with me, wrapped in a piece of the coarse paper Señor Manuel used for his stick-like cigarettes. On the slope of the Paseo de San Vicente I took the gold coin out of its wrapping and studied it. It was so tiny that I would have to put it on a ring if I wanted to hang it on my watch-chain. And I thought that really the happiest among all the people who had inherited were the poorest: we, Señora Segunda and Señor Manuel. Those two had not inherited directly, but they had a share in the inheritance.

The slope of San Vicente has nearly half a mile of iron railing set on a granite base. It was the railing of the Campo del Moro, the garden of the Royal Palace, where nobody was allowed to enter; the soldiers on guard there would have shot anyone who tried to get in. When I was a little boy and walked up the slope with my mother I used the railing to make whistles out of apricot stones. It was easy. You took one of the stones and rubbed it along the granite in walking; so it was whittled down until a small hole with an even rim appeared at its end. You took a pin and fished out the kernel so that the shell of the stone was left empty and then, when you blew sharply on the edge of the hole, it made a whistle which could be heard far away.

If I were to rub the edge of the coin along the granite now it would also be whittled away.

I passed it gently over the stone for a few steps. The edge of the coin was unchanged, but there was a very fine streak on the granite. A streak of gold.

Now who would think of rubbing a gold coin on stone? Is it because I'm still a child? A gold coin. There aren't any more left in Spain. People used to carry them in their pockets as we carry pesetas. After that only rich people kept them, and also the Bank of Spain, which stored them in steel boxes underground. The Bank of Spain keeps the gold so that people should accept its banknotes. I've heard that through the foundations of the Bank there flows a stream, the stream of San Lorenzo, and that the boxes with the gold are kept below it. If there were a fire or a robbery in the Bank, the watchmen would open the flood-gates and the whole river would pour over the boxes. But all that doesn't really interest me. What I would like to do is to take a hammer and beat out the *centén* to see whether it's true that you can make yards of sheet metal out of five grammes of gold simply by hammering it. Then I'd stick the gold sheet on the wall of our room, and our garret would have a golden wall. It must be true that I'm still a child.

In the Plaza de San Gil, which they now call the Plaza de España, they're spinning tops and people stand round in a circle to watch. The four who are playing are nearly men, they're older than I am; the youngest must be seventeen. They have drawn a big circle in the sand and each of the four throws a copper in the middle of the ring. Then one after the other spins the top and tries to make its point push the coppers out of the ring. The tops are spinning well and strongly, because the players are grown-ups. No, they're not grown-ups, they're tramps, because grown men don't play at tops and boys don't play for money. But then, they aren't tramps either, they've dumped a heap of books beside the ring. They're Law students from the college near by in the Calle Ancha. They're men, but because they're still students they have the right to be boys, to spin tops and to play hop-scotch here in the square. They can run after each other, boys and girls, grown-up men and women, and they can play. People watch them and like it: 'Oh well, they're students, it's all right for them.' And the old men with white beards who sit in the sun of the square come up, stand round while the students are spinning their tops and applaud them when they do it well. I wonder what sort of face Corachán would pull if he came by and caught us spinning a top, Medrano, Gros, and me? He would sack us. He would tell us in his ringing voice that employees of the Crédit Etranger should not behave like children or tramps, and play at tops in public. But Corachán's son is studying law here at the university. He's twenty years old. I wonder if he comes here to spin a top?

After supper Concha and Rafael came to stay with us for an hour. Concha was in service in Dr. Chicote's house and Rafael worked as an apprentice in a shop in the Calle de Atocha. They brought their wages, as it was the second day of the month. I had got mine on the first. My mother put all the money on the table and began to make her calculations and separate it into little piles. There was not much money: five duros from me, six from Rafael, eight from Concha, ninety-five pesetas in all.

'Nine pesetas for the rent, two for Pascuala.'

She put the eleven pesetas in a pile. This was the most sacred money for my mother: the money for the rent.

'Five pesetas for the Society.'

Those monthly five pesetas meant that we all had a right to medical assistance, medicines, and burial.

'Ten pesetas for my washing things.'

My mother stopped and counted her petty debts on her fingers. Then she made another pile of fourteen pesetas. The three of us were watching her in silence, hoping that the big heap would not be diminished much more. In the end she said:

'That's what we've got left to last us until the eighth, when I get my money from the Laboratory.'

Thirty-one pesetas were left. Now our turn came. First Concha.

'I need underclothes—a corset, a chemise, and a pair of stockings,'

'Well, you do look after yourself,' Rafael grunted. 'I need boots and a smock.'

'And I need shoes,' I said.

'Of course, the little gent needs shoes. He's got two pairs, but he needs a third.'

'I've got two pairs, but they're brown and I can't wear them when I'm in mourning for Aunt.'

'Dye them black.'

'That's what you say—but you must show off your breasts with a corset!'

We wrangled, all three of us. My mother tried in vain to soothe us down. In the end she took a peseta out of her pocket, put it on the remaining heap of money and divided it into four piles of eight pesetas each. She kept one of them for herself.

Rafael pocketed his eight pesetas. Concha weighed hers in her hand and said: 'What's the good of this to me?'

'Now, look here,' said my mother. 'Take a few pesetas out of your savings-book and buy whatever you need.'

Each of us had a savings-book which caused eternal discussions. Rafael and I had had ours since the time when we were given prizes at school, but we could not withdraw any money while we were minors. Concha started a savings account when she went into service, and she was the only one among us who could take out money whenever she liked. My book showed a balance of over 1,000 pesetas thanks to the money Uncle José had put in for me in the course of the years. Rafael's had over 500 pesetas; and Concha had saved nearly 1,500 pesetas in her first years of service, while she had no need to spend her wages. But then the household had drawn on her savings every time there was a difficulty, and now they amounted to no more than 200 or 300 pesetas. And so she became as angry as a wild cat whenever there was talk of drawing on her account.

'So that's why I've got to spend my life working myself to the bone? Only so as not to be able to buy myself what I need? Well, it's just not good enough that way. These two have got their cash safe while I've got to carry the whole load. Ever since the death of Uncle José you've always taken money out of my book so that the boy there can be a pen-pusher and a young gentleman, while I can go on washing up dirty plates.'

'You're jealous, that's all,' I cried.

'Jealous? Of whom? But you'll be more unhappy than any of us. We're poor, and don't mind—the children of Señora Leonor, the washerwoman. But of course—you're a nice young gentleman who's afraid to say that his mother washes at the river and lives in a garret.

I bet I'm right. I've brought along my friends and the other girls who serve with me, because I'm not ashamed to bring them to my home. But you—when have you ever brought any of your friends here? Well, there you are. A young gentleman who works in a bank, and then people might find out that you live in a garret and that your mother's a washerwoman? Oh no!'

Because she was right, I grew furious. Of course they didn't know at the Bank that I was the son of a washerwoman and lived in a garret. They might have given me the sack, they didn't like having poor people there. The bank clerk's relatives were people who wore hats and overcoats. It would not have been so good if Concha had turned up in her parlour-maid's uniform, Rafael in his grocer's smock, and my mother in her apron, with the kerchief tied round her head. But Concha didn't understand. I talked to her and tried to make her see the future in store for me, when I would earn a lot of money as an employee, and Mother would not have to go down to the river, and we would have a flat with electric light and a big lamp over the dining-room table; but she laughed in my face, shook me and screamed at me:

'You fool! What you'll be all your life is a miserable starveling—a pen-pusher—a gentleman living on bread-and-water.' She hooted with laughter, but then turned serious and burst out: 'A starched-collar slave—that's what you're going to be!' And she turned her back on me, sat down in a chair and broke into tears.

Rafael and I went off, out into the street. We bought a packet of fifty, and lit a cigarette each. Then we had coffee with brandy. Then we took a tram and went to Cuatro Caminos where we had a meal of roast lamb and red wine. When we came back, we had spent our sixteen pesetas between us. Rafael said:

'It doesn't matter. I get my tips. But don't tell Mother.'

The next morning, when I got up to go to work, my mother had already brushed my suit, as she did every day, and gave me two pesetas.

'Here, take it, you must have some money on you in case you need it.'

She did not ask me what I had done with the eight pesetas of the day before. I felt ashamed as I walked down the stairs.

VI. THE FUTURE

I felt a longing, for what, I did not know. A longing to run, to jump, to throw stones, to climb trees, to sit in the shade and look. To look without thinking of anything, to look into the far distance. To fill my mind with the country; with those groups of trees, so deeply green that they seemed a black stain far away; with the yellow of the meadows in El Pardo which the King was said to use for agricultural experiments. There was an arid patch with an artesian well in the middle, from which the water leapt up thirty feet. To fill this head of mine with snow and stone, the snow and stone over there in the Sierra de Guadarrama. To shut myself up in the garret, alone, with my mother down at the river or wherever she was. To turn the key in its lock so that Señora Pascuala should not come and see me doing nothing, filling my head with nothing at all.

I walked between the pine-trees of the Moncloa. They grew on steep slopes and their needles had carpeted the ground. People preferred the Parque del Oeste, that English park with shorn lawns and fine sand on the paths. The grass looked as though it were tended by barbers with giant hair-cutters, who scraped the ground and left it with nothing but side-whiskers; they had made a parting in the middle, a runlet with a concrete bed and an edging of rocks full of holes, like petrified sponges, and cascades like the steps of a staircase. The stream bounded down the steps and laughed at the people who watched it foolishly from the height—seven feet high—of the rustic bridges. A mamma said to her child who went near the railing made of crossed branches: 'Darling, don't lean over, you might fall in and drown.' And there were four inches of water. The boy laughed at his mother, because he would have liked to wet his feet, and the stream laughed, and the fishes laughed. The boy saw the stream as a channel of water where he wanted to splash and tumble, and to snatch at the little sleeping fishes, those stupid little fishes they had transplanted there from the Retiro Park. They were so silly that they never dared to follow the current and swim downstream to the Manzanares, because they were afraid of the running water. They were so silly that they stayed in each of the levels of the cascade, swimming round and round in their concrete tub and swallowing the crumbs that fell down from the bridge. The mother saw the stream as a roaring Niagara: 'Darling, you'll drown!' The boy and the stream laughed, but in the end they turned angry, for they wanted to play together.

I hated the Parque del Oeste. I hated it. I hated its symmetrical little lawns, I hated its narrow sand paths and little round pebbles with which the girls used to play. I hated the rustic huts, the faked rough-hewn bridges, the borders of rocks which looked cruel, but which I could have torn up and thrown into the stream. And I hated the stream itself, its belly and bottom slicked with smooth concrete, and its headspring, a cast-iron spout with an inscription in raised letters which said: 'Isabella II Canal'.

Moncloa was further away. It was open ground. There the grass grew high and stinging nettles sprouted in it. There were gullies and streams and springs with a hollow tile for a pipe, stuck into the soil by some old shepherd and lined by the years and the water with a thick, green, velvet cushion into which your lips sank when you drank from it. There were springs whose water gushed from the rock like bubbles from a boiling pot; you had to drink out of your scooped hand if you wanted to sip the froth from the cauldron of the earth. Some springs were crystal-smooth pools with sweat drops breaking out at the bottom of the hollows. The sweat of the earth filled the hole, flowed over and trickled away through the grass, unseen. When you drank from these pools the soil grew angry, its dregs rose and stained the clear glass with yellow mud-clouds. When you stopped drinking it calmed down and in the end the glass emerged, clear once more.

Here and there in the grass stood trees, thousands of lone trees. Some, at the top of the hills, had bodies that were twisted from resisting the winds, and others were straight and strong. Some, at the bottom of the ravines, clutched at the slope with their roots so as not to fall and lifted their toes out of the ground to dig in their claws more safely. There were bushes, armfuls of spices, which scented the air. And there was a soft, slippery carpet of pine needles, on which it was pleasant to sit, to lie, to roll. I wore canvas shoes with hempen soles, and the pine needles polished the hemp. As though on skates, you could start on the top of the hill and glide down on the pine needles, until you lost your stance on the slope and sat down on the needles which pricked your buttocks. The pine-trees chuckled and you laughed and rubbed your behind, and stayed on the spot where you had fallen, sitting among the pines with their chequered trunks.

When I left the house at six in the morning on Sundays, I took a black coffee in the Puerta del Sol, in a café which was open day and night. The strong, black coffee savoured of night revels. The people who met there were different from the people you saw in Madrid in daytime. Firstly there were those who had been on the spree, some tipsy from a night of wine-drinking, their mouths dry and their heads feverish from sleeplessness; they ordered black coffee without sugar.

Others were sober, but in a hurry; they had spent the night with a woman and went home, bleary-eyed, to wash in haste, brush their clothes, re-tie their bows and go to their job in an office or workshop. Then there were those who had to be up at that hour because of their profession, night-watchmen, telegraph messengers, waiters, newspaper-sellers, street-cleaners. They drank coffee with brandy or cheap spirits 'to kill the worm'. And then there were people like myself, who got up early on Sundays. Many had to catch a train and came with their suitcases, or left their cab in front of the door and came in to warm themselves. They often accompanied little old ladies who were frightened of the journey and of Madrid at dawn and who drank their scorching coffee in little sips, continually looking at their watches. Boys and girls of my age, or slightly older, came in parties on their way to the Retiro, the Moncloa or the Parque del Oeste, where they were going to spend the day. They were on the verge of becoming sweethearts, and while they drank their coffee they nudged each other, joked and laughed at the sleepy drunkards, while they came fresh from a long sleep, their faces scrubbed and clean. The boys pushed the girls against the counter and looked as though they would have liked to squeeze them then and there. Very few were alone like me, and they were only old people or boys close to manhood like me.

The old men, I knew it, would slowly walk up the Calle de Alcalá to the Retiro, sit down on a bench and watch the youngsters play like little animals let loose. They would speak with others of their age-class and recall their young years, or they would converse with some lonely little old woman who had also come to see the young people having their fun, to enjoy it and to talk in a low, slow voice.

We, half-men, half-children, we went further afield, to the pine woods of the Moncloa, with a packet for the mid-morning snack, a *tortilla* of two eggs between two slices of a loaf, or a cutlet fried in batter with breadcrumbs; with a small bottle in our breast-pocket, just enough for a glass of wine after the meal, and a book in our other pocket to read under the pines. But we did not read. We looked. We looked at the bands of young people jumping, running, and chasing each other among the trees. We would have liked to be with them, to kiss and be kissed, but we were shy. And so we despised them from the height of our pine throne and our book. The society of young people did not yet admit us to its freedom. The old people gave us advice and patted our heads, but the young people—the young people laughed at us. The lads called us 'shavers' and the girls did not want to have anything to do with us because we were 'kids', or else they treated us maternally and kissed us all over like fake mothers, to get a thrill out of it, because no young man wanted them and they could not find anyone but us, half-men, half-children.

You couldn't read with all those disturbing images in your mind, so you had to think. On my Sundays in the Moncloa I did nothing but think. Sometimes I hated thinking so much that I did not go to the Moncloa on the following Sunday. Then I went down to my old school, looked for Father Joaquín, but did not know what to say to him. Little by little, I began to speak, and then I poured out all those Sundays full of thoughts and visions. Sometimes he laughed at the things I told him. Sometimes he told me to stop, and began to play his oboe. Then the pigeons from the courtyard and the birds from the roof of the school came to listen. He only told me to stop when I started talking of women; he played the oboe as though in anger, and calmed down with the cries of his oboe and the birds. When I spoke to him of my mother, he listened for hours. One day he took from his drawer a photograph, the portrait of his mother. A big-nosed Basque woman, straight-backed and lean, with a handkerchief knotted on the top of her head; behind her his father, taller than she, big and equally lean, with little eyes, his right hand on a hoe. In the background a small house with a balcony running the whole length of its front.

'Now they've got a farmstead,' he told me. Then he looked round his cell, at the books, the birds, the music-stand like a bleak wooden skeleton in the sun. He looked as though he were missing something.

'They've got a farm. And a cow. Father is still working at seventy. The farm's down there, but you can't see it in the picture. There's a valley below the house, and the old man plants his maize there. And then Mother fries it for me when I go to stay with them.' He paused and looked without seeing. 'Each grain of maize bursts open with a crack, like a little white flower. When I go back to Madrid Mother always puts some cobs in my suitcase. But where could I fry maize flowers here?' And he passed his glance round the cell.

Then he heaved his big, elephantine body out of the chair and went to the window, pushing me before him with a hand on my shoulder. He leaned out and looked into the huge school yard where the pigeons and chickens were bickering.

'But you will be a man,' he said.

His words held something mysterious, I did not know what, something of soundless images, of a little house, of a father and mother, of children, of a wife. Something which was not this, not the cell with a number on its door and the courtyard for its horizon. Somebody who was not he in his priest's frock. I felt that he envied me something

218

which I did not yet know. When I left the school, I was sad for him and for myself, and did not return there for many Sundays.

Once he told me:

'You don't know why I'm a priest? The parents'—the Basques always say *the* parents, not *my* parents—'the parents were poor. They had four girls already when I was born. It seems I was a great eater, worse than the father. At school I was fairly clever so that the parish priest noticed me. One day he said to the mother: "Joaquín would make a fine canon." I was a hefty lad. At eight years I chopped fire-wood with my father's axe, which must have weighed a good six pounds. I carried sackloads of chestnuts on my back, up to half a hundredweight. Every time the father took me out on the field, the priest wagged his head and said to him: "Joaquín"—for the father is called Joaquín too—"let's make a little priest out of the boy." And so they did. When I was eleven they sent me to Deusto. I left it at twenty-three to sing Mass in the village. The mother wept and the father fell round my neck when I'd taken off the chasuble. "Now you're a man as I wanted you to be," that's what he said. The Fathers in Deusto wanted me to stay with them as a teacher, but I couldn't stand their mangy frocks and heavy old shoes. I couldn't be a Jesuit. So I joined the Escolapians. Here one can live, one's free and can teach children.'

I listened and saw him in my mind surrounded by children, but not as a priest. By children who were his own children, trampling the fields. I saw him with a hoe, like his father, in a fustian suit—why did I think of fustian?—which creaked on his strong, big body while he walked. I saw him putting an arm—why only one arm?—round a strong, high-coloured woman with a red handkerchief tied on the top of her head. He slapped a little boy whose nose was running, and went off to dig. 'Uuh—uuh!' Uncle Luis had shouted when I was riding on his shoulders. How Father Joaquín would shout it! If he were to lean out of the window now and shout: 'Uuh uuh!' all the windows would be crammed with the heads of priests, and Father Vesga would complain to the Father Rector.

'And what if you had sons, Father Joaquín?'

I blurted it out and watched his face to see what it would say. He looked as though he had been struck by a blow. His mouth twisted downwards, his heavy hands fell on to his frock. He looked at the music-stand, the oboe, and the window. He looked outside, at the wall opposite. No, he looked further away. He looked into the far distance beyond the wall, beyond what was behind the wall.

'I can't have sons.'

Sometimes men seem to speak inwards. The words do not come

219

out of their mouth but sound inside, in the stomach, the chest, the flesh, the bones, and resound there. They speak for themselves alone, but they do not speak. Their whole body hears them. So spoke Uncle José when he told my mother that he was about to die. And so did Father Joaquín speak now. He went on:

'But I have one.'

Then he woke up with a start.

'Don't take any notice of me. Sometimes one's so very much alone. I meant the Child Jesus. When I sang my first Mass I was in love with the Child Jesus. I saw Him even in my dreams. That's why I turned myself into a teacher.'

He was lying; and as he did it badly, he saw that I understood his lie when I looked at him. He fell silent.

You can make canoes out of pine bark. You tear off a strip, one of those deeply lined strips which come off when you push your fingers deep into one of the furrows and pull. The wood is soft and porous, you can work it with a knife like a piece of cheese. First you cut it the shape of a cigar, broad in the middle, pointed towards the ends. Then you make the belly of the keel, either rounded or with two curved flanks meeting in a sharp central ridge. Then you scoop out the upper part. You leave two bits of wood in the middle, the rowing-benches where the naked Indians sit and handle their flat oars. And the puddle in which the canoe floats becomes a lake in the jungle of Brazil or the forests of Canada, with green banks full of snakes or with frozen edges where the wolves howl.

I made canoes on Sunday mornings and set them afloat on a pool at the Moncloa, or sent them to follow the current of a streamlet, four inches wide, and to jump the rapids formed by two stones. Always there was some small boy who would turn up from somewhere and watch the course of the boat in rapt silence.

'May I have it?'

'Take it.'

He kept the canoe. He followed it downstream, he called to his parents and his friends to have a look at it. 'A gentleman gave it me.'

I would sit down with my back against a pine-tree, angry with the boy. Why had he to come and claim his right as a child? Why did he come to make me ashamed of playing and to claim his right? 'May I have it?' Of course I had to let him have it, for it was his by right. How could I go on playing with pine-bark canoes when I was already the 'gentleman who gave away boats'.

Boy or man? I liked so much to play with boats. I liked so much to look at the legs of the girls with their skipping-ropes in front of me.

A man. Yes, I was a man. I had my standing. Employee of the Crédit Etranger. My mother worked down by the river. She must stop working there. I didn't want to watch her any more climbing the stairs on Mondays and Tuesdays and saying: 'Run down and fetch the milk, will you, I'm tired.' I didn't want any more to smell the dirty linen piling up in our room during the week, with its sour smell like mouldy wine. I didn't want any more to see Señor Manuel leaning heavily against the wall by the garret door, with sweat bubbles on his forehead after the climb, easing down a six·foot stack of washing, gently, so that the bundle should not burst. I didn't want any more to count the sheets and the pants of Señor So-and-so and to make out the bills.

I didn't want to accompany her any more in the evenings, to deliver the bundles of clean linen and collect the dirty washing, and to wait in the house-doors for her to come down and say: 'They didn't pay me.' When she came back to our street, my mother went to the baker. 'Juanito, please, give me a loaf . . . I'll pay you to-morrow.' Then to the grocer. 'Antonio, give me four pounds of potatoes and half a pound of dried cod. . . . I'll pay you to-morrow.' And so we had our supper. The gentlefolk didn't pay her for washing their sweaty, mucky pants with buttons missing, and therefore the washerwoman couldn't pay for her supper. My mother was pleased because the tradesmen trusted her, I was furious because she had to beg favours and because the nobs hadn't paid her. But I ate my supper. My mother was so glad that I had something for supper although the gentlefolk hadn't paid her, that I had to eat it.

Afterwards she made her coffee, her own private luxury. She made it in a pot blackened inside like an old Dutchman's pipe, in which the grounds piled up for days on end. My mother threw in a pinch of newly ground coffee and brought the water to boil; it turned black more from the old dregs than from the fresh coffee. She drank it scorching hot, in little sips. Sometimes she would say: 'I couldn't live without my drop of coffee.' She drank coffee down by the river, too. There was an old woman, a widow with children like my mother, who sold coffee and tea. She came down to the river at seven in the morning, winter and summer, and started up her coffee-urn and tea-urn. For a copper—five centimos—she gave you a glass full of boiling coffee or of tea with a slice of lemon floating on top. Sometimes the washerwomen made room for her on the river bank and let her wash her clothes among them. Then she spread her washing out to dry in the sun and made her round of the other washing-places, to come back at ten o'clock and collect her dried things. The washerwomen often told her: 'I'll pay you to-morrow, Señora Luisa,' and she did not mind. She went off, quite happy at having money owed her. Copper upon copper, it mounted until she sat down on a heap of dirty washing one day and said: 'They owe me fifty pesetas by now.'

I saw the whole tragedy of this woman who went down to the river at seven every morning, loaded with her urns the size of buckets, and to whom the others owed—copper upon copper—one thousand coppers. But because my mother hadn't been paid by Señor So-and-so herself, she, too, owed Señora Luisa the money for four cups of coffee. She had been twenty centimos—four coppers—short!

I did not yet earn more than twenty-five pesetas, but I was going to earn more. And Rafael and Concha would earn, too. Or rather, I didn't know about Rafael. But Concha would do it. She felt herself in duty bound as I did. She had resigned herself to being a servant-girl, to washing up plates and sweeping floors. But still she wanted to become something better and worked like mad. Rafael, however, was a rebel against everything and everybody. He had walked out of his shop and when my mother wanted to get him a job in another firm he had walked out of the house and not come back. Only I knew at the time where he was; he slept in the street, on the benches of the Prado. Once a 'pansy' gave him fifteen pesetas. Rafael took the money, hit the man in the face and ran away. That night, when I came to our meeting place he invited me to supper. We had two fillets of fried cod in a tavern on the Calle de la Libertad. 'Come home,' I said to him. 'Mother cries the whole time.' He said nothing, but munched his fried cod and bread, opening his mouth very wide to take big bites, because he was very hungry. Then he answered: 'No. I don't want to be a grocer.' He walked away, up the Calle de Alcalá, and I went home. After the cod I did not feel like having supper.

My mother ate her meal in silence. Between two sips of coffee she lifted her head—the paraffin lamp was on the table between us—and asked me: 'Have you seen him?'

I ducked my head down to my cup. 'Yes,' I answered. I said no more and she asked no more. How could I tell her that he had eaten supper that evening because he had got money out of a 'pansy'? How could I tell her that his white grocer's overall was torn and chocolate-brown?

'He says he doesn't come home because he doesn't want to be a grocer,' I said.

She was silent. She looked into the flame of the lamp. She looked at her hands, those hands fretted by lye.

'Tell him to come home. If he doesn't want to be a grocer, he can do some other work. Anything but a street vagabond.'

Again she took refuge in the flame of the lamp, white, yellow, red, and smoke-black.

'Tell him to come back. I forgive him. But don't tell him that. Let him come back as if nothing had happened.'

When Rafael came back, because I made him come, he went to bed. By the time my mother came in, he was asleep. When he woke up supper was ready. My mother called gently: 'Rafael—Rafael!' He opened his eyes which were drunk from sleeping in a soft bed. During the meal none of us spoke. When we had finished, Rafael said: 'I'm going out.'

'Don't be late,' answered my mother, and gave me a wink.

'I'll come with you.'

My mother gave me a five-peseta piece and the key of the flat. 'Don't be late.'

We drank coffee at a stall in the street. I had left a full cup behind at home because I had not wanted to let Rafael go alone. We went to the pictures and afterwards we had a few glasses of wine in the Calle de Preciados. On the way home Rafael walked slowly in my wake. In the Calle de Carretas I told him: 'She'll be fast asleep by now.'

And we both went to sleep in my big bed with the gilt bars.

Sometimes he went away and strolled about, alone, or lingered at the street corners as though he were looking for something. Then Dr. Chicote gave him a recommendation and he found work in the Aguila Brewery. As it was the summer season, he worked till midnight and earned as much as six pesetas a day. When he came home at half-past twelve he sometimes fell into bed without taking off his trousers and slept till six in the morning, heavily snoring. Some days I accompanied him to the brewery which was near the station of Las Delicias in the outskirts of the city. We watched the sun rising and took a cup of tea at a stall in the factory entrance. Then, when the whistle of the brewery sounded at seven, releasing a puff of white steam, he went inside together with two hundred other workers, and I walked slowly up the slope of the Paseo de Delicias, marking time until nine, when I had to start work at the Bank. Sometimes I went home and had breakfast there. My mother gave me coffee with milk and a little pat of butter swimming on top of it, and asked: 'And Rafael?'

As though she had not seen him for days.

'He's at the brewery,' I answered.

'It looks as if he was a bit quieter now. God grant it be so.'

Since my aunt's death none of her acquaintances had kept in touch with us. Even Don Julian no longer treated me as the nephew of Doña Baldomera; I had simply become one of the staff to him, somewhat dangerous, since he felt himself responsible for my conduct. When I started work in the Coupons Section, I had gone to his room and told him: 'Don Julian, they've transferred me to Coupons.' He had looked at me from behind his spectacles and scratched his little moustache: 'Good, good. Now see that you bear yourself well, Señor Barca. I hope you won't make me look ridiculous.' It was the first time that he had addressed me in this way, and it was decisive. From then onwards I was Señor Barea to him.

I hated him. He was a bastard, a lick-spittle. After twenty years of service in the Bank he kowtowed to every head of department. He was ashamed of me. And what had he been? A poor fellow like me, a starved orphan whom his grandmother brought up between the canary, the parrot, and the tame priest who filled her house.

He still went to his grandmother's every day. He carried sweets for the parrot in his pocket, and his grandmother tittered when the bird picked them out; she kissed her grandson and sometimes gave him a banknote. Whenever the grandmother was not at home or the parrot was alone in the kitchen, Don Julian took a black pin out of his coat lapel, pricked the parrot through the bars of its cage and called it bastard. The parrot screeched, but it learnt the word from Don Julian. When he came into the sitting-room and the parrot was there, it began to shriek in a hoarse voice: 'Bastard, bastard!'

The parrot was right. Bastard, cuckold, swine, dog, slave—he was all that—all that!

But it was not only Don Julian, it was the whole Bank. If the learner was afraid of being thrown out into the street before his year of unpaid work was over, the men who were honest-to-God employees were even more afraid. That fear turned them into cowards. They told tales about the cigarettes the others smoked, about their girl friends, if they had one, about their going or not going to Mass, about the times they were late, the mistakes in their work, their visits to the bar of the 'Portuguese'. They told those tales, the subordinate employee to his superior, the higher employee to the still higher one, the still higher one to the head of his department and the head of the department to the Staff Manager, Señor Corachán, all so as to get higher marks. Then Señor Corachán would send for a clerk. 'We know that you make a habit of frequenting taverns,' and the clerk would walk down the stairs with weak knees; that Christmas there would be no rise in his salary.

One day Corachán sent for Plá. 'The management has learnt that you frequent taverns.' Plá stared at him with his short-sighted eyes and answered: 'Of course. For two reasons.'

'Two reasons for getting drunk? And pray, what are they?'

'Not for getting drunk, because I don't. Two reasons for the management to have learnt that I frequent taverns. One is that there are plenty of toadies who like telling tales. The second is that with my salary, on which I have to keep my mother and myself, I can only afford wine at ten centimos a glass. I haven't gone up in the world far enough to drink *Manzanilla* in elegant establishments such as the Villa Rosa, following your example.'

Corachán swallowed the hint. At Christmas they gave Plá a rise. I wondered whether it was so that he should be able to afford *Manzanilla* or so that he should keep his mouth shut.

And then there were the girls. In our section there were four women and two men. Three of the girls were old and ugly, and only Enriqueta was young. She was twenty. On some days it was hell. Antonio and I were the only men who counted, for Perahita was elderly and married. But we—there were days when the girls petted us as though we had been babies. Antonio touched their thighs and breasts and they only laughed. They came up to me and dictated figures, and while they did it they bent over the desk, their breasts pushed up on its surface, they leant on my shoulder, they excited me, and when in the end I stretched out my hand, they squealed: 'You naughty boy!'

Perahita laughed at them and at me and made peace. I had to make my excuses.

Enriqueta had a strong smell. Once she pushed the half-sleeve of her blouse up to her shoulder and asked me: 'Does it smell? It's too bad, I wash and wash it every day, just look.' She showed me her armpit, full of little black curls and a hot smell. I came very near it with my face and touched it with my fingertips. Later, when I came back from the lavatory she gave me a glance, her eyes smiled, and she blushed. I felt that I, too, was blushing and could not do my sums.

Once we both went down into the steel room where the section had worked before. We had to collect the coupons of the State Bonds and began to open drawers and take out bundles. She stood on one of the white steel benches, which looked like those in a clinic. I could smell her. Her stockings were stretched tight over her legs. I began to stroke softly along one of her calves and follow it upwards. We kissed, she bending down from the bench, I standing below her, with trembling legs and a burning face. We did not go upstairs together, we would have been too much ashamed. After that we used to caress each other even in front of the others. She would come and stand beside my high desk while I was sitting, and dictate to me. I plunged my left hand under her skirt, she went on dictating absurd figures to me, and my right hand went on scribbling.

These things pleased and repelled me. Once I asked her to come with me to the Moncloa. She said very seriously: 'Now listen, I'm a decent girl.' A decent girl—and once when we went to the pictures together she stroked my whole body with her fingers and never had her fill!

Why was it necessary for women to be virgins when they married? She herself said it was so. She said that we could not be together without her losing her virginity, and she would have to marry sooner or later. What we were doing was just a childish game, it did not matter and was not dangerous. 'But otherwise it might happen that I became pregnant,' she said. 'It's true that you're still a boy, but you can already have children.'

What could I have answered? Nothing. The only thing I could do was to make good use of the dark corners where she sought me out. I wanted to stop that sort of thing, but she got so angry that it was impossible.

Perhaps Plá was right. There was no prospect for anyone in the Bank until many years had passed and they had found out, not that his work was good but that he was utterly docile. Work? Work at the Bank was so organized that anybody could be dismissed on the spot without the slightest disturbance to the whole machine. It was routine work: filling in blanks with stereotyped words, making deductions and sums, always the same, mechanically. Neither Antonio nor I knew French, German, or English, yet every day we credited clients in France, Germany, and England, with their coupons and filled in the printed forms in their own languages. Then the client was bound to acknowledge the great organization of a bank which wrote to him in English and kept a special employee, who knew English, to write to him. Medina spoke English, he had gone to school in England and lived there all his childhood. But he spent his time sitting on a very high stool and making entries in a copper-plate hand on the pages of one of the Bank's day-books. It was nothing but idiotic copying, which took him endless hours. The only use he made of his English was to buy English magazines at the newspaper kiosk in the Puerta del Sol and to show them off to us, so that we should remember that he knew English. Once the Director himself passed by his desk and noticed one of the magazines. He had a look at it and asked Medina:

'Do you know English?'

'Yes, sir.'

They launched forth on an English conversation. When the Director had gone, Medina was very pleased because he said: 'Now they'll give me a transfer.'

Three days later Señor Corachán sent for him. 'The Management has learnt that you waste your working hours reading English periodicals.' Later he added: 'We had intended to promote you in June, but it is obviously impossible in these circumstances.' Medina came down in such a fury that his eyes brimmed over. The employees all started to pull his leg, asking him: 'Do you speak English?' They repeated the English phrase so often that the way they pronounced it, it became *Pickinglis* in a few weeks, and stuck to Medina as his nickname. New boys who entered as learners called him Señor Pickinglis on their first day, and all the others roared with laughter.

He swallowed it, as all of us swallowed things. 'If only I had the money to go to England,' he said sometimes. Money—money—that was the key to everything. But I would not have to bother about it much longer. Don Primo was about to wind up my uncle's estate, and soon we would each be paid out our inheritance. I was to get about ten thousand pesetas. As soon as I had it, I would be able to do as I liked and send the Bank and Corachán, that swine, to hell without worrying. We ought to manage with that money. I spoke to my mother about it, because I wanted her to stop going down to the river, but she said that we would discuss all our plans when we had the pesetas in our hands. She was scared of the money. Once Don Primo, who knew how badly off we were, called her to his office and asked her whether she would like an advance, she should ask for whatever she needed. But she did not want it. The Brunete relatives came every other day to ask for advance money. Uncle Anastasio had come several times to ask for 500 pesetas, and had gambled the money away. All the others, too, had come to nibble at their account. But my mother flatly refused. Then she said to Don Primo that she wanted to talk with him and made an appointment for one of the mornings when I was at work. When I asked her why she had gone to see him, she said she had wanted to put a few questions to him, and gave me no further explanation.

I would convince her anyhow as soon as I was paid out the money. With ten thousand pesetas we would be able to live three years, while she would not have to work and I could study. Or still better, we might buy out some tradesman and live on the shop. This meant risking the money, of course, but quite a number of shops were safe business. My brother and sister and I would work in the shop; I would finish my studies and become an engineer. Then the washer-

227

woman would be Doña Leonor and keep a servant girl to do the housework.

On my way home I went into the Experimental Farm which the Institute of Agricultural Engineers kept in the Moncloa. It had rabbit hutches, chicken coops, cowsheds, and pigsties with every kind of breed, and it had beehives and a breeding-station for silkworms. They let me have a packet of fresh mulberry leaves, and when I came home I spent my time watching the assault my silkworms made on them. Concha laughed at my worms and said they were a toy for children, but I was a man now. She made me feel ashamed of them and I almost gave them away. But then I found out at the Experimental Farm that she was quite wrong. They were by no means children's toys. The silk industry used to be one of the most important industries of Spain, but it had gone to rack and ruin. One of the professors showed me the various breeds of silkworms, their diseases and the cures for them, and the way to extract silk. He gave me a leaflet; I had the right to get free stock from the station and to sell all my cocoons to them, by weight, before they opened and the moths crept out. It might be a good business to breed silkworms. Then the laugh would be on Concha. We could go to Méntrida where mulberry trees grew along the river, and breed silkworms and chickens. We could do it on the ten thousand pesetas and still have money left to live on for a year. Whenever we wanted to go to Madrid we could do it without difficulty, it was near enough.

One of the Sundays when I went to the station for my mulberry leaves I told the professor my plan. He listened to me very kindly, asked me details about my family, and, when I had explained everything, he said:

'My dear boy, that is all very nice, but you're still a minor and will have to do what your mother wishes. And she won't wish to plunge into this maze which needs a lot of experience and a lot of money.'

So my mother can do whatever she likes with the money? I am a minor. Every time one has got something which belongs to one, one turns out to be a minor, but all the others are of age, always, and have the right to snatch away what belongs to one, just because one is a minor. But as far as working is concerned one is already of age. One is a minor when it comes to cashing in. One is paid as a minor. The family has the right to pocket what one has earned; so it happened to Gros, whose father came to the Bank and asked for his son's wages to be paid out to him, because young Gros had spent something out of his pay one month. Even when one wants to buy something people always take one's age into account. For years I've had my suits made by the same tailor. I didn't want him to make my last suit and asked my mother to give me the money to buy it for myself. I went to a tailor in the Calle de la Victoria. The good man looked me up and down, showed me his patterns and when I told him to take my measurements, he said most politely that I should ask my papa or my mama to come with me to the shop. 'You see, we're not allowed to serve minors.'

I came back to him with my mother. The tailor was extremely polite to us, took out the cloth I had chosen and showed it to my mother. The two discussed the price between them as though I did not even exist. Then my mother asked: 'Do you like it?' 'Yes,' I said. 'All right, then, will you take his measurements?' The tailor armed himself with his tape: 'Would you be so kind as to take off your coat?'

I burst out: 'I don't want to! Put your old suit where there's a hole for it. That's the only right I've got as a minor, not to have the suit made and to tell you to go to hell.'

My mother was frightfully upset and I was sorry for it afterwards. But I had to tell that fellow what I thought of him.

I went by myself to my old tailor and he made me a suit which I liked.

VII. CAPITALIST

One of the most unforgivable things in a Bank is to stay away from work. I had told Perahita that I needed a day off to go to the Notary, who had summoned all the heirs for the liquidation of the estate left by my uncle and aunt. Next day Corachán had sent for me. 'Your chief has informed me that you require a day's leave for personal reasons.'

'Yes, sir.'

He surveyed me, leisurely, as though he wanted to examine my person in every detail. If he was to play me one of his tricks I would leave the Bank. I was fed up with this fellow. Then he began to speak, stressing every word.

'And may one know what sort of "personal reasons" demand the young gentleman's neglect of his duties for a whole day?' He gave every syllable its full value, stroking his beard with his cupped hand and looking at me out of the corner of his little eyes.

'I am to receive an inheritance,' I said, also careful to pronounce each syllable.

'Ah—an inheritance? Well, well . . . then you are about to leave us, I presume?'

Leave you? Whom do you mean, sir? The Bank? No, I'll go on working.'

'Oh, is that so? It is a small legacy, then. How much are you going to receive?'

'I don't know exactly how much it is, something like two—three—four—five thousand duros, sir.'

'That's not so bad. That's not so bad.' He stroked his beard again. 'And in order to cash five thousand duros—provided that this is more than a fairy tale—you require a whole day off. Are they then going to pay it to you in coppers?'

I was dumbfounded. How was I to explain to this man, to a high official of a Bank accustomed to dealing in millions, that to receive a few thousand pesetas and to carry them to a washerwoman's attic was an event which forbade any work on the day it happened? In the Bank, thousand-peseta notes made no impression on me, but when I thought that next day a little bundle of them would be there in our attic and that we two, my mother and I, would have to stay at home to guard them until we had decided what to do with them—when I thought of this I was deeply shaken. Señora Pascuala would come and stare at the big banknotes in the glow of the lamp. 'Señora Leonor, do let me look at one of them!' Then the neighbouring women from the other attic would come, one after the other, to look at a banknote and to hold it between their fingertips, overawed.

I began to feel a resentment against this grumpy old man who was making a fool of me.

'I don't think they'll pay me out in coppers.'

The rough edge to my words made him lift his head and look into my face. Pedantically and frigidly he said:

'And who is going to prove to me that all this is more than merely a tale intended to get you off to-morrow so that you can go on the spree with a friend—or a girl·friend?'

I pulled out Don Primo's note. He read it slowly, folded it and gave it back to me.

'Very well, then. To-morrow at ten o'clock in the Calle de Campomanes. Good. You will come here to sign on and then you may leave again. You will have the morning off. In the afternoon I myself will check on whether you turn up or not. You may go now.'

I told Perahita about my interview, and he laughed at my indignation. He laughed so much that he had to clutch at the desk with his fat, short-fingered hands as though otherwise his rubber ball of a body would bounce up and down, and he dug his fingers into the desk until his flat nails went white with the pressure. Then he recovered and clapped me on the shoulder.

'Now, there, there, my boy, don't be upset. You won't come here to-morrow afternoon.'

'Will you let me off yourself, then?'

'Not me, my boy, not me. You must find someone else to oppose Corachán! But you see, to-morrow is Assumption Day and everything is closed.'

We both burst out laughing, and the whole section with us. Enriqueta came up with a bundle of coupons and installed herself beside me. 'Are you going to inherit a lot?' she whispered, and pinched me in the ribs. 'You rascal, you do keep things quiet.'

'Pooh, just some four or five thousand duros, or perhaps six thousand.'

Magdalena who overheard the figure sighed and gave me an angry look, laden with the rage of an ugly, poor spinster. Calzada stopped writing out bills. 'Six thousand duros—thirty thousand pesetas,' he said. He and I shared a secret; he was the son of a concierge who repaired shoes in a hovel, below the staircase of a poor tenement house, and I was a washerwoman's son. He realized what thirty thousand pesetas meant to us, because he thought of what they would mean to him. Thirty thousand pesetas under the oil lamp where his father hammered at shoe-soles, with his spectacles hanging on the tip of his nose. Surely his father would first wash the black dust of old shoe-soles from his hands before touching a banknote.

Perahita said: 'Well, six thousand duros isn't much, but it makes you independent. It's always useful to have something you can fall back on when you're out of a job or there's an illness at home. You never know. We'd saved one thousand duros, and thanks to them Eloisa was saved. The doctor asked three thousand pesetas for operating on her kidney. And she's quite well now, so I'm not sorry. Without those thousand duros I'd be a widower now.'

What would the fat man do without his Eloisa who brushed his suits and ironed his trousers? He went on:

'So then we started putting something by again. During the last two years we've saved three thousand pesetas. It's hard work saving up a thousand duros. But never mind, it's something towards a rainy day when we have to pay for another operation. At least we haven't got to worry about it.'

I began to laugh and all the others stared at me.

231

'I'm laughing because if that's how you go on saving, you and your wife won't have a kidney left in eight years, at this rate.'

And the whole gang burst into laughter.

For the last time in our lives we met together, all of us who had inherited. Don Primo handed each of us a sheet with the statement of account for the final liquidation; we had to sign a receipt and then he paid out the money. No-one went away; they all stayed to see how much each one was cashing in and to make sure that the Notary had not cheated. As they deciphered the accounts, rows broke out. The first to have an outburst was Aunt Braulia. She went up to the table clutching the sheet of paper and interrupted Don Primo who was just paying the money to Uncle Julian.

'Listen, mister, you read this out to me. Because I'm not learned enough.'

'Just a moment, madam.' Don Primo settled the account with Uncle Julian, took the paper from her and read aloud: 'Paid to Don Hilario Gonzalez at his request: 500 pesetas. Paid to Don Hilario Gonzalez at his request: 750 pesetas. Paid . . .' There followed a series of six advance payments on request. The balance was 1,752 pesetas.

Aunt Braulia listened very attentively. When the Notary had ended, she said:

'So it comes to this: a bit of nothing on a salver. This man'—she shot out a swarthy finger at her husband—'has been eating up all the cash. And me in the dark all the while! So that's why you went up to town so often!'

She stood there, arms akimbo, her four or five skirts and petticoats spreading and swaying, and glared at Uncle Hilario in challenge.

'All right, woman, I'll explain it all to you, but don't make a row here.'

'Of course I'm going to make a row here, and they're going to hear my say from here right to our village.'

Their quarrel gave the signal to all the others. Every wife started to examine the balance sheet and every one of them found that her husband had been up to something. Uncle Anastasio went and signed the liquidation on behalf of his wife and his daughter Baldomerita. The Notary was counting the banknotes on to the table, when Uncle Anastasio stretched out his hand with great dignity: 'Don't take the trouble to count them, it's not necessary.'

He pulled the packet of notes out of Don Primo's hand and put it in his pocket together with the account. Aunt Basilisa protested: 'Well, now, let's see.'

Uncle Anastasio bridled:

'Let's see—let's see—what d'you mean? There's nothing to see here. We'll settle everything at home. Or d'you think I'm like the others and want to cause a scandal in this gentleman's house? Thank God I'm not a village boor. I've got my education, I know how to behave in public. Let us go home.'

Aunt Braulia blocked his path.

'A boor you say—a boor? Proud to be it, you mucky squirt of a gentleman. You've done just the same as my man did, you've pinched all the cash and now you're cocky so that we shouldn't find you out. You're just as much of a shameless rascal as all the other men, so now you know.'

Aunt Basilisa burst into tears and Aunt Braulia followed suit. They fell weeping round one another's neck. Uncle Hilario and Uncle Basilio glared at each other. Uncle Julian's children began to cry. Don Primo turned angry and banged his fist on the table.

'Damnation! You're in my house, remember!'

They all stopped and fell silent. Then Don Primo called my mother and me. We both signed the liquidation sheet. Don Primo put a hundred peseta note on the table, a second, a third, and so on up to ten notes. Everybody watched him to see what was going to happen, and I was dismayed when I saw that he put no more bank-notes on the table. Then he brought out another sheet and another bundle of papers.

'This is the best thing we could purchase. Here are the certificates and here is the final account. You sign here; there is no need for the boy to sign because you are his guardian.' My mother signed labori-ously with her sprawling letters. Then Don Primo handed her a Bank of Spain receipt. I knew it well as I had to handle their bonds daily.

'Here you have the deposit receipt.'

My mother put the banknotes into her purse, folded the receipt and stuck it into her bodice. Then she took my hand.

'Say good-bye to Don Primo.'

Just as when I was eight and she had led me by the hand, a child. Just the same. I felt like crying. Aunt Basilisa went up to my mother.

'What did you do, Leonor?'

'Nothing, only what Don Primo advised me to do. You see, I'm only the boy's guardian, so he bought State Loan Bonds for him. I took out a thousand pesetas so that we can settle a few things, and as to the rest, we'll leave it for the time when he's a man, then he can do with it whatever he wants to.'

'Tell me, is it a lot?' asked Uncle Anastasio.

'At the present price of State Loan,' Don Primo said, 'we were able to purchase 12,500 pesetas nominal.'

When Fuencisla heard the words '12,500 pesetas' she turned on Don Primo like a fury. 'So you've played tricks, you robber!' she shrieked.

We all gaped. Uncle Anastasio hit the table with his heavy hand and said: 'This has got to be cleared up, eh?'

Don Primo, in his black suit, gold-rimmed spectacles, and little beard, looked as though he felt like slapping their faces for them.

'Señora,' he said hoarsely, 'I forgive you the insult because after all nobody can be forced to be knowledgeable. I spoke of 12,500 pesetas nominal, and you were aghast at the amount. The present quotation of State Loan is 69 per cent and people are selling out because the paper is not suitable for speculation.'

The country cousins were clustering round the table and staring at him with wide-open eyes. 'Quotation'—'State Loan'—'69 per cent' —what did the old man mean?

'Come now, let's have less fine words,' said Uncle Hilario, 'and let's rather get the facts clear. This young devil (may the wen on your head rot, you thief!) carries off more than two thousand duros and we get a pittance. Why?'

At three in the afternoon we left the Notary after a detailed explanation of the division of the estate, of State Loan Bonds and of the reasons why 69 per cent quotation price equalled 100 per cent nominal value. We said good-bye at the corner of the street, and it was a very rancorous good-bye. The relations from Brunete, the men in their corduroys, sashes and round hats, the women in their swaying skirts and coloured kerchiefs, and the children stumbling over their heavy boots, walked on across the square, still carrying on the dispute at the tops of their voices. People who passed them stopped and stared after them.

My mother and I went up the Calle del Arenal to the Puerta del Sol. I walked beside her, but not with her. I did not take her arm as I always had done when we went out together. I walked abreast of her, but at two feet's distance. Neither of us spoke. She went with short steps, the steps of a nervous little woman. I strode out with my long legs, one step for two of hers. I was full of resentment. I started by feeling resentment against some of the others and finished by feeling it against my mother. Nobody was excepted. I resented the relatives because of their supicious, meticulous scrutiny of the accounts down to the last centimo, their adding up of all the sums, their asking ten times for an explanation of the difference between 69 and 100 per cent, their fingering of the receipts, the certificates, the Bank of Spain deposit receipt, with faces contracted by anger. I resented Don Primo because he acted in agreement with my mother, because they both did as they liked without taking me into account, without even saying a word to me. I did not think it a bad thing for the money to stay in the bank, but I thought it wrong of them to have done it behind my back. 'There is no need for the boy to sign.' Why should he? The boy is a boy, and they are grown people who can do what they like with boys. They can make them work and cash in on them, they can buy State Loan Bonds or a new suit, and that's all right for them. In his time the boy will be a man, and when he is grown up he can protest, if he still feels like it.

No, no, and no. As soon as we are at home there will be a row. I'm going to speak my mind to my mother. If I'm a boy, then let them send me to school, bring me up, and pay for my keep. If I'm grown up, let them treat me as a grown-up. And if I'm neither, then let them go to hell, all of them, but I won't be played with like a kitten!

I wanted to smoke a cigarette to get over my nervousness. I carried cigarettes in my pocket, my mother knew that I smoked, but I had never smoked in her presence so far, and I did not care to start it now. But so much the better if she gets angry, so much the better. In the Puerta del Sol I made up my mind, pulled out a cigarette and lit it. My mother looked at me and walked on with short even steps as though it were nothing. I began to feel annoyed because she said nothing. If she had scolded me, I could have exploded. I needed to shout, to quarrel, to get rid of what I felt inside.

In the Calle de Carretas she asked me at long last:

'What are you thinking about?'

'Nothing.'

'So much the better for you.'

'Of course, if the other people do all the thinking for one, what should one think about?'

'Why do you say that?'

'Why? You know as well as I do.' I stopped and faced her. 'Because I'm fed up with being treated like a child and now you know it.'

We fell back into a sulky silence, and so we came home.

Just as I had imagined, Señora Pascuala followed us along the corridor and came with us into the attic when we opened the door.

'Well, is everything nicely settled, Leonor?'

My mother sighed, took the black handkerchief from her head and sat down.

'Yes, it's all settled. I'm glad the whole thing is over and done

235

with. I must say, if it hadn't been for the boy . . . People go crazy as soon as they see a banknote. I almost thought they were coming to blows in the Notary's office. And what for? Only to snatch at a pittance which isn't even enough to lift you out of poverty. Now look here. José's brothers had been working together thirty years. José sold the grain for them, lent them money for mules and land, and made them the wealthiest people in the whole village. Well, because of the inheritance they've separated, they've gone to law against each other about the mules and the land. The brothers and their children look as if they wanted to knife one another. And they're all the same. Even he! (She pointed at me.) Here you've got him in a fury because I've done what I thought best for him. Even the children go crazy when they see money. I've been through a lot so that the four of them should get on in life—you know something about it, Pascuala— but for myself I prefer my stew and my warmed-up coffee. So I've lived all my life and so I want to die. I'll be content if they let me die in peace in my bed and not take me to hospital. And that's not asking for much, I think.'

'I haven't said anything,' I retorted peevishly.

'No, you haven't said anything, but don't you think I've got eyes in my head? You walked beside me the whole way like an altar-boy, a few steps apart. And then the young gentleman lights a cigarette for himself in the Puerta del Sol, quite brazenly. What did you expect —that I would make a row? No, my boy, no. You can smoke as much as you like. And now, let's have it out. What is the matter?'

'You ask what's the matter?—well, it's just that I—I'm fed up with being treated like a child or a little boy and having my belongings disposed of without any consideration for me. Who told you to buy State Bonds? You may have your views about the money, but so have I. And after all, it's my money and nobody else's.'

'And what are your views about the money?'

'That doesn't concern anybody but me. You had to collect the money, because they wouldn't let me have it while I'm a minor, but afterwards we should have thought out together what to do with it. And you shouldn't have got together with the Notary and bought State Bonds. Do you know what State Bonds are? I'm working in a bank, precisely in that department which handles securities, and I must know about them. State Loan! If you'd bought Convertible Loan, then we would at least have a chance of getting a premium. But State Loan, which no-one wants! But of course, you think I'm just a little boy who doesn't understand anything about anything.'

'Of course I do, you silly.' She stroked my unruly hair, her fingers twisted its strands and soothed my taut nerves. 'Of course I think it.

Listen. I'm your guardian until you stop being a minor. That doesn't mean that I can do what I like, it means that it's my responsibility to administer your money and that I must give you an account of what I've done the day you come of age. We can't spend your money now just as you like, because then you might come when you're a man and ask me: "Where's my money?" If I then said "You've spent it," you might answer: "I? But I couldn't have spent it, I was a child. You must have spent it yourself, because you were the only person with a right to do so." And you could even send me to prison as a thief. No, your money is going to stay in the bank until you can give the order to withdraw it—and then you may spend it as you like, on business or on women, and may it bring you joy. I don't need anything. I've been poor all my life and I'll die poor. You have your life still before you, and I'm an old woman.'

Her fingers in my hair and her last words dispelled all my anger, and my eyes filled with water.

'Now, d'you see that you're a little boy and a silly?'

She wiped my face as she used to do when I was a child and kissed me on the forehead. She took out a hundred peseta note and gave it me.

'Here, treat your friends and buy yourself something, but don't do anything foolish.'

Señora Pascuala sighed. 'Goodness me, those children, Leonor, those children! What they make us suffer! And what are you going to do now?'

'Well, nothing. Just go on as always.'

'I thought you were going to move out. I've been saying to myself, as soon as Leonor's boy gets his money they'll move. I've been sorry, because by now it's a good sixteen years that we've been living side by side, with nothing but a partition between us.'

'Of course we're going to move,' I said. 'I don't want to stay in the attic.'

'Now look here, my dear, let's be sensible. This money'—she took up the deposit receipt—'doesn't make us either richer or poorer. It gives you exactly one peseta twenty-five centimos interest a day. Do you think that one twenty-five more or less settles all our difficulties? No; here we pay nine pesetas a month and don't get into debt. If we take a flat we only spend your interest and a bit over. In the end we should be in debt, and then what? When you earn more, and your brother and sister too, then we can see what we can do about it. But as things are now, you know very well that all of us together just earn what we need to live as we do live. The only thing I'd like to do is to take another attic room, like the cigar-woman's or Señora Paca's, as soon as one of them gets empty. I'd like it for your sake because you're getting older and if Concha comes home to live with us one day we can't all sleep in one room. We could do that, because the two rooms together would mean twenty pesetas rent a month, and that much we can manage.'

'All right,' I said, 'but there's something I want, and it will be done.'

'Tell me.'

'I want to install electric light in our attic. I'm sick of having my eyebrows singed by the oil lamp every time I want to read for a while.'

The electric light was granted and I promised to arrange it with the company. It would have to be a lamp screwed on in the middle of the sloping ceiling, with a very long flex so that it would light the table, but could be hung on a hook over my head when I was in bed and wanted to read; and it would need a switch in the socket so that I could turn it off without having to get up.

Next day I had to invite all my colleagues at the Bank. The commissionaire secretly brought us two bottles of Manzanilla and some pastries. We shut the door of the department so that the others should not see us eating. But then the room smelt of wine and we had to open the door and the panel in the glass roof until the draught swept out the smell.

'How much did you get in the end?' asked Perahita.

'Not much, just a little.'

'All right, keep it secret, we won't ask you for any of it. Anyhow, you wouldn't let us have it.'

'Thirty thousand pesetas,' I said.

'Good gracious, and you call that a little? Six thousand beautiful duros! Well, you must be happy! Wouldn't it be nice if a relative of that sort were to die every day?'

'It wouldn't be so bad.'

But of course it would have been bad. If Uncle José had not died, I would not have inherited, but it would have been much better for me. I would not have stayed in the attic, I would not have worked in the Bank for a miserable salary. I would have been studying to be an engineer. But how could I explain all this? I had to show them that I was happy, very happy, and that I was wealthy, very wealthy indeed, and that as far as I was concerned all my relatives could die and leave me fat legacies.

Plá was the only one to whom I told the truth. We had a glass of sherry together in the bar of the 'Portuguese', all by ourselves.

'You were right,' he said. 'Only, you ought to have told them you'd inherited twenty thousand duros. Then the Director would have sent for you, tended his congratulations and given you a rise in salary. They'll give you one in any case, you'll see. As soon as they find out that you've got money they'll give you a leg up.'

Plá was not mistaken. They increased my salary to 72·50 pesetas. My colleagues were somewhat annoyed. Sadly—for his envelope brought no rise, only a small bonus—Antonio said to me:

'You see, it's always the same thing. You and I, we've done the same kind of work the whole year, I've been in the place longer and have a greater claim than you. Well—and they go and give you a rise—and you don't need it'.

I went home, greatly pleased with my news. Now we would be able to move out of the attic.

My mother was alone, sewing by the light of the oil lamp which had only a few more hours to burn. I gave her the note which announced the rise, and kissed her on the nape of her neck where it tickled her. Then I pushed the low stool to her feet, sat down and put my head on her lap. Now at last things were beginning to go well.

'We can move now, Mother.'

Her small, slender fingers were plaiting my hair.

'You know, Rafael's been given the sack to-day. But we shall manage. Dr. Chicote will let me do the whole washing for the Disinfection Service. Señora Paca'll help me, we'll do it between the two of us. You see, with Rafael out of work, that means six pesetas a day less. And God knows when he'll find another job. He hasn't learnt any trade. . . .'

I heard her, watching her face from below, from her knees.

'To-morrow at ten the electrician will call about the light, Mother.'

He would fit the wooden plug from which the flex and the bulb were going to hang up there, just where the smoke from the oil lamp had made a round patch on the ceiling. The bulb was going to have a switch on its fitting, and when I stopped reading at night, I would turn off the light.

239

VIII. PROLETARIAN

Rafael was working again. He had started with a regular profession at last, and was a clerk like myself. He had been taken on at the Head Office of the *Fenix Agrícola*, the insurance company which insured all horses, mules, and donkeys in Spain. The inheritance had helped to get him the job. With the thousand pesetas my mother had taken out in cash we had bought clothes and linen, the two things we needed most urgently. Rafael went to the Fenix in a new suit, armed with a recommendation, and was engaged.

They employed no learners there. Every clerk started with a monthly salary of six duros. One peseta per day. That was the invariable rate. The Fenix staff had made a joke of the facts that the salary was six duros—which is thirty pesetas—and that the offices closed at six-thirty; they called it the Six-thirty Company. The management was absolutely strict in both matters. Everybody was paid thirty pesetas, everybody left the office at six-thirty sharp. At that hour, four hundred employees streamed out into the street, and only some twenty of them had a salary over six duros. Always excepting the Directors, of course, who earned thousands.

The company used its clerks only for filling in forms: insurance policies, descriptions of the horses insured, receipts, premiums. All that was required of the employee was that he should be able to read and write and calculate the percentage of the premiums.

Hundreds of thousands of animals had the mark of the Fenix—a phoenix—branded on their necks. The gipsies called it the Dove Brand and whenever they discovered it on an animal they had meant to steal they kept off it. They knew that they would never get further than ten miles along the road before meeting the Civil Guard, who would not fail to ask for the certificate as soon as they saw a horse with the Dove Brand led by two gipsies. And although it was easy enough to steal a horse, donkey, or mule, it was far less easy at the same time to steal the insurance certificate of that accursed company which had hit upon a trick to ruin poor gipsies trying to earn an honest living.

For it was a trick. The Company had invented the 'Dove' and the 'iron'. When an owner insured an animal, the company's agent pressed a red-hot iron on to its neck, and it was branded with the Dove. Then he drew up a description which enumerated everything from the beast's height to its missing teeth, so that it could neither be bought or sold without the change of ownership being entered in the certificate. You couldn't even ride on its back without risking the Civil Guard's demanding proof of your ownership, in the shape of the certificate.

The gipsies' hatred of the Civil Guard was ingrained, but their hatred for the Dove went even deeper. When you mentioned the Dove to a gipsy in the horse-breeding lands of Seville or Cordova, he touched wood or crossed himself. 'Don't make bad jokes, mate.'

Now, in order to fill in certificates, insurance policies, and receipts, the company which gave protection from robbery had set up a perfect administrative system manned by clerks paid at thirty pesetas a month. For its touts and agents it had found a different system; they kept the first premium paid as a bonus. And that was all. The high officials had only to dismiss employees who had had enough of earning thirty pesetas after two or three years' service, and to engage new ones in their place at the same rate of pay. True, anybody who was discharged received a month's salary in accordance with the Trade and Commerce Code, Paragraph four hundred odd; it was a serious firm where work was restricted to exactly eight hours and where the Wages Code was rigorously observed. But it never paid more than thirty pesetas a month to its clerks.

One peseta from Rafael, two pesetas ten from me, one peseta twenty-five interest from the inheritance, and two pesetas fifteen which my mother earned with her washing, made up our daily income. Concha did not count because she earned just what she needed for herself.

When my mother went down to the river in the mornings she left the *cocido* simmering on the little earthenware stove. Señora Pascuala came from time to time to have a look at it. The chick-peas, the piece of meat, and the bacon, all coloured yellow from the saffron, went on cooking under the joint supervision of Señora Pascuala and of Santa Maria de la Cabeza, the patroness of stewing-pots. At midday Rafael and I ate the *cocido* all by ourselves.

For a few days Señora Segunda had looked after our meals, but then one day she failed to turn up. As she lived very near, we went to see her.

She was in bed, between snow-white sheets, the crimped collar of her nightdress—an inheritance from Aunt Baldomera—tied with a piece of ribbon and Toby lying at her feet on his patchwork blanket.

'What's the matter with you, Señora Segunda?'

Rafael and I hardly had room to stand up straight in her closet. Right over our heads sounded the footsteps of people going up and down the stairs.

'Nothing, my dear boys, it's just that I'm dying.'

'But what's wrong with you?'

'Nothing, nothing at all.'

'Has the doctor been to see you?'

'Yes. The doctor was here. He said they would take me to hospital. I said no. "But you can't get well here," he said to me. "Not in the hospital either," I answered. He shut up then, and later he said: "That's true, too." He wanted to come every day, but it's not necessary.'

She spoke as calmly as though she were going to the theatre that evening.

'I'm sorry for Toby. But there's a blind man in our café who's willing to take him as his guide, and he's a very good man. You know him, Arturo, it's Freckle-Face. He's an honest man even if he's poor. When I'm dead, you give him the dog.'

Later in the evening we came back with our mother and stayed with her for a while, until Rafael and I went to the pictures. After midnight we went to fetch our mother. 'Go home to sleep,' she said, 'I'll stay with her.'

So we, too, stayed. We sat in the doorway, because the little hole was not big enough for the three of us. From time to time we walked out into the Calle de Mesón de Paredes and had a drink. She died at four in the morning.

We paid for the funeral because we did not want her to be taken away in a municipal van, wrapped in a sheet. It was a third-class funeral with two shabby black horses, and a coffin roughly painted with lamp-black, and with cotton braid along the edges of the lid. Rafael and I were the only mourners. When we came back from the East Cemetery we had a quick lunch in Las Ventas, a cutlet and roast black-pudding, and we kept Toby tied up beside us.

Toby would not take any food and died a few days later of sorrow. Freckle-Face was not able to make him eat, although he bought a whole fillet and fed it to him in the little café in front of all the beggars who never tasted meat themselves, but helped him in his vain attempts to persuade the dog to take it. In the end they fried the fillet in the frying-pan used for making crisps, cut it into small bits and ate it between the lot of them.

'Silly dog,' one of the beggars said to Toby. 'Can't you see how nice it is?'

We had been out for a stroll along the Calle de Alcalá, looking at the girls, and when we came home, my mother was getting the supper ready. She had eaten *cocido* together with Señora Paca at midday. Señora Paca was having supper with us, as she often did lately, because she liked being in our room, where the four of us could sit round the table under the lamp.

'My dear, my room drives me mad. When I'm shut up there all by myself I've simply got to drink or I'd never go to sleep.'

When she was with us she only drank a small glass of spirits after the coffee. My mother brewed fresh coffee every day since we had threatened to go out for ours if she went on boiling up the old grounds. We went to bed between eleven and twelve. Sometimes my mother and Señora Paca wanted me to read to them, and listened until Señora Paca began to nod. My mother never dozed. Sometimes when Rafael and I went to the pictures, the two women stayed behind and chatted; then Señora Pascuala usually joined them and we would find them still at it when we came home at three in the morning.

In the afternoons, when Rafael had finished his work at the Fenix and I my work at the Bank, we met our friends. We had sorted them out with the course of time. From the Bank, there were Calzada, Medrano, and Plá left; from the Fenix came Julian, big, strong, and merry, and Álvarez, a little fellow who never kept still. In the backroom of the bar we had two tables to ourselves. There we talked while we ate fried fish hot from the frying-pan.

We thrashed out the staff policy at the Fenix and the learner system of the Banks. We dug out case histories.

Two steps further along the street lived a man who had made himself rich through child labour. He set up a firm in the Calle de Alcalá, which he called *Continental Express*. It was a messenger service which delivered letters and urgent messages to people's houses. The whole business was built up on a few dozen boys in red jackets and caps, with satchels hanging from their shoulders, who ran round Madrid day and night. He paid them nothing, but they got tips. Some of them earned as much as ten or twelve pesetas a day. Even Ministers gave recommendations to boys who wanted to get into the Continental. Whoever joined the staff was fitted out with the jacket and cap of the boy who had left a vacancy, and off he went. After a time the business petered out, because most of the big stores copied the idea and employed a boy or two, paying him nothing if the store had many customers, or else fifty centimos a day. Now the whole of Madrid was full of young boys of that breed, with a satchel hanging from their shoulder, riding on the tramcar buffers or playing at pitch-and-toss with their tips in the middle of the pavement.

That man was not the only one. A solicitor established a commercial information agency and quickly acquired an impressive number of clients. He sent out hundreds of reports daily. He put advertisements in the newspapers: 'Wanted, learners who can type.' He had nearly fifty boys working for him ceaselessly. He walked up and down between the desks, his hands behind his back like a schoolmaster, and when he saw a boy not working at the speed he demanded, he boxed his ears. Later he improved on his business. When he accepted a boy as a learner, he demanded a deposit of five hundred pesetas in guarantee of his honesty. In the end the police were forced to intervene and closed down the firm.

Girls were no better off. Offices and shops had only just begun to employ women, but now they were doing so to an ever-increasing extent. They did not dare to take on girls as unpaid learners, but gave them an average salary of fifty pesetas a month. Yet the girls replaced male clerks and assistants with higher pay. It would not have been possible to man an office or shops with nothing but young boys, but it could be done with women and boys. The stores were sacking their male assistants; some of them had been thirty years with their firm and earned two hundred and fifty to three hundred and fifty pesetas a month, most of the others earned at least two hundred pesetas and were in a position to support a modest household. Now they were all replaced by young girls who looked very pretty in their black satin uniforms and white aprons, and who sold four times as much as the former shop assistants, but were paid at the most seventy-five pesetas. Hardly anyone was left of the old staff except here and there an old man who would amble through the rooms in a black cap and terrorize the girls by throwing them out on the slightest mistake, or else paw them while they were lifting down boxes in a corner, and they had no right to protest.

As this district was crammed with offices, the customers of the bar were nearly all employees and shop assistants. Day after day more of them came to tell their friends that they had been sacked. The young men had hopes, but those over thirty had to give up any idea of finding a job.

One of them told us his story in the back room:

'I found a good advertisement in the *Liberal* to-day. It said: "Wanted an accountant. Steady job." I knew that no office starts work before nine, but I went there at half-past eight all the same. There were five before me already. It was a store for surgical goods in the Calle de las Infantas, and the owner was a German. By ten o'clock there were at least two hundred queueing from the office door on the first floor down to the middle of the street. They let the first ten of us in, and we sat down on benches in the hall. On one side was a room with a counter, and the owner of the store took the first applicant in there. The owner had a round head, smooth as a baby's bottom. He began by asking the man's name, where he had worked before, and so on. The man answered in a low voice, but even so we all heard what he said. "Speak up," the old rascal said to him. Then he put him in front of a desk and started dictating calculations, entries in the day-book, problems of compound interest, foreign exchange rates—well, anything under the sun. The man worked well. You could see that he was a clerk who knew his job.

'The German looked over his shoulder while he was writing. After half an hour, when the man had finished his test, the German said: "All right, I like you. We'll check your references and if they're good we'll engage you." The man's eyes lit up. Then the German asked: "What do you expect to earn?" "Whatever the firm usually pays for the job." "Oh no, I wouldn't like to employ people who start by being dissatisfied. You tell me what you want." "Well, sir, for an accountant of a firm like this, as important as yours, seventy duros would be just about right, I think." "Three hundred pesetas? You're mad. Three hundred pesetas! No, my dear fellow, this is a modest firm, not a Bank which can afford to throw money out of the window. I'm sorry we can't come to an agreement. Let's see the next one." "But, sir, I could stay even if you paid a bit less." "No, no, I can't take you on any condition. You would be discontented from the first day, and I don't want discontented people among my staff. After three months I would have to give you a rise in salary or you would go. I'm a serious man in my dealings. This is a steady job, but there aren't any rises in salary to be had."

'He turned to the next: "What salary do you want?" "Two hundred pesetas." He simply turned to the third one with a sneer: "And you, too, have got your ambitions, I suppose?" "I could manage on a hundred and fifty pesetas. I've been out of work for the last three months." Then the seventh in the row, an elegant youngster with gold-rimmed spectacles, got up and said: "I'm an expert in commercial problems and I know both French and English, which may be of some interest to you. Thank goodness I don't depend on a salary for my living. It would be quite enough for me to get the cash to cover my little vices." The German made him pass through a lightning test. "The vacancy is filled," he told us. Then he said to the lad: "You can start work to-morrow. I'll give you one hundred pesetas a month and later we shall see how you get on."

'The man who had been out of work for three months came up to me and whispered in my ear: "I'd like to bash in that bloody swine's mug!" We walked down the stairs and out into the street together. There he saw the little commercial expert strutting along, and said to him: "So you're a commercial expert, are you?" "Yes, sir." "You're a son of a bitch, that's what you are." And he lowered his head and ran it smack into the lad's face, right on his nose, so that his spectacles were smashed and he slumped down on the ground bleeding like a stuck pig. "You won't start work to-morrow, I don't think," the man said, and ran off like a hare, and the lad had to be taken to the first-aid post. If the rest of us had had any guts, we'd have gone up to the store together and chucked that fat German out of his own window.'

Opposite the Banco Hispano a house was being built: the workers came over to the tavern for their meals and for a glass of wine at the bar after working hours. One of them was there when the story was told and said in a very loud voice:

'That's right. Serves you right for being yellow bastards. I bet our boss wouldn't dare to take on a mason at four pesetas a day. And he wouldn't find a builder in the whole of Madrid willing to work at that wage, either. The trouble with you fellows is that you want to be gentlemen and don't want to be workers. You're ashamed of saying you're hungry, because you dress like the nobs. And then every blessed soul among you goes without food when he gets home rather than not wear a tie. Of course, it's true it cost us a lot of strikes and the deuce of a lot of blows from the police and the Civil Guard before we got enough to eat. But how should gentlemen like you go on strike and how should they go to the Puerta del Sol in their starched collars to be beaten up by the police? Well, it serves you right for being a lot of cowardly bastards. And that's what I think.'

'You're right, yes, sir,' shouted Plá. 'We're a lot of bastards and cowards.' He thumped his chest. I thought he was a bit tipsy. 'Cowards, that's what we are. But not me, mate, I've got my membership card of the Casa del Pueblo!'[1] He drew a little red book out of his pocket. 'But a fat lot of good it does me! There's just a handful of us and as soon as our bosses find out that we belong to a union they'll chuck us out. We can't even form a union of our own. It's a digrace, yes, sir. Here in Madrid where everybody is an employee, we've got to join the General Workers' Union because there aren't enough of us to form a Clerical Workers' Union! And let someone else make propaganda among that bunch of lick-spittles. Twenty-four hours, and then out with you into the street, and who's going to fight for you then? Your own union can't, and the other unions won't feed you.'

Plá and the mason went on with their discussion and went on

[1] The *Casa del Pueblo*—the 'People's House'—was the seat of Socialist Trade Unions and other Labour organizations.

drinking wine. When we left the place they were still leaning on the bar with their elbows on the counter.

Next day Plá and I left the Bank together at meal-time. He lived near our street in the Calle de Relatores and we often met on our way.

'Will you show me the card of the People's House?' I asked.

'You mustn't speak to anybody about it,' he answered, and took from his wallet a little book full of receipts for two pesetas weekly contributions. It had a rubber stamp which read: 'U.G.T.[1] General Trades.'

'Don't you think that it's only me. Quite a lot of us are members. As far as I know there are ten of us in the Bank. But of course we're very few, all the same. Not enough to organize a separate Union. So they put us into the General Workers' Union with all the workers who haven't got a craft or who work in a trade with very few members. Shop assistants are there, too. To tell you the truth, the only thing we get out of it is the Friendly Society.'

He went on in answer to my unspoken question.

'Yes, that's our only benefit from it, and it's the only possible justification for our membership in the eyes of the employers. Sometimes they accept it and sometimes they don't. You see, we've got a medical assistance society which is called the Workers' Mutual Help Society, and it's the best of its kind in Spain. They give you everything, the best doctors, a dispensary and a clinic for operations. They even pay you benefit if you lose your wages through illness. But you must first be a member of the U.G.T. before you can become a member of the Society. So, if they find out that I belong to the U.G.T. I can always say that I had to do it because I wanted to have the right to a doctor and medicines through the Society. But we'll get further than that in time. Sooner or later we'll have our own union, a nd then we'll settle accounts with these rascally employers. And don't they know it! They wanted to steal a march on us and set up a Catholic Friendly Society, but nobody wants to be a member there. Quite a lot of people would join us if they weren't so frightened. Because, you see, if you're caught with the membership card in your pocket it may well be that they'll throw you out and you won't get any other job. When your former employers are asked for a reference, they'll say that you were a good worker, but a Red and a rebel who belongs to the People's House crowd. And that's quite enough for them to let you starve to death. I know a fellow who worked for Pallares, and he

[1] U.G.T.—*Unión General de Trabajadores*. The central organization for labour unions other than those under Anarchist influence, which were united in the C.N.T. The U.G.T. branches were mainly under Socialist influence.

was sacked after fifteen years with the firm, for being a union member. When he applied for a job in another firm, the manager said: "I hear you're a Socialist." "Oh no, sir." "Well, I hear from your former employers, Pallares, that you're a member of the People's House." "Well, yes, sir, I joined them because . . ." And he was going to tell the story about the Mutual Society. The manager wouldn't let him go on and said: "Stop, stop, I don't need your explanations. D'you believe I want an employee in my firm who doesn't believe in God, and parades through the streets behind a red flag, shouting threats against the Government? My firm is no hotbed of Anarchists. You can turn yourself into a Freemason and spend your time planting bombs, but this is a respectable firm!"'

I pondered over these things for days. Of course I knew what the Socialists were. But I was not really interested in political questions. It was like this: every day they fought in the Cortes, Maura, Pablo Iglesias, and Lerroux.[1] People painted the words: 'Maura—No!' in pitch upon the walls. Others sometimes scrawled in red ochre underneath: 'Maura—Yes!' I knew that those who wrote No were workers, and those who wrote Yes upper-class people. Sometimes the two groups met, each with their pot of paint; they would chuck the pots at each other and start a free fight. Sometimes a group of young gentlemen would appear in the Calle de Alcalá towards nightfall, when it was crowded with people, and shout: 'Maura—yes!' At once a group of students and workers would form and take up the cry: 'Maura—no!' People would run away. Many took the cue and left the café terraces without settling their bills. The police charged, but they never touched the young gentlemen.

In the Calle de Relatores where Plá lived, Lerroux's crowd had one of their centres. They called themselves the *Young Barbarians* and it was they who made the greatest noise. The supporters of Maura used to come to their door and shout, and then there would be a row. Lerroux himself came and spoke at the Centre; he said that priests should be castrated and nuns made pregnant. The crowd got excited by his speeches and formed up to march to the Puerta del Sol. They never got there, though. At the Calle de Carretas the police waited for them and dispersed them with their sabres.

The Socialists started a new strike every day. Sometimes it was the bakers, another time the masons, still another time the printers. They were sent to prison and beaten up, but in the end they got what they wanted. They were the only ones who had an eight-hour day and the

---

[1] *Antonio Maura*, conservative leader, repeatedly Premier, *Pablo Iglesias*, founder of the Socialist Party and leader of the Trade Unions, *Lerroux*, at that time leader of the Radicals.

only ones who were paid the wages they demanded. In their work-shops there were no learners, and boys like myself who had to work, earned two pesetas fifty a day from the start. Their leader was Pablo Iglesias, an old printer who said aloud in Parliament whatever he thought right. The workers called him Grand-dad. He had been to prison I don't know how many times, but he went on trying to turn all workers into Socialists.

I would have liked to be a Socialist. But it was a problem as to whether I was a worker or not. It sounded a simple question but it was difficult. Certainly I was paid for my work and therefore was a worker; but I was a worker only in that. The workers themselves called us *señoritos*, nobs, and did not want to have anything to do with us. And obviously we could not march through the streets with them, they in their blouses and rope-soled canvas shoes, and we in our suits made to measure, shining boots and hats.

I persuaded Plá to take me along to the People's House; one day, when he was going to pay his monthly contribution I accompanied him. The building had innumerable small rooms for the various Secretariats. In each room were one or two fellow-workers behind a desk, and a treasurer with sheets of receipt stamps and a cash box. From everywhere came the clatter of money. The corridors were crowded with workers, in front of many doors there was a queue.

'To-day's Saturday,' said Plá. 'You see, most of the organizations get their contributions weekly. Some unions are very strong. The builders' trade union, for example, must have millions, enough money to see their strikes through and to help out others when they go on strike. They pay their people unemployment relief, too, but there aren't ever many of them out of work. There's always work in the building trade.'

|He took me to the two meeting-rooms, one big and one small. In the big hall, the printers of Rivadeneyra's had a meeting. Riva-deneyra's was a big publishing firm in the Paseo de San Vicente. There were over three hundred workers present. One of the men sitting on the platform stood up and came forward. The chairman rang a bell and everyone was silent.

'Fellow-workers,' said the speaker, 'we will now take a vote for and against a strike. All those who are in favour of the strike, please stand up.'

In a wave of noise from clattering benches and trampling feet many people got up. Others followed more slowly. In the end four or five were left sitting. The others stared at them, and one by one they rose. In the first row one man remained seated, alone.

'The vote is unanimous, in favour of the strike.'

249

'I want to say something,' said the man who had kept his seat.

He walked up to the rostrum and began to shout. He did not agree w¹th the strike. Strikes were no good. Another kind of action was needed—direct action. Get rid of a number of the bosses and set the workshops on fire. He was like a madman. The others kept silent, and when a murmur started, the chairman's bell cut it short. A group of people seemed swayed by the speaker. Finally, purple in the face, he said: 'I've finished,' and gulped down a big glass of water.

Another rose to reply.

'We're not Anarchists here, we're decent men who want to do a decent job of work. We've no need to kill anybody. What—smash up the machines? But the machines belong to the workers, they're sacred to us!' Suddenly he grew heated and shouted: 'If I saw this comrade here, or any other comrade, lifting a hammer to smash up my Minerva, I'd smash his skull for him!'

The three hundred cheered him. The Anarchist crouched in his seat and grunted.

Then we went to the theatre; for the People's House had a theatre which was used for staging plays, showing films and holding meetings. Throughout the corridors we met nothing but men in blue or white blouses. When we opened the little door to the stage, a man waiting in a queue said: 'Hullo, what's this? We've got tourists here!' All the others laughed and I felt ashamed of my suit, my boots, and my hat. So I turned to face the man who had spoken and cried:

'Tourists to hell! We're workers just like you, and perhaps more than you.'

'Sorry, comrade,' he said. 'I've put my foot in it all right, but you see, we don't get many gents—I mean to say—comrades dressed like gents . . .'

I let myself be carried away by a violent impulse.

'Well, then—in spite of our suits and our soft hands and anything you like, we're workers. And what sort of workers! One year as a learner, then five duros a month, with twelve or fourteen hours of work a day . . .' And I spoke on, pouring out all my resentment. When I finished another of the men in the queue said:

'Good for the kid!'

'What the devil d'you mean by kid? I'm as much of a man as you are, and maybe more.'

An old man clapped me on the shoulder.

'Keep your shirt on, they didn't mean to hurt you. As soon as you start working you're a man!'

While we tried to find our way out of the maze of passages, I looked defiantly at all the blue and white blouses we met. I would have liked somebody else to call me a gent. I would have called them together in the big hall and shouted into their faces what we, the gentlemen employees, really were; for I saw clearly that they did not understand, that they despised us. They thought that to be a bank clerk meant sitting in a well-heated room in winter and near a ventilator in summer, reading a newspaper and drawing a salary at the end of the month.

Before we left the building, I joined the General Workers' Union.

IX. CHILDHOOD REVIEWED

That's a fine woman! If I walk a little faster I can overtake her and see what her face is like. She might be ugly. But from behind she looks all right. Her bottom shows very clearly through her skirt. The backs of her thighs are a bit curved, you see it when she walks and one of her legs moves forward, while the other is left behind so that the skirt clings to it. How well she moves her hips. Of course, you fool! She's just like the other, exactly the same. And the woman in front of me too.

People say young men like their women plump, and it must be true. I was right yesterday, anyhow. I liked that Maña better than the other girls, who were younger but thin. One of them was very pretty, with blue eyes and a face like the Virgin and she liked me too. But I preferred that Maña. She's a bit fat, it's true, but her flesh is firm and white.

What would Aunt Baldomera say if she were alive? 'Jesus! Jesus!' If anybody told her that her little Arturo had slept with a woman, with one of those bad women . . .

That Maña has a short little chemise, rose coloured, which doesn't reach as far as her thighs. The embroidered hem rides up on her buttocks. They look just like the croup of a plump little nag.

Not to mention Father Vesga's face if he knew about it. 'You have lost your purity,' that's what he would say. What about his own? That obsession of his with the Sixth Commandment—thou shalt not fornicate. I believe that sometimes he just couldn't contain himself on those wooden boards he had for his bed. Now I realize why he always looked at females as he did.

There was a woman who kept a shop in the Calle de Mesón de

Paredes, who had him for her Father Confessor. She was tall and big and had a splendid bosom. Father Vesga, tiny as he was, must have felt quite smothered by her in his confessional box. When confession was over, she always went to say her penitential prayers to the right of the altar beside the boys in rank and file. Father Vesga used to come out, red in the face from the heat in that narrow box, to stand behind her and stare at her hips and the little curls on the nape of her neck. He kept turning his four-cornered biretta round and round in his hands, and then he slapped it smack into some boy's face. 'That's for talking.' The woman turned her head, smiled, and said: 'Don't be so hard!' The boy stood there, crying silently, and Father Vesga dished out slaps with his biretta all along the file.

In the end the woman rose and walked away slowly, swinging her hips. 'Good-bye, Father,' she said softly as she passed him, and kissed his hand. 'The Lord be with you, my daughter.' He inspected the end of the file to see whether all the boys were listening to Mass, and not playing or squatting on their heels. But in reality he was looking after her, after the tall woman who swayed her hindquarters from one side to the other, like a mule. Afterwards he would kneel beside the altar, pray, and smite his breast. He unfastened his cassock and beat his flesh with his closed fist. I think he sometimes even clawed at it with his nails: once the chain of his small lady's watch was torn.

What would Father Vesga in his cassock have been like between the thighs of that Maña? The strong thighs of a woman from Aragon. She saw all right that it was the first time I was with a woman, and she made good use of me. Well, why not? But it would be funny to see Father Vesga, after always sleeping on his bare boards, between Maña's thighs on the soft, sprung bed, with her breasts rubbing against his face, because he is so small that he wouldn't reach higher. That Maña is very tall, taller than me, and I am taller than most of the men here.

If Uncle José knew it, he would say very seriously: 'Well, my boy, I won't say that you shouldn't do those things. We've all done them. But take care where you go, and above all don't let your aunt know.' He would give me a duro on Sunday, wink at me and chuckle.

When we were children—when I was a child, that is, because his hair and his moustache were already white—he used to come back from the office with the *Imparcial*; I threw myself down on the dining-room carpet to read and he would throw himself down beside me. At first he sat on the floor and then he stretched himself out on it. My aunt would cry: 'Pepe, have you gone mad?' 'Now you shut up, my dear.' He taught me the letters from the headlines, the b.s and the a.s, and taught me to read 'ba'. At half-past three he said: 'Now let's go to the pictures, the film starts at four.' And I went out clutching his hand, still dressed in a smock, in my grand overcoat with many big, shimmering mother-of-pearl buttons. That's how I learnt to read.

Uncle Luis wouldn't be angry either. He won't be angry—for he at least is still alive. As soon as he comes to Madrid I must tell him about it. Perhaps he'll burst out into one of his 'Uuuh' cries. He'll say: 'Make the most of it, boy, you'll get old anyhow. Now look at me. I've got rheumatics and can hardly move any more. But when I was your age—uuh—I knew what to do with the wenches!' He must have been a rascal. And Andrés too. His wife's eternally ill with her leg festering, and so he says to my mother every time he comes to Madrid: 'Don't wait for me this evening, I'm going to sleep at the inn.' At the inn, my foot! At the 'Lovers' Inn'. I must go and see the show called Lovers' Inn or something of the sort. It's on at the Eslava Theatre and the women come on the stage quite naked, and everybody who goes to that inn wants to go to bed with them.

Look at those two sweethearts arm in arm. I'm sure that they want each other, both of them. And that whole story with Enriqueta is over and done with. If she wants to she can sleep with me, and if not we're through. I can get a woman for a duro. I don't want any more cuddling in the cinema.

Of course, now I know what it is all about. My cousin, too, made good use of me. I was eight or nine years old at that time. She was in service in the Calle de Vergara, and her masters used to go out for a walk after lunch so that she was left alone in the house. She always kept cakes and sweets for me. It was a place where there were a lot of sweets and cakes. But sometimes my cousin may have bought them to get me there. She also gave me oranges and bananas. I used to go there towards four in the afternoon, and when I came she was always in her chemise. 'You woke me up,' she would say. Then she would give me sweets and fruit and lie back on her bed again. 'Sit down here beside me, I'm so tired. If you like, take off your things and rest a bit.' Then we romped about on the bed and tickled each other. She became excited and rubbed her body against mine and then she threw herself down, stretched out on her back, quite exhausted. I liked the warmth of her body and its smell, I liked to pull the curly hairs in her arm-pits. Once I started pulling at the little curls in the other place. She said: 'Put your hand here. You'll see how warm it is. We women aren't made like you men. Let's have a look at you,' and kissed me all over so as to tickle me, and then she burst out laughing. 'Now look at you,' she said. After that day she amused herself by playing with me and rubbing her body against me.

That was people's secret, and now I knew what it was. I don't want to have anything to do with Enriqueta any more. And if my cousin were to come now and rub herself against me, I would teach her something, the dirty bitch! She took advantage of my being a child. But in a way she was right. She couldn't go to bed with a man without being a tart, and so she consoled herself some other way. Why can't everybody do as they want? I would like to go to bed with girls, and they would like to go to bed with me, but we can't. Men have whores for that; but women must wait until the priest marries them. Or they must become whores themselves. And of course, in the meantime, they get excited. If one of them gets too hot, she must become a tart. It would be much better if they could all go to bed with whomever they liked. And why not?

Of course, then I would not know who my father is, and my mother would have been a whore who slept with anyone. It's funny. I've never imagined my mother like that, as a woman who had slept with a man and done the same with him as that Maña with me. But there's no doubt that if she had not slept with my father, I should not have been born, nor Rafael, nor Concha, nor José.

José! He must be twenty-two now. I'm sure he's never yet slept with a woman. All those unmarried, bigoted girl-cousins won't let him leave the house except to accompany them. He said in his last letter that cousin Elvira wanted to marry him. They're sure to cuddle without much on. Elvira saying that she isn't well, and José going up to her bedroom to visit her. 'Come in, come in, it's all right for you to come in,' she will say, and then the two of them will get all excited. And because it's getting too much for them, she wants to catch him for good. Perhaps she'll even get him, because he must be crazy to get a woman. And where else should he go? He hasn't got the courage to go to a brothel and to take a woman to bed with him. And besides, you can't do that sort of thing in Cordova as you can in Madrid. In Cordova everybody knows everybody else, and the next day all the world and his wife would know that José had been in such and such a house.

I seem to have turned philosopher. I talk about the facts of life. And why shouldn't I have the right to think about life? Perhaps because I'm not yet twenty-one and can't dispose freely of my belongings? Damn it all! What is life? The shutter of a camera. You press the bulb. Pff! A snap. You've seen nothing: just a little flash. Like the calves of the girl getting on to that tram. A flash! Are her legs ugly or pretty? I don't know; but to-day I like all legs. Oh well, let's leave the women out of it. What is life? That's more interesting.

From up here, from the highest spot of the slope of the Calle de

Alcalá, I'm seeing life. Sunday morning. The Church of Calatravas, with its sellers of Catholic newspapers, its blind men, its old beggar-women, its urchins on the lookout for carriages so that they can open doors and beg for a copper. With its rows of nice young ladies walking beside nice young gentlemen who bend over them and whisper into the curls behind their ears. When the girls hear something pleasant, they shake their ear-rings, which hang down like big drops, just as horses shake their ears when a motor-car passes. There are the tramcars with their clang-clang and their yellow-and-red bellies covered with advertisements. The solid stone houses, with their windows open or shuttered. The iron tram-rails between the square paving stones a-glitter with mica. The sidewalks of black asphalt, whitened by the dust of shoe-soles and studded with cigarette-ends. The round marble tables on the terraces, milk-white or mottled black. The clock of the Bank of Spain, a grave gentleman who sings out the hours with a voice like an old copper cauldron: Boom, boom! The goddess Cibele with her serious face and her bored lions who spit water in all directions. Aquatic lions. Where is the Sahara for those lions? One night, Pedro de Répide wrapped the goddess Cibele in his cloth cape the colour of well-roasted coffee, and so the dawn found her. She had icicles hanging from her nostrils, but she was sweating under the cape. Pedro de Répide had to pay a fine. Who had asked him to cloak statues? And up there, in the Puerta de Alcalá, the gate with its three arches and the Latin inscription, *Carolus Rex . . .*

Is that life?

Of course, in Paris and London and Peking there are streets just like this, ant-heaps where people take their walks or go to Mass. The stories tell that Chinese temples have a lot of pointed roofs, with a silver or even a golden bell on each point tinkling in the wind, and outside the gate, slung on three huge posts, an ancient bronze gong over a thousand years old. When Mass is going to be said—Chinese 'Mass', of course—the oldest of the bonzes—their priests are called bonzes—comes out with a wooden mallet and strikes the gong. It sounds in the far distance like a cascade of quavering 'ploms'. The Chinese come with short little steps, bounding on their toes, their hands hidden in their sleeves and the knobs on their skull-caps dancing, and they climb the temple stairs in short little leaps. They kneel down and double up their bellies a thousand-and-one times in front of a grave Buddha with a polished navel. Then they burn strips of paper, which are their prayers. Rather like when Father Vesga told me to copy the Credo a hundred times. When the Chinese grow old, they have pigtails curved outwards and long

255

moustaches that hang down in two lanky strands. But it's funny: in pictures and photographs I've seen a lot of Chinese with white moustaches and beards, but I've never seen a Chinese with a white pigtail, and I've never seen a Chinese woman with white hair.

But there are so many things in the world. Trains starting punctually, with their punctual passengers and their punctual engineers and station-masters. The station-master blows a whistle and the train starts. Harbours with ships riding close to the stone walls of the jetties, while people laden with luggage climb up a small wooden gangway and blow kisses to those who stay behind. A bell tolls and the gangway is withdrawn. A whistle blows and the ship begins to move. Some people stay quietly on land, waving their handkerchiefs, and others lean over the ship's railing. When a ship leaves, everybody has a clean handkerchief, a handkerchief without a snivel, because people would speak badly of anyone who used a dirty handkerchief to wave farewell.

Is that life?

To run up and down the Calle de Alcalá in Madrid, or some other street like it in Paris or London or China. To get on a train, to board a ship. To hear Mass or to burn strips of paper on an altar, before Our Lady or before Buddha's paunch. To ring great cathedral bells or to strike a bronze gong with a mallet or to let the wind sway little bells.

And that is life?

Old people, grown-up people, teach children what life is like. I am no longer a child. I am working, I am already sleeping with women. But the school still sticks to me as bits of egg-shell stick to a chick's bottom. Let's sit down here on the bench in the Retiro Park. I'll review what the old people have taught me about life. Back—back—think. Look into the far distance.

What do you want, you sparrows? I haven't got any crumbs in my pockets. Don't flutter up and down in front of me. This is serious, and you're a lot of little rascals. Let me see whether I can remember the time when I was small, like you, and then I may discover what the grown-up people have taught me about life.

My grandmother told me—but no. Before they told you anything where were you then? Before you understood what they told you, where were you?

First was a morning. It snowed fat flakes, like big white flies tumbling down from high up in a daze. My mother dressed me up in petticoats and woollen stockings which she tied round my middle with white ribbons full of knots. She put on my boots, boots with plenty of buttons, and we went out into the streets. I in her arms,

wrapped in a shaggy shawl like a sheepskin that hasn't been clipped.
Beautifully warm, and my nose sticking out of the cowl of the big
shawl. A column of steam rose into the air every time I breathed out
of my open mouth. I had fun blowing, because it made a funnel of
grey air which drifted away in the street like smoke from a cigarette.
The trolley of the tram was covered with blobs of ice. In a big portal
two soldiers were standing near a huge brazier filled with burning
coal. One of the soldiers had his foot on the edge of a dark blanket.
the other held its other end and waved it like a fan. The current of air
hit the brazier and the coal burst into a shower of sparks which the
wind carried down the street and smothered in the snow. They
hissed, they squealed because the cold hurt them. Then I felt that my
feet were cold. They were sticking out from under the shawl and
snow had fallen on them. I laughed, because one of my boots was
black and the other brown. My mother looked at my boots and
laughed with me. We stayed for a while in the warmth of the brazier
and we all laughed, the soldiers, my mother, and I, while the melting
snow dripped from my boots. When they stopped dripping, my
mother bundled me up, with my feet inside the shawl, and we walked
down the street. The snow drifted against our faces.

That is my first clear childhood memory. Then came a black hole
from which everything emerged by and by, I don't know when and
how: uncle and aunt, brothers and sister, the attic, Señora Pascuala,
. . . one day they came and put themselves into life, into my life.
Then they began to fill life for me with 'do's' and 'don't's'. 'Don't
do this'—'Do that'. Sometimes they themselves didn't agree. 'Do
this,' one said; 'don't do it,' said the other.

Once we were in a theatre, I don't know which. I only remember
the red velvet of the chair, just like the red velvet of the sofas in the
Café Español, and the bright stage where men and women were
singing. I wanted to make water. 'Uncle, I want to pass water.' He
nodded. 'All right, come with me.' 'What's the matter with the
child?' asked my aunt. 'He wants to do his little business.' 'He can
wait.' 'But, my dear, he's a child.' 'He must wait. Arturito, be good.'
I wetted the red velvet seat and no-one heard the small splash, because the music made so much noise. When the curtain had fallen,
my uncle said: 'Now come along.' 'I don't need to now,' I answered.
They both went on scolding me for days and days.

At that time they all started teaching me when it was right and
when it was wrong to make water or the other, when it was right to
speak and when it was right to be quiet. When I was crying, they
told me: Men don't cry. Then, when somebody died, men and
women came in tears to tell us about it. Don't scream! Children must

not say blasphemies! And then grown-up people shouted at each other and most of them blasphemed against God and Our Lady. Uncle, too, swore and said dirty things at times. Even the Fathers at school. There was Father Fulgencio who played the organ and was our chemistry teacher. He used to scribble formulas all over the blackboard, take a few test tubes, mix salts and acids, explain their reactions and then say: 'Have you got it?' Hardly any of us had understood it. Then he banged on the table: 'You've bloody well got to understand. What the bloody hell is the use of my teaching you if you don't understand?' There was a daft boy in the class, another of those sons of rich fathers, I don't remember his name. One day Father Fulgencio fastened on him: 'Have you got this?' 'No, I can't understand the bloody thing,' he answered. Father Fulgencio boxed his ears for him. 'What do you mean by using bad language? Who taught you such an ugly word? What a bloody life one has with these boys!' One day he sat down at the organ and pressed one of the keys, but the pipe gave no sound. He stopped playing and pushed away at the key. The organ sounded pffff, in a long wheeze, but no more. He got up and marched us off through the cloisters. There he met another of the priests who asked him: 'What is it, Brother Fulgencio, why are you in a bad temper?' 'Well,' he said, 'there's an *f*, a bitch of a key, that doesn't sound at all.' With Chinese ink we painted its name, 'Bitch', on the yellow key. Father Fulgencio went quite mad. 'Who's done this? You shameless rascals!' And he struck the key hard. The organ pipe, thick as an arm, gave back: Pfff!

⸢They taught us the Catechism and Biblical history before anything else. They taught me to read, and then they taught me to read nothing except what they permitted. They taught me to count, to add, to subtract, to shunt figures and letters, to use the signs of plus and minus, of minus-plus and plus-minus, roots, powers, logarithms. To draw beautiful letters of the kind called English writing, with fat strokes and thin strokes, which you had to write slowly with your hand placed right and your arm placed right and your body poised right and your bottom sitting right in its chair and the sheet of paper in its right place. Then the Bank: 'This handwriting is no good—discount must be calculated like this—interest must be calculated like that—pounds sterling must be calculated in such-and-such a way.' And the postures for the English script, and the rule-of-three are just good for nothing, and Biblical history too, and the Catechism even more so.

'Be good,' they all said. 'Don't fight with the other boys.' Once I came home with a black eye. The whole family jumped on me: 'You little runt, you cry-baby, you let them beat you! You ought to have knocked his brains open with a stone, you ought to have kicked him in the belly!' I went away, out into the street, and looked for the boy who had hit me. I was sorry for him, because he was weak and small, and he had hit me in the eye without meaning to while we were playing. But I had a fight with him and hit him with my fists in his face, mainly the eyes, so that they should turn black like mine. A trickle of blood ran from his nose. I threw him on the ground and kicked him in the ribs and loins. He screamed. Then Pablito's father, the plasterer, came and separated us. First he boxed my ears, then he picked me up and carried me upstairs to our flat, the other boy in front of me, bleeding and with torn clothes. What a row they made! Uncle José slapped me, my aunt pinched me, my mother spanked me. They all shouted at me and called me a savage and I don't know what else; but they stuffed the other boy with sweets, biscuits, and coppers. He went off grinning and crying, and I would have liked to hit the whole lot of them. 'It's he who gave me the black eye! I kicked him in the belly and smashed his face for him because you told me to. And now you thrash *me* and give *him* biscuits!' I cried, tumbled on the dining-room carpet. Uncle José said: 'But, my goodness, if you beat somebody you must do it within bounds.'

And so I learnt to respect the grown-ups. Señor Corachán is a grown-up man, a 'gentleman'. One day he pulled my ears and called me a vagabond. I kept silent, but I would have liked to kick him in the belly, too.

They have all taught me how to live. And nothing they taught me is any good for living. Nothing, absolutely nothing. Not their figures and not their Biblical history. They've deceived me. Life is not what they teach it to be, it's different. They've deceived me, and so I must learn for myself about life. Plá has taught me more than all the others. And so has Uncle Luis with his rude words, and Señor Manuel with his innocent labourer's mind, and my cousin with her hot stuff, and that Maña in her short chemise. But the others who educate boys so as to turn them into 'men'—what have they taught me? Only Father Joaquín once told me that I should believe what I felt to be good, and to say that cost him an effort as though he were betraying a secret.

Why rack one's brains about it?

But I would like to know what life is. I don't know what my mother was like as a little girl; when she was young she was in ser-vice, then she married and my father earned only just enough to keep them going, then he died and she was worse off than ever with her four children. Without my uncle and aunt the five of us might have starved to death. So off with her to wash clothes in the river, the mucky linen of rich people who can pay a washerwoman. The rich people. What are the rich?

Do you know who the rich people are, you sparrow? Of course you know, it must be those who throw you crumbs not of bread but of cake. Those are the rich ones for you. As soon as one of the women who sell buns passes, I shall buy one for you and throw you crumbs. Then you'll say I'm rich. The rich are people who throw cake crumbs to the birds and bread crumbs to the poor like my mother. You know —do listen, you little fool, don't fly away, the cake will come afterwards. You know, there's Señor Dotti, the millionaire for whom my mother does all the washing. He's married, and his wife once said to my mother: 'Leonor, do you know how much we spent this year on toys for the children?' 'No, madam,' said my mother. 'Twenty-four thousand pesetas, six thousand duros. And still they aren't content, just imagine, Leonor.'

My mother said: 'Madam, with that money we could have lived for a whole year, without my having to go to the river.'

They gave me all the old toys of the year before, so many that I had to make three trips by tram to fetch the things home. There were enough toys for us all. I got an engine which could run by itself; it had a little spirit lamp in place of the boiler and when you poured water in it started running just like a real engine. There were hundreds of lead soldiers, and motor-cars with doors which opened and shut, and dolls which could say 'Mama' and 'Papa'. Concha came home after her washing-up and carried the dolls off. She was already in service, but she was still a little girl. In her spare time she knitted frocks for the dolls. Why did they ever buy dolls for their two boys? Señora Dotti told my mother: 'They were keen on them—so what could I do about it?' Then the boys got tired of the dolls and threw them aside. Those old toys are still stowed in a corner of our attic, behind my books. But I don't feel like having them out. I'm no child any more. Sometimes it amuses me to play with a huge gyroscope, to let it gyrate on the rim of a glass or run along a string stretched across the attic.

Well, that is what being rich means. Señor Dotti has got a telephone in his house, and he has two houses, one in Madrid, one in Barcelona. When he stays in Madrid he rings up Barcelona every morning, and when he stays in Barcelona, he always rings up Madrid. When he's told that there's nothing new at the other end, he goes off to the Exchange. There he makes a few thousand pesetas, and goes home again. He puts on a frock-coat or a cutaway and invites people home to tea. His boys wash and brush their hair and go in to kiss the hands of the lady visitors. Once one of the boys,

Alejandro, was not allowed to sit at table during meals for a week, as a punishment. His father had come home from the Exchange, very pleased with himself because he had made a lot of money. He opened the door with his latchkey, took off his hat, and by chance went into the kitchen. There he found Alejandro sitting on the floor together with the dog, a very beautiful bitch, and the two of them eating the dog's *cocido*. For in Dotti's house a special stew for the dogs was cooked every day, with meat, sausage, and chick-peas; Alejandro used to come to the kitchen and share it with the bitch. When my mother heard the story and how they had punished him, she said to his mother: 'Send him to our attic for a week and you'll see how quickly he gets tired of eating *cocido*.' That's how things go with the rich.

One day a few masons were sitting under the arches of the Plaza Mayor and eating saffron-yellow *cocido*, the kind my mother always cooks down by the river. An elegant carriage stopped in front of them, a gentleman and a lady got out, and he said to one of the workers: 'Let me buy your *cocido* off you.' The mason stared at him and said, 'I don't want to.' 'Now look here,' said the other, 'my wife is expecting a baby and she feels she wants to eat *cocido*.' The mason answered: 'Well, she'll have to do without.' But the mason's wife was there and made him give them the *cocido*; they carried the pots with the dish to the carriage and gave the worker fifty pesetas. He said to his wife: 'I wouldn't have given it them—perhaps she would have produced a boy with the mark of a stew-pot on his belly.'

And is this life, then? A rich man can afford to spend six thousand duros on toys, and to telephone to Barcelona just to know whether there's anything new at home, and to buy a mason's *cocido* off him?

Be quiet, you sparrow. Where did you get those grains from? Now look, there's a whole column of ants crawling backwards, each carrying a grain of wheat. Aren't you ashamed to eat the grain they carry with so much labour, and perhaps to swallow the ant as well while it sticks to its grain, clutching at it with its horny, black teeth? I wonder where they get hold of corn here in the Park? Perhaps from the ducks. I don't know whether I ought to make you drop the grain or not. Perhaps there's a little sparrow in your nest, waiting to swallow the ant and the grain you bring with you. I remember the swallows in the courtyard of the Palace chasing flies and gnats with those shrill hunting cries of theirs, carrying them off and dropping them into the square, wide-open, never-filled beaks of their young. Perhaps you're right, sparrow, perhaps you have a right to the ants' grain.

Is this life? To take away each other's food? To devour each other?

Watch out, sparrow, here's a little boy with a bun who wants to feed you. Silly, why do you run away and fly off? Now then, do go and eat—closer to him. Look how he smiles and holds out crumbs between his fingertips. He wants you to come and peck at them. That fat crumb is meant to tempt you. Is that life: to give for the pleasure of giving, to take for the pleasure of taking?

People are taking their walks, nursemaids keeping the children in front of them so that they shouldn't get lost, and screaming as soon as the children go too far away. Lovers leaning against each other. Old women sit there knitting socks on long steel needles, with quick, deft movements and flashes as from sword blades. When they get up they limp from rheumatics, but now while they're sitting their fingers fly like a conjurer's. They call to their grand-children who shovel sand into brightly painted tin buckets. How sad the little boy is, the one over there in the perambulator with rubber tyres, kicking his feet and waving his arms and wanting to run about, instead of being stuck among the cushions that keep him from crawling on the ground. Now he starts crying. You fool of a mother, take him out of that black oilcloth box on wire-spoke wheels, put him on the ground, tumbled on his back or his tummy, let him scratch about in the sand or catch ants or splash in the mud and smear his face with black streaks. Don't you see he's crying because that's what he wants? The papa lights a cigar and goes on reading the paper: 'Can't you keep the boy quiet?' 'But what shall I do with him?' 'Give him the breast and he'll shut up.' The lady sits down on the fretted iron chair which has produced coppers for so many years, and pulls out one of her breasts. A flabby breast with a big, black nipple which looks as though it were hairy. The kid doesn't take it. Of course he doesn't. He wants to stick his fingers in the earth and make mud-balls with the palm of his hand. He goes on crying, and the mother doesn't understand him. You silly goose, you animal, why do you slap and shake him and scream: 'Be quiet—be quiet!' Do you think he understands you? You nasty brute. You lay him out in his perambulator as if he were a stuffed sack. I can see it in your face that, if you could, you would throw him away from you, like a dead frog—you would hold him by one leg and dash him on the ground so as not to hear him crying any more. 'Now see what a silly fool you are,' says the papa, and he's right. But he is as much of a silly fool as she is.

Is this life?

The path by the lake is deserted. The sunlight pours down, the sand is scorching hot. Why not bathe in the sun? Why not go where nobody else goes? In the big lake people are rowing boats, but the steam launch which takes children twice round the square basin is anchored. Anchored. No, it's tied to a rope, ridiculously anchored. There is no tide here. Just now the benches of the launch are clean. When it's full of children they can stretch out their hands and trail them in the water without fear of sharks biting them. The mammas imagine they are at sea and get sick behind their black mantillas. Then the boatman's lad, who always sings out the number of boats which have been out for the full half-hour of their hire, takes the ladies by the arm, gives them a cup of tea, gets a peseta's worth of a tip out of them, and shows off, standing up and walking about in the boats without falling, like a real sailor. 'There you see, lady, it's quite easy, it's just practice.'

But I'm grown-up now, and this is life. All this, all this together. So much the better. This is life, life is like this. One day I'll throw crumbs to the fishes or the sparrows, another I'll get sick in a boat, and still another I'll fish fishes or shoot birds. Yes, sir, it's necessary to scold little children when they cry. What, you've given him a perambulator and he cries? A perambulator with rubber tyres? That couple must be rich. Some day I'm going to have a son, but my wife won't have black nipples like that woman's. How can a rich man marry a woman with black nipples? That's to say, she may be the rich one of the two, and then he's right, of course. What do black nipples matter if one's rich? For that is the only thing that counts: to be rich. That's living.

But perhaps not. We aren't rich in our attic, but we're happy.

Oh, there's Father Joaquín. He must have come here for a walk after Mass. Really, he's a fine man. I would like to look like that, tall, strong, broad-shouldered, as they say all Basques are. His cassock suits him well, because he's got no belly and a chest like a barrel. With most other priests the buttons on their cassock—how many are there, thirty to forty?—mark a curve that sinks in under their chin and protrudes over their belly in a row of shiny dots. But not his. The buttons curve out on his chest and recede on his stomach and then go straight down to his legs, which seem to break out of the cassocks as he walks.

I don't know the people with him. A lady leading a little boy by the hand. The boy is very serious for his age, but strong, much stronger than I had been.

Hat in hand, I walked at Father Joaquín's side. The woman and the boy came behind us.

'Are you out for a walk, Arturo?'

'Yes, I've got one of my attacks. I was thinking.'

'What have you been thinking?'

263

'Well, I don't know, really. Stupid things. About life and death and animals. I've been laughing over a sparrow and a little boy in a perambulator with rubber wheels. What do I know? My mother says it's my growing up. I don't know what it is. And then . . .'

'Then, what?'

'Nothing . . . no . . . Nothing.'

I had gone red, I felt it in my cheeks. But how could I have told him that I had slept with a woman for the first time in my life and that she wore a short pink chemise. . . .

Father Joaquín stroked my head as so often before and turned round to the others, to the woman and the boy who walked so gravely behind us.

'Do come here,' he said.

He took the woman by the hand and drew her closer. He put his other hand, broad and strong, with fair fluff on the knuckles, on the boy's shoulder and pulled him nearer. He placed them in front of me; and the three of us, the woman, the boy, and I, were waiting for something to happen, waiting for something very big.

He only said: 'My wife and my son . . . Here you have Arturo.'

We walked together on the sun-filled path along the lake, silent, without a word, and looked at the water in the square basin so that we should not catch each other's eyes. We walked slowly and the path had no end.

Then I left them with an awkward good-bye, stumbling over my own feet. And I never dared to turn my head so as not to see the three of them looking at each other, looking at me.

X. REBEL

Everything was arranged. We four men would sleep in the old attic, Rafael and I once again together in my gilt bed, and Uncle Luis and Andrés in my mother's double-bed with its green frame and the faded saints on sheet-iron panels fretted by the years and insecticides. The women, my mother and Concha, were going to sleep in the other attic which was formerly Señora Francisca's.

Señora Francisca had died and left behind nothing but a few blackened pots and pans and a basketful of monkeynuts, sweets, and squibs such as she used to sell to children in the Plaza del Progreso. We took over her attic room, as it was next door to ours, and inherited her belongings, the old clothes, cooking-pots, goods for sale, and a truckle-bed with a black wool mattress. Nobody claimed this inheritance, so we chopped up the bedstead for firewood, and shared the rest with the tenants of the other attics.

Rafael and I moved into the new room. In daytime it was used as the kitchen, because it had a little stove with a chimney-pipe in a corner under the sloping roof, and as Concha's workshop. Concha had left Dr. Chicote's service and had learnt the laundry trade, paying for the training herself, because she did not want to go on working as a housemaid. As my mother was a washerwoman, Concha easily found customers. She spent the days heating her irons in the corner under the roof and ironing clothes or linen on a deal table more than three yards square, which filled the middle of the attic. Now the two women slept by themselves, and so did Rafael and I; sometimes we stayed away for a night, thanks to our independence. Yet at the same time we were together. Besides the two big beds, the round table my father had made, our crockery and our linen were still in the old attic—all our wealth. That day we had to make room for four and needed the big beds, so we changed places with the women.

Uncle Luis and Andrés had arrived together, but each on a different errand. Andrés was on his way to Toledo where he meant to spend three days with his son Fidel, the seminarist; his wife Elvira had stayed behind in Méntrida, bedridden because of her festering leg. Uncle Luis had come, as he often did, to buy the iron for his horseshoes, iron in rods, soft and black, which had never been touched by fire since it left the crucible.

Every time I saw Uncle Luis buying iron I was reminded of the times I had seen him tasting wine. He would make the round of the underground wine-cellars of Méntrida with a dipper, and take a small quantity out of each wine-jar, just enough to fill half the glass which he had rinsed most carefully. He would look at the wine against the light, take a sip 'to wash his mouth', roll it round his tongue, say nothing, rinse his glass, and try another wine-jar. Suddenly he would firmly grasp the glass, plunge it into the jar as though it were the dipper, draw it out filled to the rim, and pour it down his gullet. And so a second time, and a third. The owner of the cellar would ask him: 'What do you think of it, Luis?' 'This jar here is our Saviour's own blood, the rest can be poured away.'

He did the same with the iron. He would enter the stores of the *Cava Baja*, stooping his huge body, and ask for iron, just like that:

265

'I want iron.' All the owners knew him and would get out rods two and four yards long. He would weigh them, stroke them with the tip of a finger, make them ring with his knuckles, and drop them back on the heap, until he came to a heap where he would stop, holding the iron rod high, and ask: 'How much?' When he had made the deal, he would double the finger-thick rods with his bare hands, tie them up in a bundle and carry them away on his shoulder, as though he were going to march straight from the Cava Baja to Méntrida and so start forging them then and there. Sometimes he would pat the rods and say: 'Pure gold!'

Rafael and I fixed the centre leaf of the table so that six of us should have room. My mother produced one of her white tablecloths and started laying the table. At eight both of our guests were back from their business. Andrés arrived laden with parcels, good things to eat and clothing for his boy. Uncle Luis carried a single parcel which he handled like a club. He banged it on the table and guffawed: 'It sounds hard, doesn't it?' Then he unwrapped it and took out a smoke-cured ham, dry and hard as wood. 'Give me a knife, Leonor.'

He cut it in the middle to show the almost purple meat, of which he sliced off a strip for each of us. My mother protested:

'Now look, leave that to take home.'

'Never mind, eat and shut up, you never know what willl happen to-morrow.'

He filled a glass to the brim with wine and tossed it off: 'And now let's have supper.'

At the beginning of the meal we were all silent, for the slice of ham had made us hungry and anyway we did not know what to say first. Uncle Luis started the ball rolling. He addressed me:

'Well, and what about you?'

'I'm working.'

'He's settled for life,' said Andrés. 'He's had better luck than my boy who'll have to stay nine years in that seminary.'

Uncle Luis crunched a chop between his teeth, wiped his greasy lips with the back of his hand, and turned round to Andrés:

'Well, it'll be funny if in nine years' time the boy hangs his cassock on a nail and runs after some skirt or other!'

'If the boy does that to me, I'll kill him. There I have been sacrificing myself for him all my life, and if he goes and chucks away the priest's habit and becomes a good-for-nothing I'll kill him!'

'T-t-t, what d'you call sacrifice? The seminary doesn't cost you a thing. They're letting him study free, because they need more silly

266

little priests, and you've a mouth less to feed at home. You've even got savings by now.'

'But you forget that it's a sacrifice to be separated from one's son for eleven years, only because one wants him to become a man.'

'To become a man! Come now, d'you think I'm a silly fool? You may do it because you want him to become a priest, but not a man. Priests can be men, but they can't act as men. And that's your doing. When your boy's grown up he'll be either a man or a priest, but never both things at the same time.'

'Let's leave it, Luis, there's no discussing things with you.'

'Of course there isn't. I'm such a rough brute that I won't swallow anything which might hurt me inside. I call bread, bread and wine, wine.' To stress his words he wiped his plate with a chunk of bread big enough to fill his mouth, and poured down another glass of wine. Then, when his plate was clean, he planted both elbows on the table and went on:

'Now listen. You're wrong, both of you. She here'—he nodded towards my mother—'and you. You've got the same bee in your bonnets as all the other starvelings, you want your boy to be a Prince of the Blood. Look at him'—he pointed at me—'so smart and fine, so nice to look at, with his white face, starched collar, silk tie, elegant suit—with two pesetas salary, living in a garret and his mother washing clothes. They've taught him to be ashamed of his mother being a washerwoman.'

'I'm *not* ashamed because my mother's a washerwoman,' I said.

'Oh no? And how many of your friends at the Bank come to visit you here?'

I flushed and gave no answer.

'D'you see it?' Uncle Luis said to Andrés. 'Just like you. I bet your boy doesn't tell it to others in the seminary that he's a master-mason's son, and I bet you don't have the guts to turn up at Toledo in your white overall. In Leonor's case one can still excuse it, because she's a woman, and because of a lot of other things as well. But what have you got to say? You're as well off as me. God won't forgive you—if there's such a thing as God anyhow. Every man to his trade. My boys are hammering iron now, and when they're men they can do what they feel like, but they'll always be able to earn their bread and they won't be ashamed of being blacksmiths like their father. And if it comes to being well off, you bet they won't be slow, they're going to be richer than you and your boy, even if he is made a canon.'

'That's just what I don't want,' said Andrés in a slightly hoarse voice. 'I don't want my boy to have to carry pails, mix plaster, and

267

whitewash walls in a blazing sun. What I'm doing is for his good, and one day he'll thank me for it.'

'And when he sees a pretty girl passing and feels like having a woman, he'll call his father a bastard, cassock and all.'

'Now come, come, the boy isn't quite a fool, and when he feels like being with a woman he'll take one to bed.'

'That's just it. And you'll have turned him into a hypocrite or a poor wretch. My boy, Aquilino, already has an eye on the girls. Now he's hammering iron at the forge, and when a girl passes he tells her she's pretty. And if she let's him go on, the worst that happens is that the next day he finds the sledge-hammer a little heavier than before. But he does his work with more pleasure than ever and eats like a devil and walks with his head high because he's got nothing to be ashamed of. The boy here's lucky in that it will be the same with him. But then all he'll ever be is a pen-pusher, a little gentleman who marries some consumptive girl in a hat, and afterwards the two of them will go crazy with hunger on thirty duros a month.'

'So in your opinion one oughtn't to worry about one's children becoming something better?'

'Better than oneself, yes. But not something different. Now I've got everything. I've got my wife and my children and the smithy, and thank God we're all in good health. And then there's my bit of wheatland and my strip of orchard, and the pig and the wine, and the figs for dessert. Well, my boys have got all that too, and later on they can make it more by working hard, just as I did. In my house there's no God and no King and no nothing. I'm the master there, and nobody's my master. So why should I want to be richer if I'm my own master and have all I need?'

'What should I have done then?' asked my mother, who had listened to the men, silent and quiet.

'You? You've done quite enough by bringing them up and not turning them into priests. Now it's up to them to take care of you.'

'Well, I work like a donkey,' Concha said.

'What else did you imagine, my dear girl? I work like a horse. And that's just our lot in this world, to work like beasts. But at least we must have the right to kick now and then,' said Uncle Luis.

Rafael lifted his head for the first time and said:

'All it comes to is that because we're poor we must put up with things. You've got everything settled, and so you're happy. But I'd like to see you in my office writing out invoices and getting thirty pesetas at the end of the month.'

'Well, d'you know what I'd do? I'd take my cap and shut the door from the outside. The trouble with you is that you've got an easy life

268

in your office and you don't want to work. Come with me to Méntrida to handle the sledge-hammer, and I'll teach you the trade and keep you. Of course you'll get black, and it won't wash off, and your hands will get horny.'

Until that moment I had kept out of the discussion because I knew I was near bursting point. But when I found that all of them put things in the wrong way, I cut in.

'I think you're all wrong. You're in love with your trade, Uncle, and you've been happy at it. But your sons won't be able to live on your trade, and you know it. Hand-forged horseshoes and wrought-iron grilles are all over and done with. You and I, we've seen horseshoes of pressed steel in all sizes, like boots, when we were in the stores of the Cava Baja. The only customers you've got left are old friends of yours. Now ask Andrés, who's a master builder and has built houses, how many orders for wrought-iron grilles he's given you. He'll tell you that he buys them from stock in Madrid, cheaper than the iron rods you buy for horseshoes.'

'There's nothing like a forged horseshoe from the fire straight on to a horse's hoof. It's like boots made to measure,' shouted Uncle Luis, and banged on the table.

'Just so,' I answered. 'When Uncle Sebastian was thirty he shod the whole village. But to-day—to-day he's glad if he's given shoes to sole, because sneakers are cheaper and last longer than half-soles on an old shoe.'

'That's just what I'm saying,' cried Andrés.

'No, it isn't. I may be a pen-pusher, but after all I'm doing a job. But your son is a budding priest, and that's no job. And then, there will always be clerks, but very soon it will be all over with priests. People are getting fed up with feeding loafers who bellow Latin.'

'That's just being rude. But never mind. There will always be religion.'

'Are you religious?' I asked Andrés.

'Well, to tell the truth, it's of no matter to me. If I feel like saying a bad word I do it, because it's a relief.'

'So why do you want your son to become a priest? You don't believe in God, or you don't mind whether you do or don't. But you turn your son into a priest so that he can exploit the others with the help of a God you don't believe in. And the worst of it is that you leave him without having learnt any trade or profession, and, as Uncle Luis says, you've prevented him from being a man.'

'Now that's all hot air. Everybody acts as he thinks best, and my boy will do what I want him to. That's my good right as his father.'

'You've no right at all. Parents have no rights.'

269

Andrés and Uncle Luis gaped at me. My mother looked at her hands. Rafael lifted his hanging head once again and gave me a side-wise look. Concha put her two fists on the table as though she were going to knock me down. I spoke on, looking round from one to the other.

'Yes, you needn't all stare at me like that. Parents have no rights. We children of theirs are here, because they brought us here for the sake of their own pleasure. And so they must put up with what had been their pleasure. I never asked my mother to bring me into the world, and so I can't allow her any right over me, such as you claim over your son. If I had a father and he said to me what you said just now, I'd tell him to go to hell.'

Each of them reacted in his own manner. Andrés said: 'You're a shameless rascal.' Uncle Luis said: 'If you were my son I'd break your leg to make you walk straight.' Concha said: 'Then Mother ought to have chucked us into the Foundlings' Home?' Rafael said: 'Go on.'

After all the others, my mother said slowly:

'Yes. Having children is a pleasure for which you pay dearly.'

At that I saw tumbling visions of my uncle's house, of heaps of dirty linen, of her lye-bitten hands and her meek, silent forbearance, a smile for ever on her lips. Kisses in the kitchen and behind the curtain of the Café Español. The struggle for centimos. Her falling into a chair, utterly worn out. Her fingers in my rumpled hair, my head on her lap. It all surged up in me and it put me in the wrong, but not the outcries and protests of the others who disputed and shouted.

'Let's go, Rafael.'

We went downstairs, and out into the street. Rafael said: 'You've given it them.'

I grew indignant and began to speak. I spoke without pause for streets on end, trying to convince him that I was wrong about our mother, that we three, he and I and Concha, had the obligation to take her away from her work by the river, from washing clothes, from breaking up the ice and being roasted by the sun and coming home worn out. That we had to get her away from all this if we had to smash the whole world for it.

Rafael let me speak and then said:

'All right, that's easy. To-morrow we'll ask for a rise, you at the Bank and I at the Fenix. We'll speak to our managers of our mamma the washerwoman, and you may be sure they'll give us a good salary so we can support her. . . .'

It's the easiest thing in arithmetic to add up sums, but it's also the most difficult. To add up ten or twelve sheets of fifty lines with six or seven figures in each is more difficult than to handle the rule-of-three or the table of logarithms. At the end there is always a centimo too much or too little—or a thousand—and you have to start again at the beginning.

I was adding up and never took in what the messenger said, but answered 'Coming', automatically. After a short time he came back, touched me on the shoulder, and said: 'Señor Corachán's waiting for you. I told you a while ago but you forgot.'

I was startled and sprinted up the stairs, since the staff had no right to use the lift which was reserved for customers and the high officials of the Bank. What did that old fellow want of me? The commissionaire left me for a long while cooling my heels in the management's reception room. I used the breathing space to master my agitation and to wonder what the man wanted. Surely nothing pleasant. Anyhow, I would soon know, whatever it might be. I was sitting in a deep leather arm-chair the seat of which tipped backwards and rocked. For a while I amused myself swaying backwards and forwards, forwards and backwards in see-saw movement. There was a silver box on the polished table in the middle of the room. I opened it; it was filled with Virginia cigarettes. I wavered for a moment, then I took out a fistful and put them away in my coat pocket. The commissionaire opened the door to the office and announced me.

Don Antonio was meticulously scanning a letter, as usual, and spent long minutes over it. Finally he signed it, deigned to raise his head and looked at me through his pince-nez.

'You're the employee of the Coupons Section who broke the plate-glass the day before yesterday?'

'Yes, sir.'

'Well, well. This time no strong measures will be taken in view of your past conduct. The Management has decided to deduct the cost of the plate-glass from your salary. It amounts to 37·50 pesetas. That is all. You may go.'

I walked slowly down the stairs and went to the washroom to smoke one of the Virginia cigarettes and think the whole injustice over.

Less than a month ago every desk had been covered with a sheet of plate-glass. Most of the desks had a centre piece lined with red or green oilcloth, and a broad frame of varnished wood. They had laid the plate-glass directly on the frame, which meant that a hollow space was left under the glass in the centre. The backs of the coupons we sent out to the provinces or abroad had to be stamped with the initials of the branch office, to prevent their being stolen and circulated. We had to stamp thousands of coupons with a metal stamp, and there were days when the only noise in the department was that of the stamps hitting the ink-pad and the coupons. When the desks were covered with the glass panels, I asked for a rubber sheet, because I foresaw that I would inevitably break the glass. I was told that no rubber sheet was necessary, and had to go on stamping coupons on the glass. The day before yesterday the glass was starred. They put a new one on and I gave it no further thought. And now that nasty old fellow said I had to pay for it. Well, I would pay, but I wouldn't stamp any more coupons as long as they didn't let me have a rubber sheet.

When I came down to our section they were all waiting to hear what had happened. The story of the plate-glass went round the whole Bank immediately. Discontent was general, because the building was full of glass-covered desks and metal stamps; all the employees were afraid that the same thing would happen to them sooner or later. Plá sent for me to come to the lavatory—to our club —and there I found him in the midst of six or seven others, swathed in cigarette smoke. Somebody was keeping watch by the stairs against Corachán's coming.

'Now come along,' said Plá, 'and tell us what happened.'

I reported my interview and told them that the price of the plate-glass would be deducted from my salary.

Plá grew angry: 'They're a set of robbers. All that glass is insured, and then they cash in on us when something gets broken. We must protest against it.'

'Yes, but how?' said one of the others. 'We can't just go up to the Management as a protest delegation, because if we do they'll give us the sack.'

'Well, we must do something. If we let them get away with it we must expect to pay for all broken glass. And besides we must show that gang our teeth. Remember what happened on the First of May. They swallowed it and never said a word.'

Years before the First of May had been recognized by law as the Labour holiday. In the morning a procession crossed the city and went to the Premier's seat to present a paper with the demands of labour. Employers regarded the demonstration as an insult to themselves, and did what they could to make their men work the whole day. The Second of May was a National holiday, in commemoration of the Second of May 1808, when the War of Independence began with the rising of the people of Madrid against Napoleon's army of occupation. The employers used the second day to scotch the first. Only workshops shut down on the First of May, while the other trades, particularly commerce and the banks, treated it as a normal working day.

That year we had agreed that members of trade unions employed in banks would not go to work on the First of May, but take part in the procession, come what might. We felt certain that we should be sacked; but then *El Socialista* would start an intense publicity campaign, because we were within our legal rights. There were about a hundred of us from the Madrid banks, who all tried to encourage one another and threatened cowards who wanted to shirk with reprisals. When the procession was marching through the Calle de Alcalá where all the banks have their head offices, the group of gentlemen in starched collars, so conspicuous before, dwindled away and disappeared down side streets. Only a few of us marched on, enough, however, to make the fact known. On the following day we went to work awaiting instant dismissal.

Nobody said anything. Cabanillas, who years later became chief editor of the *Heraldo de Madrid*, had no occasion to publish the article he had already prepared against the Crédit Etranger, an impassioned article describing the fury of French Capitalism which sacked employees for staying away from work, although they were acting within the law, but then shut up the Bank on the Second of May and decked the balconies of the building with banners and streamers, as a French firm's contribution to the celebration of Napoleon's defeat.

We were very proud of our success, and very much ashamed of the desertions in the Calle de Alcalá, and very much afraid of the reprisals which would later on hit us one by one. If they were going to dismiss us one after the other, taking their time over it, it would have been better if all of us had decided to march through the Calle de Alcalá among the workers, our heads high. Of course, if you asked each member of the group individually, it turned out that none of them had left the files even for a moment, except to take a quick glass of vermouth or to satisfy an urgent physical need.

That was the story of the First of May, of which Plá never ceased to remind us.

More employees joined us in the lavatory until the whole space between the basins and the cabins was crowded. Chubby little Plá was submerged in a mass of people, but his fury grew and he kept on shouting:

'We must do something! We must make a big row! If we don't we're a pack of cuckolds and bastards!'

One of our more moderate colleagues found a solution.

'It's quite simple. If we pay for the plate-glass between the lot of us, the whole thing is settled. Every time a glass cover is broken we'd solve the problem by paying ten centimos each, and so nobody will be ruined.'

'Your big idea is to avoid any trouble.'

'Of course it is, we've got trouble enough as it is. If they had sacked all of us, at one go, on the 3rd of May, the People's House would have supported us and in the end they would have had to take us back at the Bank. But now the first of us to open his mouth will find himself in the street—and can you tell me what he's going to live on?'

'The trouble with us is that we're a pack of cuckolds,' said Plá. He thought a moment and then shouted: 'I've got it.'

He would not explain, but said: 'Wait here a moment.' He ran upstairs, and came back with a sheet of white paper at the top of which he had typed: 'Since the Crédit Etranger, with 250,000,000 frcs. capital, lacks the means to pay for a glass pane, value thirty-eight pesetas, its staff have pleasure in paying for it.'

Pressing the sheet against the wall, he put down his signature, all curves and scrolls. 'And now—anyone who doesn't sign this is a yellow bastard!'

The sheet filled sluggishly with signatures. One of the men tried to sneak away, but Plá caught him by the coat-tails.

'Now where are *you* going?'

'Upstairs.'

'Have you signed?'

'No, I haven't.'

'And you're a trade unionist? You sign. You sign, God's truth! The others who are not our comrades have no obligation to sign, but you will do it, or I'll take away your membership card and slap your face with it! You bastard!'

The timorous man put down a shaky signature. After that the paper was passed in secret from one department to the other. In the end, when it bore over a hundred signatures, one of the Heads of the Department got a hold of it in the Deposit Section, and took it up to the Management. Now what? We tried to console each other: 'They can't sack all of us!' Tense hours of waiting passed, while we all watched the big stairs every time a messenger came down. Towards the end of the evening Corachán sent for me. This time I did not have to wait in the ante-room, I went straight into his office. He was sitting under the lamp which made the plate-glass on his conference table glitter, turning the pages of a dossier. My dossier, probably. He kept me standing in front of his table for a while, until he said:

'You are the employee of the Coupons Section, who broke the 'ate-glass?'

'Yes, sir.'

He had the sheet of paper filled with signatures lying beside him. He spoke in a chilly voice, somewhat hoarsely.

'The Management of the Bank has decided not to deduct the price of the plate-glass from your salary, because the Bank fortunately does not need the money. But since matters of this order cannot be left without appropriate punishment, an entry will be made in your dossier.'

'What entry, sir?'

'What entry—a bad mark, of course. You won't persuade me that it is possible to smash a sheet of plate-glass with a stamp. Plate-glass the thickness of this!' He caught the rim of the glass panel on his table between his thumb and forefinger. 'The only way to break this is by playing with it, as you did. After all, you're nothing but young cubs, you people. But I'm no fool.'

"You're no fool,' I burst out, 'but you're an idiot. With this blotting paper weight, which is of wood'—I lifted the blotter and held it over the glass sheet—'I can smash your glass cover here, and your head, and the head of your bitch of a mother. You're just angry because of the subscription list. Yes, sir, it's a shame that the Bank should want to take away half my salary to pay for a glass pane which is insured anyhow. You're a pack of robbers and scoundrels.' Gently, but firmly, Carreras, the Assistant Director, grasped my arm from behind.

'Are you mad, boy?'

'Yes, I'm mad with disgust and rage and contempt! This fellow here in his frock-coat who hides in the lavatories to catch employees smoking, because that's how he shows he's worth his salary and his job in the Management—this fellow is a swine and the Bank is a pig-sty!'

I went out, slamming the doors and going on shouting even when I was on the stairs.

At my desk I wrote out a receipt for my salary until that day and asked Perahita to get me a testimonial for my work.

'A clean testimonial, with no black marks, for my three years of hard labour. Tell Corachán that if he refuses I'll go straight from here to the People's House, because I'm a trade union member.' I waved my membership-card in his face.

The cashier took my receipt and said:

'I can't pay you out without the endorsement of the Manager.'

'Go up and get it, then.'

'You go yourself, or I can't pay you.'

'Listen,' I said to him in a low, tense voice, 'I don't want to get you into trouble. Ring up Corachán, do whatever you like, but pay me out, or I'll make the biggest row there ever was in front of all the clients.'

The man gave in and paid me half a month's salary, 37·50 pesetas.

Perahita came down on an errand of conciliation.

'I've spoken to Corachán, there's no need for you to leave. All you've got to do is to apologize, and you can stay on in the Bank without any bad mark in your dossier.'

'D'you imagine I'll climb these stairs again to lick that man's bottom? And what for? So that my mother has to go washing clothes by the river? No, my dear friend, no. I'm too much of a man for that!'

I picked up the testimonial and walked to the entrance door. The huge hall of the Bank was studded with desks whose plate-glass covers shone like diamonds under the milky globes of electric light.

The Calle de Alcalá was full of noise. Newspaper vendors went by shouting, with enormous sheaves under their arms. People tore the papers out of their hands. The European War had begun.

At home my mother listened to me, sitting on her low chair, a piece of needlework fallen from her hands, her hands on her lap. I told her what had happened, with a heavy heart. At the end I swallowed and said:

'So I've left the Bank.'

We were both silent. Her fingers played with my hair, plaiting and unplaiting it. After a short while she said:

'See what a child you still are!'